Thomas McGuire

Science Coordinator
Briarcliff High School
Briarcliff Manor, New York

Reviewing Earth Science

THE PHYSICAL SETTING

With Sample Examinations

AMSCO SCHOOL PUBLICATIONS, INC.
315 Hudson Street/New York, N.Y. 10013

The publisher wishes to acknowledge the helpful contributions of
Neal Grasso, Geologist, Ossining, New York, in the preparation of this book.

Please visit our Web site at:

www.amscopub.com

When ordering this book, please specify: *either* **R 705 P** *or*
REVIEWING EARTH SCIENCE: THE PHYSICAL SETTING

ISBN 0-87720-159-5

Printed in the United States of America

3 4 5 6 7 8 9 10   06 05 04 03 02 01 00

To the Student

You are embarking on an adventure. Adventures are known for the challenges and accomplishments they bring, as well as for the trials that are a part of the process. The challenge will be understanding Earth systems. Rather than just memorizing numerous facts, you will be expected to use information sources, such as the Earth Science Reference Tables, to help you gain an understanding of our planet. These tables are printed near the back of this book, and should be used in class, during labs, and for reference during tests.

Reviewing Earth Science: The Physical Setting will help you place factual information in context. This skill will allow you to answer challenging questions. Each section of text is followed by a set of questions. In addition, there are Chapter Review questions. This wealth of questions provides practice in answering both multiple-choice items and questions that require longer answers. In many cases, these questions test your ability to apply your knowledge and skills in new ways.

The best learning takes place as a cooperative venture. You will work with your teacher and this book to learn the principles of earth science. In my thirty years of teaching, I have seen that the majority of students in late middle school or high school can meet the demands of this course. I wish you success in this course. Remember that success will require effort on your part. Adventures are seldom easy. But the rewards can make the effort worthwhile.

To the Teacher

Every course of study needs guiding principles. The Physical Setting: Earth Science core guide is the product of a committee of distinguished earth science teachers convened by the New York State Education Department for the purpose of writing an earth science document based on the Learning Standards for Mathematics, Science, and Technology. This book is based on those documents.

Reviewing Earth Science: The Physical Setting is abundantly illustrated with clearly labeled drawings and diagrams that illuminate and reinforce the subject matter. Important science terms are boldfaced and defined in the text. Other terms that may be unfamiliar to students are italicized for emphasis. The large work-text format makes this book easy for students to read. Within each chapter are several sets of multiple-choice questions and a Chapter Review that test students' knowledge and reasoning while provoking thought. These questions can be used throughout the year for review, exams, and homework assignments.

No book alone can impart the skills your students will need in this course. The most important part of instruction will be the learning activities that you provide in your classes. Your classroom learning activities should be physically and intellectually engaging and stress an inquiry/problem-solving style of learning. Your students may have had little experience in courses that develop these higher-level skills. Patience, planning, and keen professional judgment will be needed to guide the students in this important mode of learning.

Contents

Prologue

WHAT IS EARTH SCIENCE?

What is our planet made of? How old is it? How can we accurately predict the weather? Why do the stars and planets seem to move together through the night sky? The methods used to investigate questions like these are part of earth science. **Earth science** is the study of our planet, its changing systems, and its setting in the universe. (Sometimes the term "earth and space science" is used to make it clear that we include the investigation of objects outside Earth such as planets and stars. However, in this book it will be understood that we include the whole of astronomy in the earth sciences.)

Science is centered on conducting experiments and making observations. When many earth scientists reach similar conclusions (**inferences**) based on a variety of investigations, the shared body of knowledge that is assembled becomes a part of earth science. So earth science is a method of investigating our physical surroundings as well as the commonly accepted knowledge that has been assembled from these endeavors. One of the most important characteristics of science is that science is dynamic. As we refine our methods and as we apply new ideas and technology, we make new discoveries, which, in turn, change both the methods and the information that constitute earth science. But throughout our investigations we also encounter new questions that lead us to a constantly expanding understanding of our physical surroundings.

There are a variety of disciplines within the earth sciences. **Geology** is the study of what our planet is made of and how it changes. **Meteorology** is the study of the changing conditions of Earth's atmosphere, which we know as weather and climate. **Astronomy** is study of the motions of Earth and other objects in space. Figure P-1 shows how the earth sciences are related to the basic sciences of biology, chemistry and physics. Each of these three disciplines includes more restricted specialties. For example, some geologists concern themselves with the recovery of commercial earth resources and are therefore known as economic geologists. Petroleum geologists are even more specialized because they concentrate on the geological and environmental aspects of locating and extracting oil. In this course, you will learn about many career and academic opportunities in earth science, as well as our efforts to conserve resources and protect our environment.

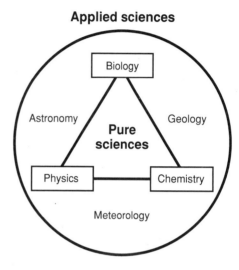

Figure P-1. The earth sciences are applied sciences because they use the methods of pure science to investigate systems of Earth and space.

OBSERVATIONS AND MEASUREMENTS

Observations and measurement are basic to all sciences. Observations are information obtained directly from any of our five senses; sight, touch, smell, hearing or taste. In some cases, we use instruments to extend our senses. (See Figure P-2 on page 2). In other cases, instruments, such as mass scales and thermometers, are used to make our observations more precise. Instruments can be as simple as a meter stick, or as complicated as the Hubble Space Telescope.

Measurements are expressed with numbers and units of measure, such as "25 meters" or "0.4 light years." (Both meters and light years are units of length.) These units give precise and universal meaning to our observations. You may be more familiar with the system of units now known as U.S. Customary measures. These units include the foot, the pound, and the degree Fahrenheit. Scientists prefer to use the International System of Units (SI, or the Metric system) because of its simplicity (most SI/Metric units relate to larger and smaller unit by factors of 10 (100, 0.1, etc.)) and because it is commonly used over most of the world.

Figure P-2. We use instruments to help us make better observations.

Converting units within the metric system is often as easy as changing the position of the decimal point. For example, 3.5 meters = 350 centimeters = 0.0035 kilometers. Table P-1 shows the basic units of measure and Table P-2 includes the most common metric prefixes.

Some units of measure are combinations of **basic units**, such as the basic units shown in Table P-1. When we measure speed we must express it in terms of distance per time. That might be meters per second or kilometers/hour. These combinations of basic units are known as **derived units**. In some cases, a single name is applied to a derived unit that can also be expressed as a combination of basic units. For example, a liter (L), a unit of volume, is actually 1000 centimeters^3. The pound (or its equivalent metric unit, the Newton) can be expressed in basic units as kilogram meters/second^2. You are probably familiar with metric prefixes, such as *milli-*, *centi-* and *kilo-*. These prefixes express multiples of units, but they do not change basic units into derived units.

Exponential Notation. Scientists often work with very large or very small numbers. These numbers are easier to read, write, and use in calculations if they are expressed in a mathematical shorthand known as **exponential**, or **scientific notation**.

Table P-2. Common Metric Prefixes

Prefix	Meaning	Exponential Notation
micro-	millionth	$\times 10^{-6}$
milli-	thousandth	$\times 10^{-3}$
centi-	hundredth	$\times 10^{-2}$
deci-	tenth	$\times 10^{-1}$
kilo-	thousand	$\times 10^{3}$
mega-	million	$\times 10^{6}$
giga-	billion	$\times 10^{9}$

A number written in scientific notation is written in the form

$$M \times 10^n$$

where M is a number between 1 and 10 (but not 10), and 10^n is a power of 10.

The number 2500 written in scientific notation is 2.5×10^3. The first factor, 2.5, is a number between 1 and 10; and the second factor, 10^3, is a power of 10. So 2.5×10^3 really means 2.5×1000.

OBSERVATIONS AND INFERENCES

We use our observations to draw conclusions, or **inferences**, that may include generalities, predictions, or extensions of our beliefs to situations where observations are inconvenient or impossible. Inferences that are based upon a wide range of observations can be nearly as reliable as our best observations. For example, we might be able to imagine a strange set of events that would prevent the sun from rising into the sky tomorrow, but the quantity and quality of observations leading to the prediction that the sun will indeed rise are so great that we consider sunrise a virtual certainty.

If our observations do not support our scientific beliefs, it is science that must change. For example, in Chapter 3 you will learn how a variety of observations contradicted our beliefs that the global positions of the continents are permanent. Over a period of half a century, evidence accumulated that gave rise to the modern paradigm (scientific thought framework) of plate tectonics. From these observations evolved a comprehensive theory to encompass a wide variety of observations from both the continents and the oceans. Plate tectonics has enabled us to understand observations that were difficult to explain under our former set of beliefs, and

Table P-1. Basic Units of Measurement Used in Earth Science

Physical Quantity	Metric Basic Unit	Metric Symbol	U.S. Customary Measure
Length	meter	m	inch, foot, mile
Mass	gram	g	ounce, pound, ton
Time	second	s	(same as metric)
Temperature	degree Kelvin	K	degree Fahrenheit (°F)
	degree Celsius	°C	

it has guided new scientific inquiry to expand our understanding of planet Earth. In fact, many of the most important discoveries of science came about when our traditional beliefs came into conflict with new observations.

Sample Problems

1. Write 27,508 in scientific notation.

Step 1: Determine M by moving the decimal point in the original number to the left or right so that only one nonzero digit is to the left of the decimal.

$$2.7508$$

Step 2: Determine n, the exponent of 10, by counting the number of places the decimal point has been moved. If moved to the left, n is positive. If moved to the right, n is negative.

$$4\ 3\ 2\ 1$$
$$2.7508$$
← 4 places to the left
$$27,508 = 2.7508 \times 10^4$$

2. Write 0.00875 in scientific notation.
Step 1: $\qquad$ 0.008.75
Step 2: $\qquad$ 1 2 3
$$0.0087 5$$
3 places to the right →
$$0.00875 = 8.75 \times 10^{-3}$$

A negative power of 10 does not mean a negative number. $8.75 \times 10^{-3} = 0.00875$. What a negative power of 10 *does* mean is a number less than 1.

QUESTIONS

1. Which of the following is **not** considered to be one of the earth sciences? (1) Meteorology (2) Physics (3) Astronomy (4) Geology

2. Which of the following is an inference, rather than an observation? (1) The sun often appears red just before sunset. (2) Some stars are visible only with a telescope. (3) Tomorrow the weather will be cool and rainy. (4) The outside temperature is 18° Celsius.

3. The earth sciences apply the knowledge and methods of chemistry, biology, and physics to real world problems. For this reason, the earth sciences are generally known as (1) soft sciences (2) qualitative sciences (3) theoretical sciences (4) applied sciences

4. Who is probably **not** doing science? (1) an artist making an abstract painting (2) a student measuring the mass of a mineral sample (3) a surveyor determining the boundaries of a building lot (4) an astronomer looking for the most distant stars and galaxies

5. Which expression is given in basic (not derived) metric units? (1) 7 pounds (2) 13 kilograms (3) 2.5 cubic centimeters (4) 100 kilometers/hour

6. A scientist observing the light given off by a star discovers that this star emits a kind of starlight never before observed by other scientists. Which of the following reactions would **not** be good science? (1) He contacts other astronomers to help him observe and understand this unusual star. (2) He extends his idea of what a star is to include this newly discovered object. (3) He changes his observations to conform to what he has learned from textbooks. (4) He repeats his observations to be sure that he has not made some kind of error.

7. 3.5×10^3 equals (1) 0.0035 (2) 3.5 (3) 350 (4) 3500

8. Which of the following numbers is the largest? (1) 3×10^8 (2) 8×10^3 (3) 5×10^5 (4) 5.069×10^5

9. 805,000 equals (1) 8×10^5 (2) 8.05×10^5 (3) 8×10^6 (4) 8.05×10^6

10. The circumference of Earth is about 4.0×10^4 kilometers. This value is equal to (1) 400 km (2) 4000 km (3) 40,000 km (4) 400,000 km

11. The average distance from Earth to the sun is approximately 149,600,000 kilometers. This distance correctly expressed in scientific notation (powers of ten) would be (1) 1.496×10^6 km (2) 1.496×10^8 km (3) 1.496×10^9 km (4) 1.496^9 km

Determining Percent Error. Percent error is a convenient way of comparing a measurement with the commonly accepted value for that measurement. To calculate percent error, divide the difference between the measured and accepted value by the accepted value, and then multiply by 100%. (Note: You always subtract the smaller value from the larger value.)

No measurement is perfect. All measurements can be made with more care or by using better instruments. That's why this formula uses the term "accepted value" rather than "correct value" or "true value."

Percent Error

$$= \frac{\text{Difference From Accepted Value}}{\text{Accepted Value}} \times 100\%$$

Sample Problem

In measuring a table, a student found its length to be 1.9 meters. If the accepted value is 2.0 meters, what is the percent error of the student's measurement?
Solution:

Percent Error

$$= \frac{\text{Accepted Value} - \text{Measured Value}}{\text{Accepted Value}} \times 100\%$$

$$\text{Percent Error} = \frac{2.0\ m - 1.9\ m}{2.0\ m} \times 100\%$$

$$= \frac{0.1\ m}{2.0\ m} \times 100\% = 5\%$$

12. A student measures the length of a room to be 6.9 meters. If the actual length of the room is 7.5 meters, the student's percent deviation (percent error) is (1) 20% (2) 14% (3) 8% (4) 6%

13. A student determines the volume of a cubic crystal to be 8.6 cubic centimeters. What is her percent error if the correct volume of the crystal is 8.0 cubic centimeters? (1) 6.0% (2) 6.5% (3) 7.0% (4) 7.5%

14. What is the percent error of an error of one meter in a kilometer? (1) 0.1% (2) 1% (3) 10% (4) 100%

15. A student calculates the specific heat of ice to be 0.40 cal/g C°. According to the *Earth Science Reference Tables*, what is the student's percent error from the accepted value? (1) 2.5% (2) 2.0% (3) 20.% (4) 25.%

Types of Graphs.

A graph is a visual way to organize and present data. Instead of reading paragraphs of information or studying columns of figures, you can see the data in a graph and make comparisons between variables almost at a glance. Unlike a data table, a graph helps you to visualize changes in data, to understand relationships between variables within the data, and to picture trends or patterns in data.

Line Graph.

A line graph, such as the one in Figure P-3, shows how a measured quantity changes with respect to time, distance, or some other variable.

Line graphs are constructed by plotting data on a **coordinate system** that is set up on vertical and horizontal axis. The horizontal (x) axis is usually used for the independent variable. It usually indicates a uniform change, such as hours, years, or centimeters. The vertical (y) axis is used for the dependent variable. It usually indicates the amount of the measured quantity being studied, such as temperature, height, or population. Normally, you know in advance the regular change expected in the independent variable. The values of the dependent variable are what you are trying to find or know more about. You draw the graph in order to see how the dependent variable changes with respect to the independent variable.

The rise or fall of the line in Figure P-3 shows the increase or decrease in noon temperature during the week. When the line graph moves upward to the right, it represents a continuous increase. When the line graph moves downward to the right, it indicates a continuous decrease. No change is represented by a horizontal line. The steeper the line segment in a graph rises to the right, the greater the slope of the segment and the greater the increase in temperature. Likewise, the steeper the line segment falls to the right, the greater the decrease in temperature.

Not all line graphs are straight lines. Some line graphs are curved. You can still determine the general slope of a curved line by observing the way it runs on the graph.

Pie and Bar Graphs.

Sometimes a line graph is not the best kind of graph to use when organizing and presenting data. In earth science, you will sometimes see the bar graph and the pie graph used. The bar graph is useful in comparing data about one thing at different times. For example, the bar graph in Figure P-4 compares monthly rainfall, or precipitation (PPT), over a period of a year.

Average Monthly Precipitation for Lake Placid, N.Y.

Month	PPT (mm)	Month	PPT (mm)
J	81	J	107
F	71	A	84
M	86	S	86
A	71	O	74
M	81	N	86
J	94	D	86

The pie graph is used to show how a certain quantity has been divided into several parts as well as to show the comparison between these parts. The pie graph in Figure P-5 shows the most abundant chemical elements in rocks of Earth's crust.

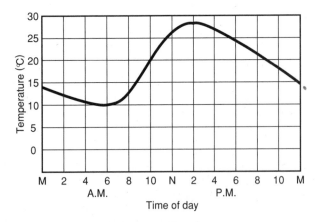

Figure P-3. This line graph shows the temperature changes at a central New York State location on a typical summer day. Note that with a line graph like this you can read the graph value at any point in time.

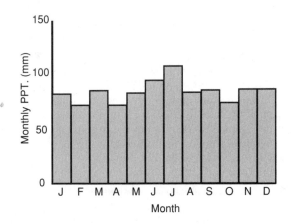

Figure P-4.

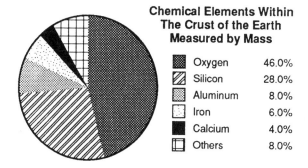

Chemical Elements Within The Crust of the Earth Measured by Mass

■	Oxygen	46.0%
▨	Silicon	28.0%
▦	Aluminum	8.0%
▫	Iron	6.0%
■	Calcium	4.0%
⊞	Others	8.0%

Figure P-5.

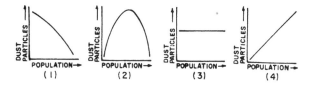
QUESTIONS

16. The data table below shows average dust concentrations in the air over many years for selected cities of different populations.

Population in Millions	Dust Particles/ Meter^3
Less than 0.7	110
Between 0.7 and 1.0	150
Greater than 1.0	190

Based on this data table, which graph best represents the general relationship between population and concentration of dust particles?

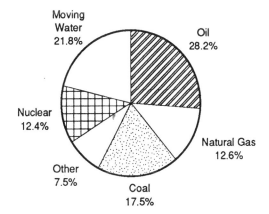

17. The circle graph below shows the sources of the electrical energy used in New York State in a typical year.

Moving Water 21.8%
Oil 28.2%
Nuclear 12.4%
Other 7.5%
Coal 17.5%
Natural Gas 12.6%

The largest amount of electrical energy came from (1) coal (2) oil (3) moving water (4) natural gas

---

Directions: Base your answers to questions 18 and 19 on the graph below and on your knowledge of earth science. Write the *number* of the word or expression that best completes *each* statement or answers *each* question.

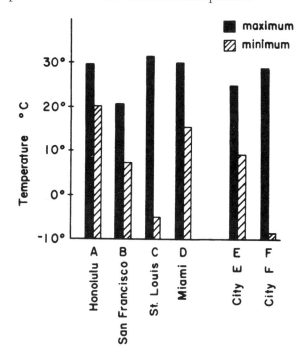

The graph above represents data collected from six cities, showing the average maximum and the average minimum temperatures for a 12-month period.

18. Which location has the highest average maximum monthly temperature? (1) A (2) B (3) C (4) D

19. Which location has the largest difference in average monthly temperatures? (1) A (2) B (3) E (4) F

Density.

Finding the density of an object involves two steps. First, you must determine both the mass and volume of the object. **Mass** can be defined as the quantity of matter in an object. Mass is measured in kilograms (kg), grams (g), or milligrams (mg). **Volume** is the amount of space occupied by an object. Volume is usually measured in liters (L), milliliters (mL), or cubic centimeters (cm^3). (The milliliter and the cubic centimeter are the same size; they are just expressed in different units.)

The second step is to use the formula below to calculate density.

Density = mass/volume

An example might help. If an object has a mass of 20 grams and a volume of 10 milliliters, its density is 2 grams per milliliter. Please note that dividing these quantities results in the unit grams per milliliter (g/mL). You can also express the result as grams per cubic centimeter (g/cm^3).

Water is a special substance. On Earth, water is commonly found in all three states of matter: solid, liquid, and gas. (Because there is so much water present, Earth is sometimes called the water planet.) Liquid water is

---

essential for life. Since water is matter, it has mass, volume, and density. One gram of water occupies a volume of one milliliter. Therefore the density of water is one gram per milliliter (1 g/mL). Since one milliliter is equal to one cubic centimeter, the density of water also can be expressed as one gram per cubic centimeter (1 g/cm³).

Density is a property of a given substance, no matter how much or how little of that substance you consider, the density of the substance will always be the same. For example, the density of 1000 grams of liquid water is 1 g/cm³ and the density of one gram of water also is 1 g/cm³.

Water provides us with a simple way to test the density of a substance. When placed in water, materials like a piece of iron or a rock usually sink because they are more dense than water. However, objects made of certain types of wood or objects filled with air usually float. They are less dense than water. Density is related to an object's ability to sink or float in water, as shown in Figure P-6. For objects less dense than water, the lower the density of an object, the greater the portion of the object that floats above the surface of the water. That is, with regard to water, the lower the density of an object, the higher it floats. The density of some common substances are shown in Figure P-7.

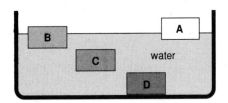

Figure P-6. Density and Flotation. Substances that are less dense than water, like A and B, float in water. The lower the density, the greater the portion above water. C remains suspended because its density is equal to that of water. D sinks, like all objects that are denser than water.

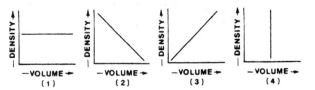

20. A student calculates the densities of five different pieces of aluminum, each having a different volume. Which graph best represents this relationship?

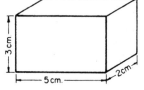

21. An unknown sample has a density of 6.0 grams per cubic centimeter. If the sample were cut in half, each half could have a density of (1) 12.0 g/cm³ (2) 9.0 g/cm³ (3) 3.0 g/cm³ (4) 6.0 g/cm³

22. The diagram right represents a solid object with a mass of 60 grams. What is the density of the object? (1) .16 g/cm³ (2) 2 g/cm³ (3) .5 g/cm³ (4) 6 g/cm³

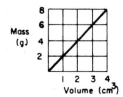

23. The graph shows the relationship between mass and volume for a certain material. The density of this material is (1) 0.5 g/cm³ (2) 2.0 g/cm³ (3) 5.0 g/cm³ (4) 8.0 g/cm³

24. What is the density of a rock that has a mass of 35 grams and a volume of 7.0 cubic centimeters? (1) 5.0 g/cm³ (2) 0.20 g/cm³ (3) 28 g/cm³ (4) 42 g/cm³

25. If a wooden block were cut into eight identical pieces, the density of each piece compared to the density of the original block would be (1) less (2) greater (3) the same

26. Compared to the density of water the density of ice is (1) less (2) greater (3) the same

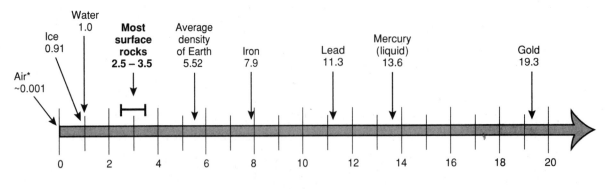

Density in grams/cubic centimeter

*The density of any gas changes dramatically with changes in temperature and pressure.

Figure P-7. Densities of selected Earth materials. Most of the rocks and minerals we find at or near Earth's surface have densities in the range of 2.5–3.5 grams/cubic centimeter.

27. The following diagram represents two beakers, each containing an ice cube and clear liquid. In beaker A the ice cube floats, and in beaker B the ice cube rests on the bottom.

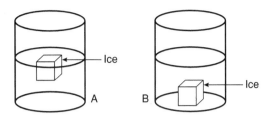

What is the most probable cause for the difference in behavior of the ice cubes in the two beakers? (1) The ice cube in beaker B is heavier than the ice cube in beaker A. (2) The ice cube in beaker B is less dense than the ice cube in beaker A. (3) The liquid in beaker B is less dense than the liquid in beaker A. (4) The liquid in beaker B is more dense than the liquid in beaker A.

Directions: Base your answers to questions 28 through 29 on your knowledge of earth science and on the diagram below which represents five different materials several minutes after they have been placed in a container of water at constant 20°C temperature. The distances between the marks on the various materials are equal.

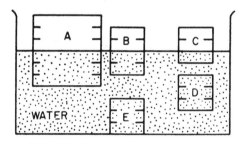

28. Which material has the greatest density? (1) A (2) E (3) C (4) D

29. Which materials have the same density? (1) A and B (2) A and C (3) B and C (4) C and D

30. The original block of material A is cut into several pieces. When compared with the density of the original block, the density of each piece will be (1) less (2) greater (3) the same

31. Material D is removed from the container and compressed to half its size. If it is then returned to the container it will (1) float at the surface (2) float beneath the surface (3) sink to the bottom

Preserving Earth Systems.

No other species has the ability to use and modify Earth as humans have. We live in a time when great changes in planet Earth are taking place. Our planet home is subject to ever increasing stresses. The products of modern technology demand increasing amounts of limited resources, and it places the natural environment under more stress than ever before. However, people can use technology to minimize its harmful effects. We can even use technology to help restore the natural environment. For example, strip mining of coal and metal ores has left great scars on Earth's surface. Sometimes, the land in these scars cannot even support a covering of weeds. The same earth-moving machines that exposed and extracted the ores can be used to smooth the land and cover it with a productive layer of soil.

We have the opportunity and the responsibility to protect and preserve Earth's natural environment. Over time, changes in human attitudes toward the environment have occurred. For example, the use of leaded gasoline released tons of dangerous lead compounds into the environment. (Lead was added to gasoline to prevent a condition called "engine knock.") Laws were passed. All cars built since the early 1980s, use only unleaded gasoline. As a result, air quality in many urban areas has improved over the past few decades. However, other pollutants added to the air from the burning of fossil fuels are still a problem. Perhaps this is a problem that you might be able to help solve in the future.

Societal pressures also play an important role in changing human behavior. People's attitudes toward recycling have changed, in part, because of the costs involved with disposing of trash. A market for recyclable materials has also helped change attitudes by giving value to materials that were once discarded. Recent campaigns to recycle materials that were once buried or burned have benefited greatly from public acceptance. This acceptance has, in large measure, been the result of favorable publicity in the media and in educational forums. In addition, laws have been passed in numerous cities and towns that mandate the recycling of some materials.

Everyone should assume responsibility for protecting the environment and for supporting scientific research. It is the nature of our legal, social, and economic systems that the laws and conventions we adopt are only as good as our commitment to work to implement them. It would be wonderful if all students using this book developed professional skills in scientific research and the applications of science. However, most people do not grow up to become scientists. Nevertheless, leadership in government and in business requires the support and encouragement of an enlightened public. Scientific literacy is a necessary part of that enlightenment; and a general understanding of Earth's systems is a crucial part of scientific literacy.

QUESTIONS

Directions: Base your answers to questions 32 through 36 on the following diagram, which shows air, water, and noise pollution in a densely populated industrial area, and on your knowledge of earth science. Write the *number* of the word or expression that best completes *each* statement or answers *each* question.

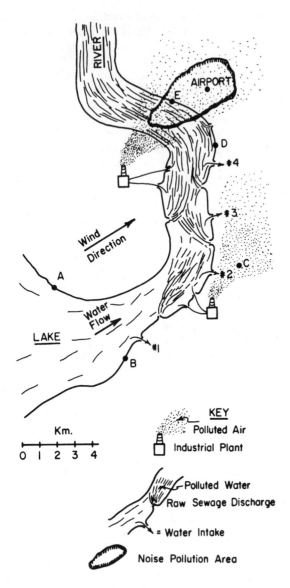

KEY

Polluted Air

Industrial Plant

Polluted Water

Raw Sewage Discharge

⇒ = Water Intake

Noise Pollution Area

32. Air pollution would probably be greatest at which location? (1) A (2) B (3) C (4) D

33. Water pollution would probably be greatest at which location? (1) A (2) B (3) C (4) D

34. Noise pollution would be greatest at which location? (1) B (2) C (3) D (4) E

35. Which location is subjected to the greatest number of pollution factors? (1) A (2) B (3) D (4) E

36. If the water intakes supplied drinking water to the area, which intake would most likely require the most extensive purification procedures? (1) #1 (2) #2 (3) #3 (4) #4

The Scientist, Engineer, and Citizen

Should the United States make the complete change to metric measures? Why haven't we done so already? Formulate detailed plans to abandon our system of "U.S. Customary Measures" (pounds, miles, etc.) and change to the measures used in the rest of the world.

1. What are the most likely units of measure obtained by using the instrument shown below?

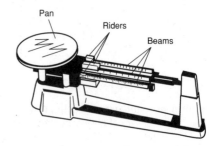

(1) meters (2) grams (3) liters (4) kilometers

2. Four students calculated the density of lead, based upon their measurements of mass and volume. The numbers that follow are the percent errors of each student. Which student has the most accurate calculation? (1) 5% (2) 10% (3) 50% (4) 100%

3. A sample of rock has a density of 5 g/cm³. If the rock were cut into two equal pieces, what would be the density of these smaller fragments? (1) 2 g/cm³ (2) 2.5 g/cm³ (3) 5 g/cm³ (4) 10 g/cm³

4. A scientist decided to investigate the properties of a certain substance. The first thing she did was to place a piece into a large, ordinary bucket of water. What property was she probably observing? (1) mass (2) length (3) weight (4) density

5. A 1-kilogram sample of which of the following four substances would be the smallest volume? (1) air (2) water (3) iron (4) gold

Densities of Four Common Substances	
Air	0.0013 g/cm³
Water	1.0
Iron	7.9
Gold	19.3

6. If 3.7×10^9 is written as a standard decimal number, it is equal to (1) 37.9 (2) 3 700 000 000 (3) 0.000037 (4) 37 000 000 000

7. Why do ships float higher in sea water than they do in fresh water? (1) Sea water is more dense than fresh water. (2) Sea water is less dense than fresh water. (3) Sea water and fresh water have the same density. (4) The ship took on more cargo when it went from the fresh water into the salt water.

8. The diagram below shows four objects that have been placed in a container of water. Which object is the *least* dense?

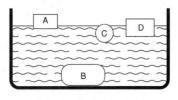

(1) A (2) B (3) C (4) D

9. A floating object can be made to sink by decreasing only its (1) mass (2) volume (3) density (4) pressure

10. Which object probably has the same density as a carpenter's nail? (1) an oak board (2) a brick (3) an ice cube (4) an ax head

11. In scientific notation, -562.3 is equal to (1) 562×10^3 (2) 5.623×10^{-2} (3) -5.623×10^2 (4) -5.623×10^{-2}

12. Which units would be the best in expressing how large an empty box is, or how much space is inside? (1) grams (2) liters (3) meters (4) pounds

13. What percent error would mean that the error is the same size as the accepted value? (1) 0% (2) 50% (3) 100% (4) 200%

14. Which of the following objects is the most dense? (1) a large bucket of water (2) a human body (3) an ice cube (4) a thumbtack

15. Which of the following has the greatest length? (1) a kilometer (2) a centimeter (3) a millimeter (4) a meter

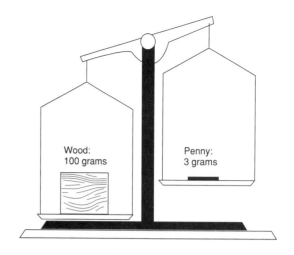

Object	Mass	Flotation
Wood	100 grams	Floats
Penny	3 grams	Sinks

FREE-RESPONSE QUESTIONS

(Answer the following questions on a separate sheet of paper)

1. A student estimated the height of a tree to be 20 meters. Careful measurement revealed that the tree was actually 16 meters high. What was the percent error of her estimate? (Show the algebraic formula and show your steps to the solution.)
(Algebraic Formula, +1; Substitutions correct, +1; Correct number, +1; Correct Units, +1)

2. Make a list of procedures that could be used to find the density of a cube of lead 2 cm on a side. List each step, 1, 2, 3, … . Each step must be written as a complete sentence.
(Complete Procedure, +2; Numbered Steps, +1; All Steps in Complete Sentences, +1)

3. Pat learned that heavy objects sink, and light objects float. But, when she did the experiment shown below, she found that the heavier object was the one that floated. Explain why the heavier object was the one that floated. (Please answer in one or more complete sentences.)
(Complete sentence, +1; Correct but incomplete reasoning, +1 or, Correct and complete Reasoning, +2)

4. The following data represent four samples of the same material. Show this data as a line graph. Graph the mass on the vertical (up and down) axis and the volume on the horizontal axis. Be sure to follow the graphing rules you learned in class.
(Labeled axes, +1; Points plotted, +1; Graph line, +1)

Four Samples of the Mineral Magnetite	
15 g	3 cm³
40 g	8 cm³
50 g	10 cm³
25 g	5 cm³

5. In a contest to estimate the mass of a stone, Jill's guess was 190 grams. Careful measurements established the accepted mass at 200 grams. What was Jill's percent error?
(Appropriate formula, +1; Correct substitution, +1; Correct answer, +1)

6. Explain why an important feature of science is that our beliefs about the world remain flexible and adaptable.

7. If scientists value precision, why do they say the universe is approximately 10 to 15 billion years old, rather than giving a more exact figure?

CHAPTER 1 Planet Earth

THE SHAPE OF EARTH

A model is a representation of an object or a natural event. Many models of Earth, such as a globe, show Earth shaped round like a ball or a sphere. For most purposes, these models are good representations of the shape of Earth, because Earth is *nearly a perfect sphere*. Earth is actually an **oblate spheroid**, slightly flattened at the poles and bulging a little at the equator. The following evidence shows that Earth is not a perfect sphere—that it is slightly oblate. However, you must be careful not to exaggerate Earth's "out of roundness" based on this evidence, for the same evidence supports the view that Earth is *nearly a perfect sphere* and that it can be modeled as a round object.

Although Earth looks flat to those of us who live on its surface, we live on an almost perfect sphere nearly 13,000 kilometers (8000 miles) in diameter. Due to its daily rotation (spin), Earth bulges about 40 kilometers at the equator. Still, Earth is so close to the shape of a sphere that from any point in space it looks like a perfect sphere. Even the tallest mountains are insignificant when we compare them with the size of our planet. From outer space Earth looks perfectly round and smooth.

How do we know that we live on a gigantic sphere? We have photographs of Earth taken from outer space. All of them show Earth's round shape. In addition, we notice the changing positions of the sun and stars, especially the North Star (Polaris), as we move over great distances on Earth. These changes are consistent with the expected changes as we move over a round planet as shown in Figure 1-1.

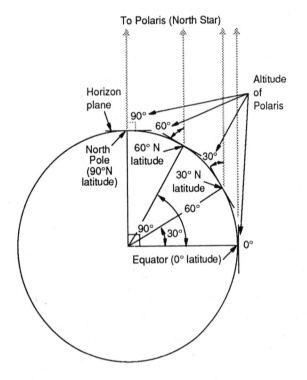

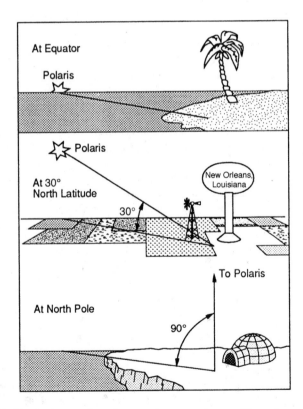

Figure 1-1. Our observations of changes in the angular altitude of Polaris as we travel north or south are consistent with a spherical planet.

Diameter and Circumference. Earth measurements, taken either on Earth's surface or from orbiting satellites in space, have uncovered the following facts:

	Diameter	Circumference
Polar	12,714 km	40,008 km
Equatorial	12,756 km	40,076 km

THE STRUCTURE OF EARTH

The outer portion of Earth is generally classified into three major parts: lithosphere (solid), hydrosphere (liquid), and atmosphere (gas). The **lithosphere** is the dense, solid shell of Earth composed of rock and soil that surrounds the more fluid inner layers. It varies in thickness from about 70 to 150 kilometers. Oxygen and silicon are the two most common elements within the minerals that compose the lithosphere. It also contains many other elements in smaller amounts, including aluminum, iron, and calcium.

The **hydrosphere** consists of the waters of Earth—the oceans, lakes, rivers, and water in the ground. The oceans extend to an average depth of 3–5 kilometers and cover about 70% of Earth's surface. Water is a chemical compound composed of oxygen and hydrogen with various other elements and compounds present in solution.

The **atmosphere** is the shell of gases that surrounds Earth. It extends out several hundred kilometers into space and is stratified, or layered, into zones.

The principal layers of the atmosphere, listed in order of increasing altitude, are the *troposphere*, the *stratosphere*, the *mesosphere*, and the *thermosphere*. Each layer is characterized by the pattern of vertical temperature trends shown in the *Earth Science Reference Tables*. The names of the layers of Earth's atmosphere end in "-sphere." The top interfaces (boundaries) of those layers end in "-pause."

The lowest layer, the **troposphere**, is the most important to life on Earth since it contains the gases necessary to support life. Although it extends from the surface to an elevation of only about 12 kilometers, it contains most of the mass of the atmosphere. The composition of the troposphere is generally 78% nitrogen and 21% oxygen, with water vapor, carbon dioxide, argon, neon, and other gases making up the remainder. Strong winds, storms, and turbulence occur in this layer of the atmosphere. Most of the water vapor in the atmosphere is in the troposphere and, hence, most of the clouds. Temperature in the troposphere generally decreases with increasing altitude.

The *tropopause* is the boundary separating the troposphere from the stratosphere. Likewise, the *stratopause* is the boundary between the stratosphere and the next layer of the atmosphere, the mesosphere. And the *mesopause* is the boundary layer between the mesophere and the thermosphere.

Note that Earth's layers become progressively more dense as they get closer to Earth's center. That is, less dense layers always sit above more dense layers.

QUESTIONS

1. According to the *Earth Science Reference Tables*, as the elevation above sea level in Earth's atmosphere increases, the measured atmospheric pressure will (1) decrease (2) increase (3) remain the same

2. According to the *Earth Science Reference Tables*, which part of the atmosphere has the *smallest* distance from the bottom to the top of its zone? (1) troposphere (2) stratosphere (3) mesosphere (4) thermosphere

3. The hydrosphere is mostly (1) solid rock (2) liquid water (3) gaseous air

4. According to the *Earth Science Reference Tables*, nitrogen is the most abundant element in the (1) crust (2) hydrosphere (3) troposphere (4) mantle

5. According to the *Earth Science Reference Tables*, nearly all the water vapor in the atmosphere is found within the (1) mesosphere (2) thermosphere (3) troposphere (4) stratosphere

6. In which sequence are Earth layers arranged in order of increasing average density? (1) atmosphere, hydrosphere, lithosphere (2) hydrosphere, lithosphere, atmosphere (3) lithosphere, atmosphere, hydrosphere (4) atmosphere, lithosphere, hydrosphere

7. Which of the four models shown below best represents the volume of each of the gases found in the troposphere? [To help answer this question, refer to the *Earth Science Reference Tables*.]

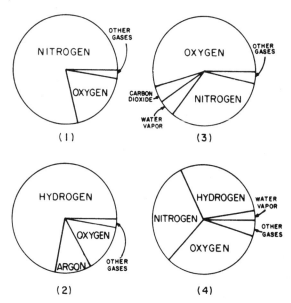

Directions: Base your answers to questions 8 through 11 on the following graph, which represents the temperature of a parcel of air as it is lifted through the atmosphere.

Write the number of the word or expression that best completes the statement or answers the question.

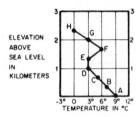

8. The temperature of the air at an elevation of 2 kilometers is most likely to be (1) −2.5° (2) 2.5° (3) 3° (4) 0°

9. As the air rises from the surface to 1 kilometer, its temperature (1) decreases, only (2) increases, only (3) increases, and then decreases (4) remains the same

10. The temperature change is *least* between letters (1) B and C (2) D and E (3) E and F (4) G and H

11. Between which two points does the temperature increase with an increase in elevation (a temperature inversion)? (1) A to D (2) D to E (3) E to F (4) F to H

LOCATING POSITIONS ON EARTH

Scientists have established a surface grid, a system of lines, that you can use to locate any position on Earth. This type of system, a **coordinate system**, assigns to every position on Earth a pair of coordinates (two numbers) called *latitude* and *longitude*. Like any other coordinate system the latitude-longitude system's grid has two main reference lines—the equator and the prime meridian.

The reference line for latitude is based upon the rotation of Earth. The spin of Earth determines the positions of the North and South poles. (Although which was called "north" or "south" was an arbitrary decision). The **equator** is an imaginary line that circles Earth halfway between the North Pole and the South Pole. Angular distance in degrees north or south of the equator is called **latitude**. Imaginary lines drawn around Earth parallel to the equator, represent lines of equal latitude and are often called **parallels** since they never meet. The latitude of the equator is zero degrees (0°). The highest degree of latitude are 90° N at the North Pole and 90° S at the South Pole. See Figure 1-2.

Unfortunately, there is no natural location for the line from which to begin measuring longitude. The *prime meridian* is an imaginary line (semi-circle) that runs through Greenwich, England, from the North Pole to the South Pole. The prime meridian was located here because that was the location at which English navigators set their clocks to the apparent motion of the sun. Angular distance in degrees east or west of the prime meridian is called **longitude**. Imaginary semicircles (**meridians**) drawn around Earth from the North Pole to the South Pole represent lines of equal longitude. The longitude of the prime meridian is zero degrees (0°). See Figure 1-3. If you move east and west away from the prime meridian, the farthest you can get from

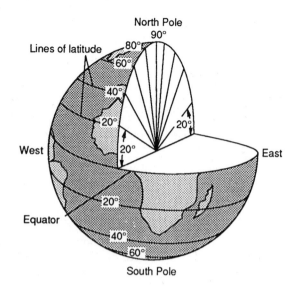

Figure 1-2. Latitude

it is 180°. The 180th meridian is half the distance around Earth. The half of the world that is west of the prime meridian has west longitude. The half of the world that is east of the prime meridian has east longitude. See Figure 1-4.

Many students learn latitude as the lines that circle Earth, parallel to the equator. In this course, however, you will need a greater depth of understanding. Remember that your latitude is your *angle* north or south of the equator, and your longitude is the *angle* east or west of the prime meridian. Terrestrial coordinates are angles, not lines.

Navigation.   **Navigation** is the science of locating your position on Earth. Any location can be expressed as the measure of your angle north or south of the equator (latitude) and as the measure of your angle east or west of the prime meridian (longitude). In other words, each place on Earth has its own unique coordi-

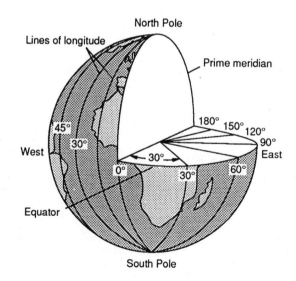

Figure 1-3. Longitude

Reviewing Earth Science: Chapter 1

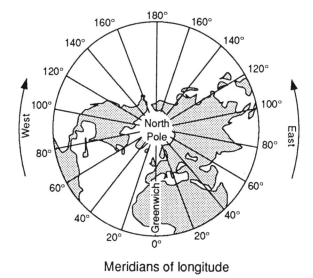

Meridians of longitude

Figure 1-4.

nates of latitude and longitude. Any location north of the equator has a latitude that is equal to the angle of Polaris (the North Star's altitude) above the horizon. For example, New York City's latitude is 40° N, the angle of Polaris above the horizon at New York City.

To find Polaris in the night sky, look for the Big Dipper. If you have a clear northern horizon, the Big Dipper will always be visible in the northern part of the sky, although it may be tipped on its side or upside down. (See Figure 1-5.) The two stars at the end of the bowl of the dipper are known as the pointer stars because a line connecting these two stars always points to Polaris,

regardless of where the Big Dipper is in the sky. Although there are dozens of stars brighter than Polaris, it is one of the brighter stars in the Little Dipper, which seems to rotate around Polaris with the Big Dipper.

Residents of the Northern Hemisphere are fortunate to have a bright star located almost exactly above Earth's North Pole. Residents of the Southern Hemisphere, however, must use certain other stars when locating the South celestial Pole.

Finding the Altitude of a Star With an Astrolabe. The altitude of a heavenly body is its angular height above the horizon of an observer. You can measure the altitude using an *astrolabe*. An astrolabe is a protractor from which a heavy weight is suspended. See Figure 1-6, on page 14. When you sight a star along the edge of the astrolabe, the weight hangs straight down toward Earth's center, or center of mass. A line at a right angle to the line formed by the string from which the weight is suspended represents the plane of the horizon. Therefore, the line on the protractor where the string of the weight falls indicates an angle that is equal to the altitude of the star above the horizon.

Solar Time and Clock Time. Our system of clock time is based on observations of the sun. Noon is defined as the time the sun reaches its highest point in the sky. Note that for all locations in the continental United States the noon sun is never straight overhead. For us, it is always in the southern half of the sky. The day is divided into 24 divisions we know as hours. Each hour is further divided into minutes, which are in turn divided into seconds.

Approximate longitude can be calculated if you know the present clock time along the prime meridian at

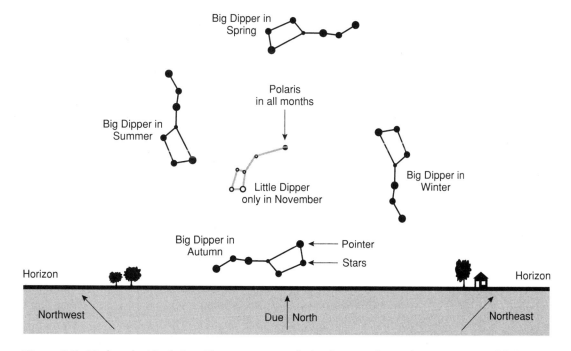

Figure 1-5. Finding the North Star. The easiest way to find Polaris is to locate the Big Dipper and follow the pointer stars at the end of the bowl as they point toward Polaris. This diagram shows the way the Big Dipper looks in the evening sky at the middle of each season. The Little Dipper also rotates around Polaris, but it is shown only in its autumn position.

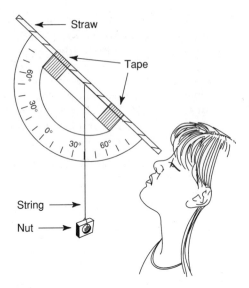

Figure 1-6. How an astrolabe is used to measure the angular altitude of an object in the sky.

Greenwich (**Greenwich Mean Time**) and if you know the local clock time. To find longitude, you must first find the time difference, in hours, between local clock time and Greenwich time. Your longitude will then be this time difference multiplied by 15° per hour. (The rate at which the sun appears to move from east to west is 15° per hour.) If local time is earlier than Greenwich time, your position is west of the prime meridian or west longitude. If local time is later than Greenwich time, your position is east of the prime meridian or east longitude.

For example, there is a time difference of 5 hours between London, which is located at the prime meridian (0° longitude), and New York City. Multiplying 15° by 5 (hours), you find a difference of 75°. The fact that New York time is 5 hours earlier than London time indicates that New York is west of London. Therefore, the longitude of New York is 75° W. See Figure 1-7.

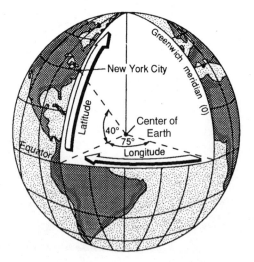

Figure 1-7. Coordinate system for locating positions on Earth. The parallels of latitude and the meridians of longitude enable us to locate positions such as that of New York City (latitude 40° N, longitude 75°W).

12. Polaris is used as a celestial reference point for Earth's latitude system, because Polaris (1) always rises at sunset and sets at sunrise (2) is located over Earth's axis of rotation (3) can be seen from any place on Earth (4) is a very bright star

13. What is the latitude of the observer shown below?

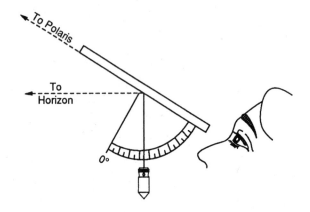

(1) 35° N. (2) 55° N. (3) 90° N. (4) 125° N.

14. The diagram below indicates the altitude of Polaris as measured at three locations in Earth's Northern Hemisphere.

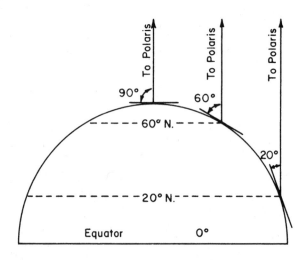

These observations could lead to the inference that Earth (1) has a curved surface (2) has an elliptical orbit (3) rotates 15° per hour (4) revolves around the sun

15. What is the latitude of point A in the diagram below?

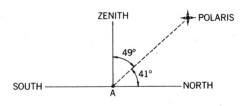

(1) 8° N. (2) 41° N. (3) 49° N. (4) 59° N.

16. At what latitude would an observer on Earth find the altitude of Polaris to be 37°? (1) 37° South (2) 53° North (3) 37° North (4) 90° North

17. A navigator aboard a ship measures the altitude of Polaris as shown in the diagram. What is the latitude of the ship's position at the time the measurement was taken?

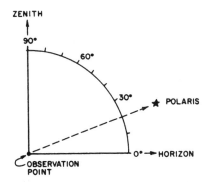

(1) 10° North (2) 20° North (3) 40° North (4) 70° North

18. At which latitude will Polaris be overhead? (1) 0° (2) 23½° N. (3) 90° S. (4) 90° N.

19. Upon what measurement is Earth's latitude and longitude system based? (1) star angles (2) gravity intensity (3) magnetism direction (4) apparent solar diameter

20. The diagram below represents a portion of a map of Earth's grid system. What is the approximate latitude and longitude of point A?

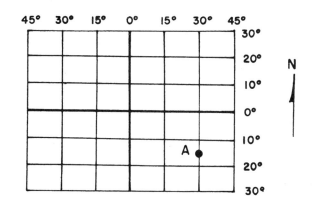

(1) 15° N. 30° W. (2) 15° S. 30° W. (3) 15° N. 30° E. (4) 15° S. 30° E.

21. As an observer travels eastward along the 40° N parallel of latitude, the altitude of the North Star will (1) decrease (2) increase (3) remain the same

22. Ship *X* and ship *Y* are sailing along the equator. The difference in local solar time between them is 2 hours. What is their difference in longitude? (1) 0° (2) 15° (3) 30° (4) 45°

23. As a ship crosses the prime meridian, the altitude of Polaris is 65°. What is the ship's location? (1) 0° longitude, 65° South latitude (2) 0° longitude, 65° North latitude (3) 0° latitude, 65° West longitude (4) 0° latitude, 65° East longitude

24. Cities located on the same meridian (longitude) must have the same (1) altitude (2) latitude (3) length of daylight (4) solar time

25. A person knows the solar time on the prime meridian and the local solar time. What determination can be made? (1) the date (2) the altitude of Polaris (3) the longitude at which the person is located (4) the latitude at which the person is located

26. An observer on a moving ship notices that the altitude of Polaris increases each night. Local solar noon occurs at the same time each day. In what direction is the ship moving? (1) due east (2) due south (3) due west (4) due north

27. Based on the Generalized Bedrock Geology Map of New York State in the *Earth Science Reference Tables*, what could be the approximate location of an observer if he measured the altitude of Polaris to be 41 degrees above the horizon? (1) Watertown (2) Massena (3) Buffalo (4) New York City

FIELDS

A **field** is a region of space in which a similar quantity can be measured at every point or location. **Isolines** connect points of equal value on a field map. See Figure 1-8. Types of isolines include isotherms, isobars, and contour lines. **Isotherms** connect points of equal temperature. **Isobars** connect points of equal air pressure. **Contour lines** connect points of equal elevation.

A.

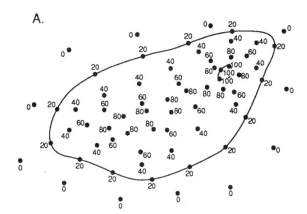

B.

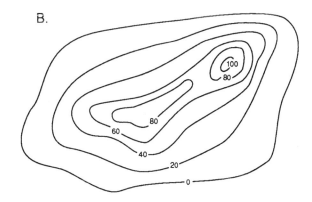

Figure 1-8. Elevation above sea level is being measured in this topographic field. Many points in a region have been measured and plotted on a map, and isolines (contour lines) have begun to be drawn in. Isolines are drawn in and connect points of equal value in a region.

Topographic Maps. A **topographic**, or **contour**, **map** shows the shape of Earth's surface. The measured heights may be shown as numbers on a topographic map. *Contour lines* (isolines) drawn on the map give **elevations** (heights above sea level) for a region and show the shape of the land. See Figure 1-9. Each contour line is separated from the next by a uniform difference in elevation known as the **contour interval**. In other words, the contour interval is the difference in height between two adjacent contour lines. Where the contour lines are close, the slope of the ground is steep. Where the contour lines are far apart, the slope of the ground is gentle. *NOTE*: Do not confuse a contour interval, which shows a difference in height, with horizontal distance along the ground. You measure the horizontal distance between two points by using the map scale.

From the shape of a set of contours you can recognize landscape features, such as hills, valleys, depressions, escarpments (cliffs), etc. See Figure 1-10 on page 17. A topographic map may also use other symbols or colors to represent bodies of water, vegetation, and structures such as buildings and roads. A key or legend describing the symbols is usually provided.

It is important for you to remember that throughout time, the shape of the land changes. Our landscape has been formed by a combination of erosion and uplifting forces. Those forces have been active for the billions of years of Earth's history, and they seem certain to continue in the future. Earth is constantly changing, although, in many cases, too slowly for a person to notice. When we look at Earth, it is as if we are seeing a single frame of the motion picture that is Earth's history. Some Earth scientists say that nothing on Earth is unchanging, except the process of change itself.

Note the following features of the topographic contour map Figure 1-10:

1. The contour lines on this map connect places with the same elevation. The darkest lines are the index contours. Some of the index contours are labeled with their elevations. This one is 450 feet above sea level. What is the contour interval on this map? (Ans. 10 ft.)

2. This is a stream valley. The streams are located in the lowest parts of the valleys. Notice that where contour lines cross streams, the contour lines make "V"s. Also note that the "V"s always point upstream. If you can visualize the shapes represented on this map, you have acquired an important skill in map reading.

3. The slope (gradient) is the steepest where the contour lines are closest.

4. The highest elevations on this map are found where the contour lines make small closed curves.

5. A closed depression is shown by a contour line with small marks projecting toward the lowest part inside the depression. On this map, the depression contour must have an elevation of 250 feet, the same elevation as the dark line to the left. Therefore the elevation at the center of this closed depression must be a little lower than 250 feet above sea level. Can you see why? (If not, ask your teacher to show you why these two lines must be at the same elevation.)

QUESTIONS

28. The diagram below is a contour map. Between which two points is the slope of the hill steepest?

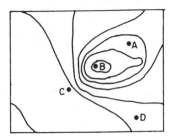

(1) *A* and *B* (2) *B* and *C* (3) *C* and *D* (4) *A* and *D*

29. Which is true of isolines on a weather map? (1) They are of equal length. (2) They are evenly spaced. (3) They connect points with equal readings. (4) They never change.

30. What is the elevation of the highest contour line shown on the map below?

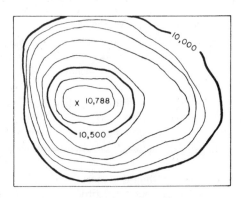

(1) 10,000 m (2) 10,688 m (3) 10,700 m (4) 10,788 m

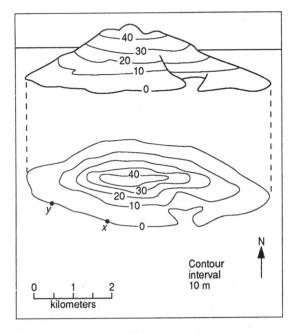

Figure 1-9. A topographic map of an island. The contour interval is 10 meters. However, the distance from point *X* to *Y* is approximately 1.5 kilometers based on the scale.

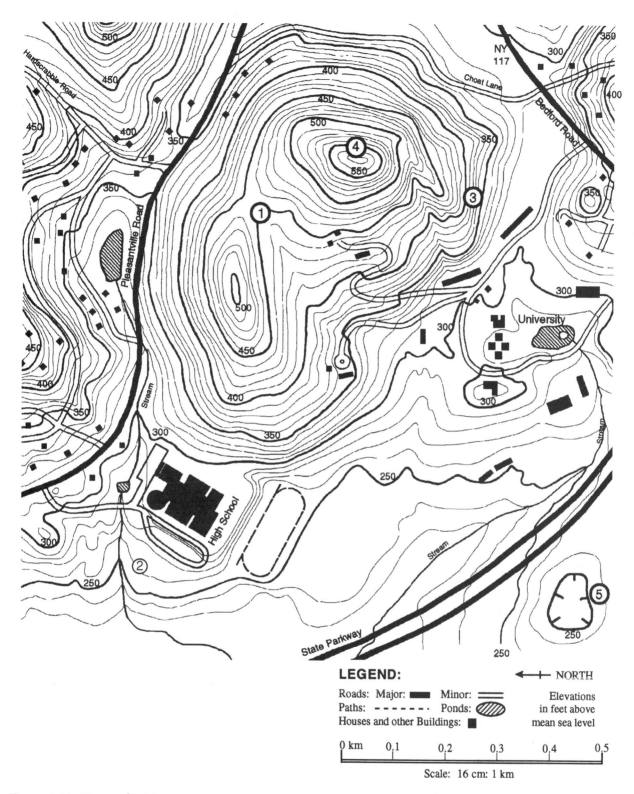

Figure 1-10. Topographic Map

Earth's Magnetic Field. If you place a thin sheet of window glass horizontally on top of a bar magnet and sprinkle iron filings onto the glass, the slivers of iron will show the magnetic field of the bar magnet as they come to rest on the glass. (See Figure 1-11 on page 18.) An invisible magnetic field surrounds every magnet.

The Earth itself also has a magnetic field that lines up within about 12° of Earth's spin axis. In that way the Earth is like a gigantic bar magnet. When you use a magnetic compass, the compass needle points toward Earth's magnetic pole that is located relatively close to the geographic north pole. (You may recall that the

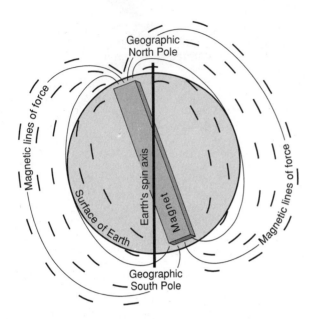

Figure 1-11. Earth's Magnetic Field. Our planet has a magnetic field as if a giant bar magnet were buried within Earth. The short, dark lines show the pattern obtained by sprinkling iron filings near a bar magnet.

geographic pole is where Earth's spin axis intercepts Earth's surface.) This can be a convenient way to find directions if clouds cover the sun and stars.

Topographic Profiles. Topographic maps include information about the third dimension: A **topographic profile** is a cross sectional view that shows the elevations of the land along a particular baseline. It is a vertical slice of the topography. It shows the ups and downs along a chosen route. Wherever the baseline crosses a contour line, the exact height above sea level can be plotted on a vertical scale as shown in Figure 1-12.

Making a Profile from a Topographic Map. You will need two sheets of blank paper in addition to the topographic map.

1. Use a straight edge to draw the baseline on the topographic map. In Figure 1-12 the end points are labeled M and N.

2. On one of the blank papers draw parallel horizontal lines to show the elevations of the contour lines along your profile. These lines need to be as long as the profile line, M-N.

3. Label the elevations of these horizontal lines at the appropriate contour interval; one line for each contour elevation crossed by the profile line. (The profile may cross the same elevation several times.)

4. Place an edge of the second sheet of blank paper on the topographic map along the profile line, M-N. Mark M and N at the appropriate places along this blank edge. Then mark the same edge where the profile crosses each contour line. Label these marks so that you know the elevation of each.

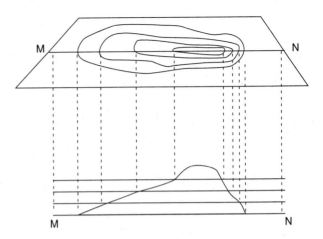

Figure 1-12. The relationship between a contour map and its profile. Notice that along baseline M-N, the gradient (slope) is the steepest where the isolines are closest.

5. Now move the sheet with the marked edge to the bottom of the parallel lines. Use the marks and elevation labels to project where the profile crosses each horizontal line.

6. Connect the points on the profile to show a vertical cross section along line M-N.

Some people are able to visualize a profile simply by looking at the numbers or the isolines on a field map. This skill can be useful in map reading or in choosing the best profile from several possibilities in a multiple-choice question.

QUESTIONS

Directions: Base your answers to questions 31 and 32 on the information and temperature chart and on your knowledge of earth science.

The temperature data (°C) plotted on the chart below was taken at the same elevation and time in a room. Letters A through G represent specific locations in the room.

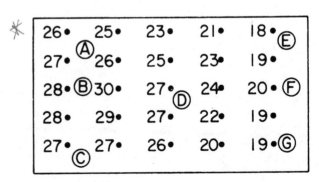

31. Which diagram best represents the 26°C isotherm?

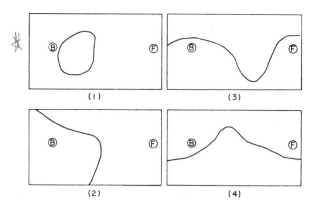

(1)   (3)

(2)   (4)

32. Which graph best represents the temperatures between *B* and *F*?

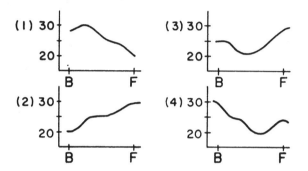

(1) 30 20   B   F

(2) 30 20   B   F

(3) 30 20   B   F

(4) 30 20   B   F

Determining a Gradient, or Slope. You can determine the rate of change of a value within a field by finding the gradient. **Gradient**, or average slope, is the rate of change in field values between two points in a field. It is calculated by comparing the difference in field values at two points with the distance between those two points. For example, the average slope, or gradient, between any two points (A and B) on a mountain can easily be determined from a contour map. If you know how many meters the mountain drops or rises between A and B in a given distance, you can calculate the average slope by using the following equation:

$$\text{gradient} = \frac{\text{change in field value}}{\text{change in distance}}$$

$$= \frac{\text{difference in elevation between A and B (m)}}{\text{distance between A and B (km)}}$$

Please notice that the units of gradient will be the unit of the field value divided by units of distance. Since the field value in the example above is elevation in meters, the units of gradient are meters/kilometer. If the field value were the temperatures in a classroom, the units might be °Celsius/meter.

Sample Problem

Calculate the average slope of a mountain trail from the 980-meter contour line to the 480-meter contour. The distance between these two elevations measures 4 kilometers.

Solution:

$$\text{gradient} = \frac{\text{change in field value}}{\text{change in distance}}$$

$$= \frac{\text{difference in elevation (m)}}{\text{distance between the points (km)}}$$

$$= \frac{980 \text{ m} - 480 \text{ m}}{4 \text{ km}}$$

$$= \frac{500 \text{ m}}{4 \text{ km}}$$

$$= 125 \text{ m/km}$$

QUESTIONS

33. A stream has a source at an elevation of 1000. meters. It ends in a lake that has an elevation of 300. meters. If the lake is 200. kilometers away from the source, what is the average gradient of the stream? (1) 1.5 m/km (2) 3.5 m/km (3) 10. m/km (4) 15 m/km

Directions: Base your answers to questions 34 and 35 on the diagram below which represents a contour map of a hill.

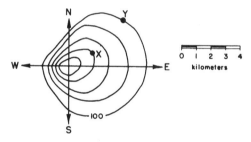

CONTOUR INTERVAL = 10 METERS

34. On which side of the hill does the land have the steepest slope? (1) north (2) south (3) east (4) west

35. What is the approximate gradient of the hill between points X and Y? [Refer to the *Earth Science Reference Tables*.] (1) 1 m/km (2) 10 m/km (3) 3 m/km (4) 30 m/km

Directions: Base your answers to questions 36 and 37 on your knowledge of earth science and on the topographic map below.

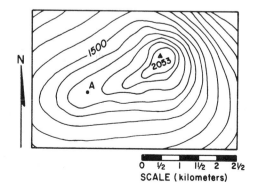

SCALE (kilometers)

36. What is the most likely elevation of point A? (1) 1,250 (2) 1,650 (3) 1,750 (4) 1,850

37. Which section of the map shows the steepest gradient? (1) southeast (2) northeast (3) southwest (4) northwest

Directions: Base your answers to questions 38 through 42 on your knowledge of earth science, the *Earth Science Reference Tables*, and the topographic map below which represents a coastal landscape. The contour lines show the elevations in meters.

38. What is the approximate distance along the dirt road from points *G* to *H*? (1) 2.1 km (2) 2.6 km (3) 3.2 km (4) 4.0 km

39. What is the general direction of flow of the stream between points *E* and *F*? (1) north to south (2) south to north (3) west to east (4) east to west

40. What is the elevation of the highest contour line shown on the map? (1) 140 m (2) 150 m (3) 155 m (4) 180 m

41. Which diagram best represents the profile along a straight line between points *C* and *J*?

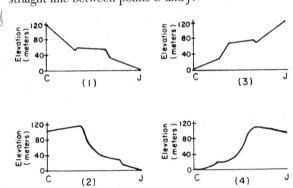

42. What is the rate of change in elevation (gradient) of the land from point *C* to point *D*? (1) 10 m/km (2) 15 m/km (3) 20 m/km (4) 25 m/km

CHAPTER 1 REVIEW QUESTIONS

1. Which direction could you travel along Earth's surface, so that your latitude would not change? (1) East (2) South (3) South-East (4) North-West

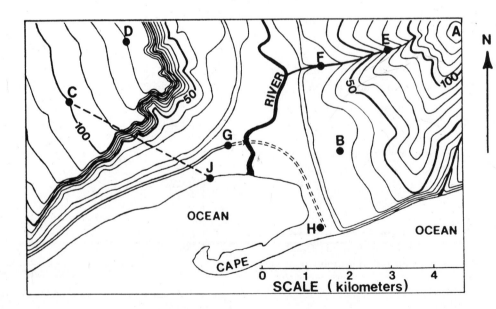

2. Which pie chart below best shows the elemental composition of the oceans by volume?

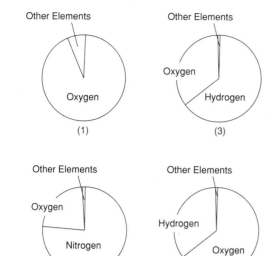

Directions: Use this map to answer questions 3–7.

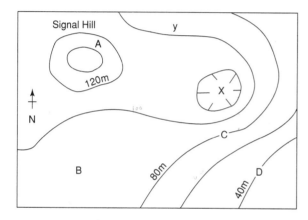

3. What is the highest elevation in the contour map? (1) 100 m (2) 130 m (3) 140 m (4) 150 m

4. Where is the topographic gradient the smallest? (1) A (2) B (3) C (4) D

5. What is the approximate elevation at the place marked "X"? (1) 70 m (2) 80 m (3) 90 m (4) 100 m

6. What is the contour interval on this map? (1) 10 m (2) 20 m (3) 40 m (4) 100 m

7. If a heavy rain fell onto the ground at point y, and the water could not soak into the ground, in which direction would the water flow? (1) North (2) South (3) East (4) West

8. For observers in Niagara Falls, New York, how high in the night sky would Polaris be? (1) 43° (2) 45° (3) 79° (4) 90°

9. What are the most common units of measure for expressing your longitude? (1) km east or west (2) km north or south (3) degrees east or west (4) degrees north or south

10. Students in New York and Florida observed Polaris on the same, clear night. How will their observations differ? (1) Polaris will appear higher in New York (2) Polaris will appear brighter in New York (3) Polaris will move faster in Florida (4) Polaris is not visible in Florida

11. Which of the following objects would be the best scale model of the true shape and smoothness of planet Earth? (1) a dried out apple with a wrinkled skin (2) a golf ball that has been played a lot (3) a bowling ball without finger holes (4) a pizza with pepperoni

12. According to the Generalized Bedrock Geology Map in the *Earth Science Reference Tables*, what is the approximate longitude of Watertown, NY? (1) 44°N (2) 44°30'N (3) 76°E (4) 76°W

13. What part of Earth is mostly nitrogen? (1) hydrosphere (2) atmosphere (3) lithosphere (4) crust

14. According to the *Earth Science Reference Tables*, what is the approximate distance from the North Pole to the South Pole straight through the Earth? (1) 6000 km (2) 13,000 km (3) 24,000 km (4) 50,000 km

15. What is the exact shape of Earth? (1) a perfect sphere (2) nearly a perfect sphere (3) a round object half as tall as it is wide (4) flat and broad, like a pancake

16. A topographic map is a two-dimensional model that uses isolines to represent places of equal (1) elevation above sea level (2) temperature gradient (3) barometric pressure (4) magnetic force

17. Measuring the angular altitude of Polaris would enable us to determine our (1) elevation above sea level (2) average surface temperature (3) longitude (4) latitude

18. The Big Dipper, part of the star constellation Ursa Major, is shown below.

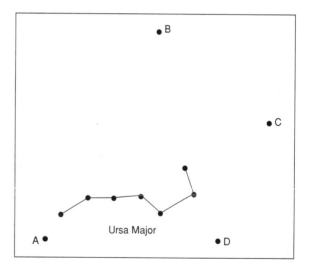

Which letter represents Polaris (the North Star)? (1) A (2) B (3) C (4) D

FREE-RESPONSE QUESTIONS

(Answer the following questions on a separate sheet of paper.)

1. Briefly describe an experimental procedure to determine your latitude if you know you are located north of the equator.

(Reasoning, +1; Sentence, +1)

2. Briefly explain one way that we know that Earth is round.
(Reasoning, +1; Sentence, +1)

3. Draw isotherms on the following temperature field map at an interval of 2°C.
(Each of three Isotherms, +1)

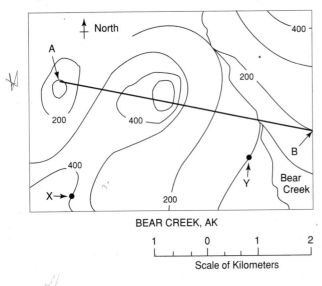

25	26	27	27	26
24	25	27	28	27
25	26	28	29	28
25	26	26	25	26

Summer Temperatures
in a Warm Room

4. Calculate the gradient from point X to point Y on the map below.
(Algebraic Formula, +1; Substitutions, +1; Answer and Units, +1)

BEAR CREEK, AK

Scale of Kilometers
1   0   1   2

Elevations in Meters

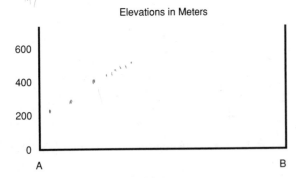

5. Draw a profile view of line A–B from the map above onto the profile box below the map.
(Length, +1; Shape, +1; Elevations, +1)

6. The numbers in the box below represent land elevations, in meters, in a geographic region. Use this diagram to draw a topographic map at a contour interval of 5 meters.

Map Scale – 10 cm: 1 km

29	34	36	38	37	36	33	30	27	24
26	31	35	44	41	35	30	28	26	24
24	27	30	34	34	31	28	24	21	19
22	23	26	31	32	27	25	22	19	17
21	22	24	26	28	23	21	18	16	15

Accuracy, 1 point; Neatness, 1 point; Correct Interval, 1 point;

7. Copy data map (below), draw contour lines at an interval of 50 meters. Label each isoline with its elevation. The places marked "0" are in the ocean. The shoreline has been drawn for you.

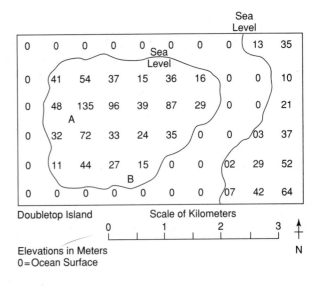

Sea Level									
0	0	0	0	0	0	0	0	13	35
0	41	54	37	15	36	16	0	0	10
0	48	135	96	39	87	29	0	0	21
0	32	72	33	24	35	0	0	03	37
0	11	44	27	15	0	0	02	29	52
0	0	0	0	0	0	0	07	42	64

Doubletop Island

Scale of Kilometers
0   1   2   3

Elevations in Meters
0 = Ocean Surface

N

8. Calculate the gradient from point A to point B on the map (above). Start with the algebraic formula, show your work, and label your answer with the appropriate units.

9. Define latitude.

10. What place (or places) on the Earth have the greatest latitude?

11. List the latitude and longitude of the place marked X on the map on page 23. You must include the number, the units, and the direction for each.

Directions: Use the information that follows to answer questions 12–15. The box on page 23 shows data from an experiment to measure air pollution particles from a single source over part of a small town. Small glass slides were covered on the upper side with petroleum jelly and left outside overnight. In the morning, they were collected and the pollution particles on each slide were counted. The

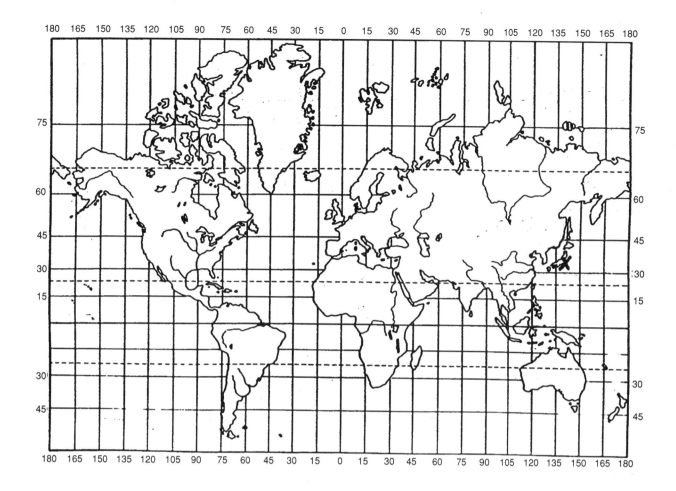

numbers below show the amount of pollution counted on each slide and where each slide was placed.

↑ N	0	1	0	3	7	9	10	12	14	13	13	10	9
	0	0	8	13	19	23	22	21	19	15	13	9	6
	1	5	11	20	28	25	24	23	18	17	12	7	5
	0	7	24	31	30	26	23	20	16	14	10	6	3
	2	9	37	32	27	21	19	15	14	8	5	3	2
	0	3	10	9	7	5	3	4	3	0	2	0	0

12. Draw isolines showing the amount of particle pollution at an interval of 10 particles, starting with the 10 particle isoline. (The 0 line need ***not*** be shown.)
(Each isoline +1)

13. Write an "S" on the map to show the most likely source of the pollution.
(+1)

14. What direction was the wind apparently blowing from that night?
(+1)

15. Write a capital "G" in the location where the field gradient is the greatest.
(+1)

16. A traveler observed and measured the angle of the North Star (Polaris) above the horizon, as she traveled from the North Pole to the South Pole (that is, when it would be visible in a clear sky). Label the vertical (up and down) axis with appropriate **numbers** and **units**. Then, use this grid to **show how the angular altitude of Polaris would change during this whole journey**.
(Numbers on the vertical axis, +1; Units on the vertical axis, +1; Appropriate trend from the North Pole to the Equator (Northern Hemisphere, +1; Appropriate indication of observations in the Southern Hemisphere, +1)

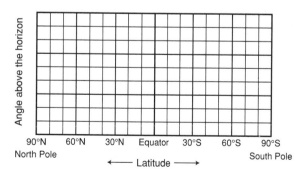

CHAPTER 2 Minerals, Rocks, and Resources

MINERAL RESOURCES

Earth's mineral resources include minerals, rocks, and fossil fuels (coal, oil, and natural gas). Minerals are an important part of our lives. Steel, copper, aluminum, gold, and other metals come from minerals or combinations of minerals. Minerals are also essential ingredients in computer chips, concrete, and even foods. Rocks, which are made up of minerals, make up the planet on which we live, and weather to form soil and sediments. Although fossil fuels are found in naturally occurring underground deposits, they actually are not minerals. This is because they are organic, or formed from living things.

WHAT ARE MINERALS?

Minerals are naturally occurring, homogeneous (uniform) substances that are **inorganic**. Inorganic means that the substance was not formed by or from living things such as plants or animals. As a result, inorganic substances such as minerals do not contain the complex carbon-containing compounds made by living things.

Some minerals are chemical elements or compounds. Graphite and diamond are different forms of elemental carbon (C). Quartz (SiO_2, also called silica), and calcite ($CaCO_3$) are chemical compounds composed of elements in set ratios. A third group of minerals are mixtures, for which complete chemical formulas cannot be written. For example, minerals in the feldspar family contain potassium, calcium, and/or sodium in varying proportions along with silicon, oxygen, and aluminum. Minerals are the substances of which rocks are made.

Although thousands of minerals have been identified and classified, less than a dozen are commonly found. Clay, feldspar, quartz, and calcite make up the bulk of rocks found near Earth's surface. Pyroxene, amphibole, and olivine are common deep underground, but less common at or near the surface. Oxygen and silicon make up more than half of the mass of these minerals. With just another dozen elements, you can account for about 98 percent of Earth's mass. Figure 2-1 shows the chemical composition of Earth's crust by mass and by volume. You can usually identify minerals on the basis of their physical and chemical properties. Always use a fresh, unweathered sample or an unweathered surface when you try to identify a mineral. Table 2-1 lists about two dozen of the most common minerals, which you should be able to identify.

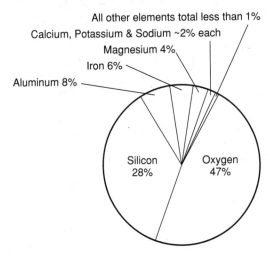

Elemental composition of Earth's crust by mass

All other elements total less than 1%
Calcium, Potassium & Sodium ~2% each
Magnesium 4%
Iron 6%
Aluminum 8%
Silicon 28%
Oxygen 47%

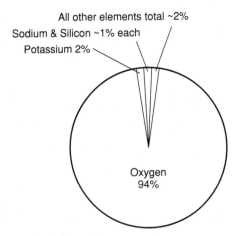

Elemental composition of Earth's crust by volume

All other elements total ~2%
Sodium & Silicon ~1% each
Potassium 2%
Oxygen 94%

Figure 2-1. The two elements oxygen and silicon make up most of Earth's crust both by mass and by volume.

Color. Many minerals have a characteristic **color**. Pyrite ("fool's gold") is usually a brassy yellow color. Almandine garnet is valued for its deep red color. But, certain colorless or white minerals are often discolored by impurities. Quartz and calcite are usually colorless, although they may be pink, green, or even black, depending on the impurities they contain. Dark-colored minerals, such as the amphibole and pyroxene families,

Table 2-1. Common Rock-Forming Minerals

	MINERAL	COLOR	LUSTER	STREAK	HARD-NESS	BREAK-AGE	SPECIFIC GRAVITY	COMMENTS, HABIT	COMPOSITION[2]	Igneous[1]	Sedimentary	Metamorphic
Mafic Minerals	Olivine	Green	G	-	7	Fracture	3.8	Common deep within the Earth	$(MgFe)SiO_4$	+		
	Pyroxene	Black to Green	G	-	$5\frac{1}{2}$	2 cl, 60°	3.3	60° cl	Mg Fe Na Ca Al Si O	✓		
	Hornblende	Black	G	-	$5\frac{1}{2}$	2 cl, 90°	3.3	90° cl	Mg Fe Na Ca Al Si O OH	✓		✓
	Biotite Mica	Black to Brown	G	-	3	1 cl	3.0	One perfect cleavage	K Mg Fe Al Si O OH	✓		✓
Felsic Materials	Feldspars: Plagioclase	White	G	-	6	2 cl, ~90°	2.7	The most common family of minerals	(Na Ca) Al Si O	✓	✓	✓
	Potassium	Pink							$(K)AlS_3O_4$	✓	✓	✓
	Muscovite Mica	Silver to Colorless	G	-	$5\frac{1}{2}$	1 cl	2.9	One perfect cleavage	K Al Si O OH	+		✓
	Quartz	Colorless to White	G	-	7	Fracture	2.7	Hexagonal crystals, resistant to weathering	SiO_2	✓	✓	✓
Other Minerals	Clay	Any	N	-	Soft	Variable	2.6	Weathering product of many minerals	Mg Fe Na Ca Al Si O OH		✓	
	Calcite	White	G	_	3	3 cl, Oblique	2.7	Bubbles with acid	$CaCO_3$	+	+	
	Dolomite	White	G	-	$3\frac{1}{2}$	3 cl	2.9	Alteration of calcite	$CaCO_3 \cdot MgCO_3$	+	+	
	Galena	Silver	M	Gy-Bk	$2\frac{1}{2}$	Parting	7.4	Metallic luster, ore of lead	PbS	—	—	—
	Garnet	Red[3]	G	-	7	0-1 cl	4	Official NYS mineral	Mg Fe Al Ca O OH	+	+	
	Graphite	Silver	M	-	1-2	~1 cl	2.2	Pencil "lead," dry lubricant	C			—
	Gypsum	White	G	-	2	1 cl	2.3	Used in sheetrock	$CaSO_4 \cdot 2H_2O$		+	
	Halite	Colorless	G	-	$2\frac{1}{2}$	3 cl, 90°	2.2	Rock salt, cubic crystals	NaCl		+	
	Hematite	Redish Brown	D-M	R-Bn	5-6	Uneven	5	Ore of iron; often colors sedimentary rock	Fe_2O_3	—	+	—
	Magnetite	Black to Silver	M	Bk	3	Fracture	5.2	Strongly magnetic, ore of iron	Fe_3O_4	+	—	—
	Pyrite	Brassy	M	Gn-Bk	$6\frac{1}{2}$	Poor	5.1	"Fools Gold"	FeS_2	—	—	—
	Sulfur	Yellow	R	-	2	Poor	2.1	Widely used in the chemical industry	S	—	—	
	Talc	White	P	-	1	1 cl, wavy	~2.7	Used in baby powder, cosmetics, and paint	Mg Si O OH	—		—

[2]Symbols & Abbreviations:

cl = cleavage	G = glassy	M = metallic	N = nonmetallic	P = pearly	R = resinous	Bk = black
Bn = brown	Gy = Gray	Gn = green	O = oxygen	Si = silicon	Al = aluminum	Mg = magnesium
Na = sodium	Fe = iron	Ca = calcium	K = potassium	OH = hydroxide	H_2O = water	C = carbon

[1] Abundance: ✓ = Usually present, + = common, — = minor   [3] Varies considerably with the variety of this mineral.

are easier to identify because impurities are unlikely to cause color variations.

Luster. **Luster** describes the way light is reflected from the freshly cut surface of a mineral. Minerals with a metallic luster have a hard, shiny look, like polished metal. This is because light is unable to penetrate the surface and almost all the light is reflected. Minerals with nonmetallic luster can also be shiny, but nonmetallic luster differs from a metallic luster because some of the light is transmitted into and through the mineral while some is reflected. Nonmetallic lusters include glassy, waxy, pearly, and earthy, which is dull.

Streak.   The test for **streak** is performed by rubbing a fresh corner of the mineral across a white, unglazed streak plate. The streak is the powdered form of the mineral. Some metallic minerals leave behind a powder that is not the same color as the mineral. The test for streak is shown in Figure 2-2.

Crystal Structure.   A **crystal** is a regularly shaped solid formed by an ordered pattern of atoms. Minerals form characteristically shaped crystals. Calcite and quartz can look very similar. Both are fairly common and are often white or colorless with a glassy luster. However, their crystals are very different. Quartz crystals are hexagonal (six-sided) in cross section, while crystals of calcite form rhombohedral solids. (A rhombohedral solid resembles a rectangular solid that has been pushed over to one side so that all the faces have parallel edges, but none meet at right angles.) Pyrite

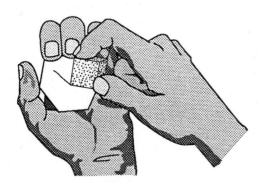

Figure 2-2. The streak test is used to find the color of the powder of a mineral with a metallic luster. A corner of the sample is rubbed across an unglazed porcelain streak plate.

Crystal Form, Fracture, and Cleavage As Keys to Mineral Identification

QUARTZ forms six-sided (hexagonal) crystals that break along wavy, curved surfaces. This is called conchoidal fracture.

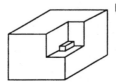

HALITE is the primary mineral in rock salt. The crystals are cubic. Halite breaks (cleaves) into tiny cubes and rectangular solids.

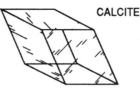

CALCITE crystals look like rectangular solids that have been squashed over to one side. This is called a rhombohedral shape. Calcite crystals split (cleave) in three directions parallel to their crystal faces.

MICA crystals cleave into thin sheets. This is called perfect cleavage in one direction.

ASBESTOS fractures into tiny fibers.

Figure 2-3. Crystal form, fracture, and cleavage are keys to mineral identification.

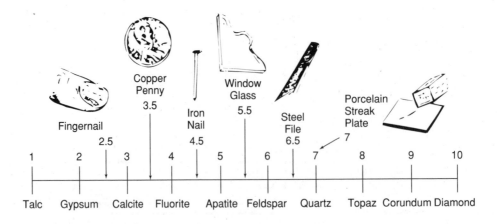

Figure 2-4. Mohs' scale of hardness is a relative index based upon the hardness of selected common minerals. This is not an absolute scale because the changes in hardness from step to step are not always the same. For example, diamond is much harder than corundum, in spite of a change of only one step on Mohs' scale.

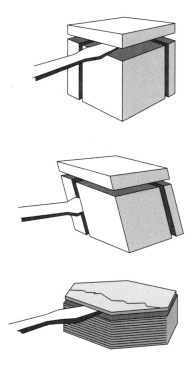

Figure 2-5. Halite (rock salt) shows cubic cleavage (top). The cleavage in calcite (middle) is rhombihedral, while mica (bottom) shows cleavage in one direction (sheets).

and galena form cubic crystals. The crystals of mica grow in "books" of thin, flexible sheets. Many minerals form distinctive and beautiful crystals. Figure 2-3 shows the characteristic crystal forms of five minerals.

Hardness. Minerals also differ in **hardness**. You test for hardness by scratching the unknown mineral with the edge or point of other minerals of known hardness.

Quartz is able to scratch most other minerals. Because calcite is softer than quartz, calcite cannot scratch quartz, but quartz can scratch calcite. The geologist Friedrich Mohs created a scale of hardness that uses relatively common minerals. On the Mohs' scale, talc is the softest mineral. The hardness of talc is 1. The hardest natural substance is the diamond. Its hardness is 10. The hardness of a fingernail is 2.5, calcite is 3, window glass is 5.5, and quartz has a hardness of 7. See Figure 2-4 for the hardness of other common materials.

Cleavage. If a mineral breaks readily along flat surfaces it shows cleavage. Cleavage comes from a Latin word meaning to cut, or cleave. Many minerals break along flat surfaces called **cleavage planes**. These cleavage planes are sometimes, but not always parallel to the sides of crystals. For example, halite (rock salt) breaks into small cubes and rectangular solids, the same shape as its crystals. However, quartz, which forms hexagonal crystals with flat faces, does not break along parallel planes. Minerals that break along even surfaces that do not follow the atomic arrangement (crystal faces) are said to show **fracture**. Quartz breaks along curved surfaces, a property known as conchoidal fracture. Figure 2-5 shows cleavage directions in halite, calcite, and mica.

Density. Minerals also vary in density and **specific gravity**. Specific gravity is a ratio of the density of a substance to the density of water. Water's density is 1 g/cm^3. Therefore, a mineral with a density of 4 g/cm^3 has a specific gravity of 4. As shown in Table 2-2, the density of many minerals falls within the range of 2.5 g/cm^3 to 3.5 g/cm^3. Gold, the densest substance you commonly see, has a density of about 19 g/cm^3, and the density of lead is about 12 g/cm^3. You can determine density in two ways: dividing the mass of a sample by its volume, or by flotation. A substance will sink in a liquid

Table 2-2. Density of Selected Materials

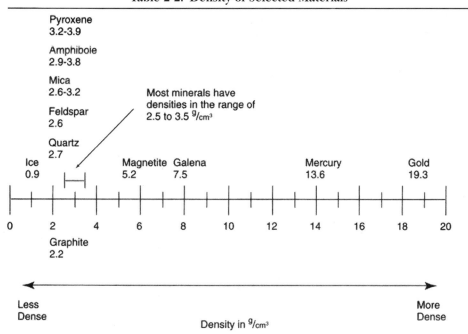

that is less dense than it is and float in a liquid that is more dense than it is.

QUESTIONS

1. A student broke a mineral sample with a tap of a hammer on a sharp chisel. What property was she investigating? (1) streak (2) specific gravity (3) cleavage (4) luster

2. Which of the following is a family of minerals? (1) sandstone (2) mica (3) air (4) water

3. How can you determine the hardness of a mineral? (1) Crush it in a vice. (2) Drop it onto a concrete surface. (3) Use it to scratch other solid materials. (4) Drop it into a graduated cylinder half-full of water.

4. Minerals are related to rocks as (1) automobiles are related to highways (2) chairs are related to tables (3) night is related to daylight (4) words are related to paragraphs

5. Many mineral samples are composed of (1) crystals (2) rocks (3) ice (4) plastic

6. What is the most common element in the crust of Earth, both by mass and by volume? (1) silicon (2) potassium (3) oxygen (4) carbon

7. How many different minerals are there in the rock shown below?

(1) 1 (2) 2 (3) 3 (4) 4

8. 100 people in different places around the world are told to walk outside and pick up the first natural mineral object they find. How many different minerals would you need to know to identify most of these samples? (1) about a dozen (2) just over 50 (3) about 100 (4) several thousand

9. Which of these mineral characteristics would *not* be useful in identifying a mineral sample? (1) density (2) volume (3) luster (4) streak

10. Which of the following elements is the *least* common in rocks of the Earth's crust? (1) magnesium (2) oxygen (3) aluminum (4) silicon

11. Which mineral property depends upon how light is reflected from a fresh mineral surface? (1) streak (2) specific gravity (3) cleavage (4) luster

12. If you observe a wide variety of samples of quartz, which property is likely to change the most, from sample to sample, because of minor impurities? (1) luster (2) hardness (3) density (4) color

13. What mineral property is shown being tested in the diagram below?

Screwdriver pushing the layers apart.

(1) luster (2) cleavage (3) streak (4) specific gravity

14. Which of the following terms best describes a surface that reflects almost *all* the light that hits it? (1) metallic (2) shiny (3) opaque (4) dark

15. What is the best way to test the hardness of a mineral? (1) Squeeze the mineral with calibrated pliers. (2) Measure the mass and volume of the sample. (3) Use the mineral to scratch a glass plate. (4) Break the mineral by hitting it with a hammer.

16. Which of the following mineral properties is something you can't just see by looking at a mineral sample? (1) luster (2) color (3) crystal form (4) hardness

17. Which property of quartz is always the same from sample to sample? (1) hardness (2) size (3) mass (4) color

ROCKS

Nearly all rocks are composed of one or more minerals. Limestone is made of calcite, while halite is the mineral in rock salt. But most rocks, such as granite, basalt, and sandstone, contain a variety of minerals. The minerals in granite—quartz, feldspar, amphibole, and biotite mica—are illustrated in Figure 2-6. Coal and organic limestone, which form from the remains of plants and animals, respectively, are rocks that are not composed of minerals.

Geologists classify rocks according to their origin (how they were formed). **Igneous** rocks form when molten rock, known as magma (or lava, when it reaches the surface), cools and solidifies. **Sedimentary** rocks usually result from the compaction and cementing of layers of sediment. The third kind of rock is called **metamorphic**. Metamorphic rocks form when igneous, sedimentary, or other metamorphic rocks are changed by heat and/or pressure.

Igneous Rocks.
Igneous rocks are always the result of the solidification of magma or lava, and only igneous rocks form from a hot liquid. When a liquid cools below its melting temperature (usually about 600°C to 1,000°C), it **crystallizes**, or becomes a solid as molecules arrange themselves into an ordered pattern that forms crystals.

The size of the crystals provides a clue to how quickly the rock solidified. Slow cooling allows the molecules enough time to form large crystals. Granite may have crystals one centimeter in length. Rapid cooling, such as occurs at the surface of a volcano, produces rock with

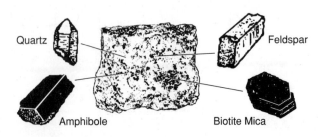

Figure 2-6. As most rocks are, granite is composed of a variety of minerals. These four are especially common.

crystals too small to be visible without the use of a magnifier, for example, basalt. In fact, volcanic glass (obsidian) cools so quickly that crystals do not have time to form. In general, igneous rocks that cool slowly deep within Earth, where temperatures are just below the melting temperature, are composed of large crystals. But rocks that form at or near Earth's surface usually cool quickly, and therefore have small crystals or no visible crystals at all.

Another characteristic of most igneous rocks is their general lack of layering. However, successive lava flows can form a layered igneous rock structure.

Classification. The most common igneous rocks are classified using just two characteristics: crystal size and color. For example, basalt is relatively dark in color (black to gray) and usually contains crystals too small to be obvious. On the other hand, granite contains crystals that are easily seen, and it is relatively light in overall color (gray to pink). Rhyolite is light-colored and fine-grained, while gabbro is dark-colored and coarse-grained. See Figure 2-7. Light-colored rocks are usually rich in feldspar and silica; they are called **felsic**. Darker rocks, such as basalt and gabbro, are called **mafic** because they contain more minerals rich in magnesium and iron (Fe), such as those in the amphibole and pyroxene families.

There are three relatively common igneous rocks that do not fit this scheme. Although obsidian (volcanic glass) is dark in color, it is almost always felsic in composition. Scoria looks like cinders, full of large air pockets. Pumice contains smaller air holes that make it look frothy. Sometimes pumice contains so many air pockets it floats in water.

It is important to remember that igneous rock is the only kind of rock that is formed from hot magma, and that all rocks that crystallize from melted rock are igneous.

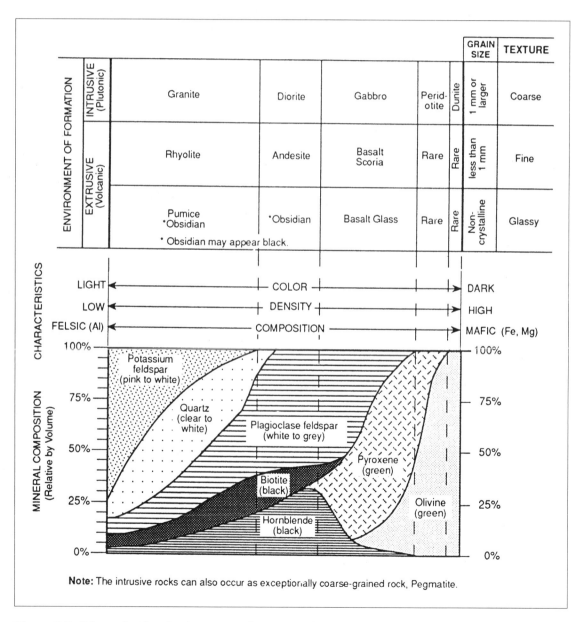

Figure 2-7. Scheme for identifying igneous rocks

18. According to the *Earth Science Reference Tables*, which of the graphs below best shows the relative grain sizes of the minerals in basalt, granite and rhyolite?

Key to Graph Abbreviations

B — Basalt
G — Granite
R — Rhyolite

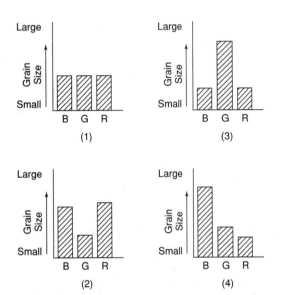

19. Which observation of an igneous rock would lead to the conclusion that the rock formed by the slow cooling of magma deep within Earth? (1) The rock has well defined layers. (2) The rock has large mineral crystals. (3) The rock is about 50% plagioclase feldspar. (4) The rock is light in color and low in density.

20. According to the *Earth Science Reference Tables*, what is the percentage of the mineral quartz in a typical granite? (1) 5% (2) 10% (3) 35% (4) 75%

21. Which choice best characterizes an igneous rock? (1) layers of rounded grains (2) a mass of intergrown crystals (3) banded layers of light and dark minerals (4) distorted and wavy layering

22. How do igneous rocks form? (1) high pressure at low temperatures (2) erosion and deposition (3) compaction and cementing (4) melting and solidification

23. According to the *Earth Science Reference Tables*, which mineral is found in a wide variety of igneous rocks? (1) orthoclase feldspar (2) plagioclase feldspar (3) quartz (4) dark (biotite) mica

24. According to the *Earth Science Reference Tables*, how does gabbro differ from basalt? (1) only in grain size (2) only in mineral composition (3) in color and grain size (4) in mineral composition and color

25. If an igneous rock is composed of large mineral crystals, we can conclude that (1) it contains both plagioclase and pyroxene (2) it is felsic and low in density (3) it formed near the earth's surface (4) it cooled slowly as it formed

26. According to the *Earth Science Reference Tables*, which of these is a fine-grained, dark-colored igneous rock? (1) basalt (2) granite (3) shale (4) diorite

27. Large crystals in a rock show that the rock formed (1) by rapid cooling at the Earth's surface (2) by slow cooling underground (3) from particles of weathered sediment (4) without melting and recrystalization

28. Sand collected from a beach contains a mixture of pyroxene, olivine, hornblende, and plagioclase feldspar. According to the *Earth Science Reference Tables*, what can we conclude about the rock the sand came from? (1) It was mafic in composition. (2) It was relatively low in density. (3) It contained only light-colored minerals. (4) It was either granite or rhyolite.

29. According to the *Earth Science Reference Tables*, what is the approximate percentage of plagioclase feldspar in igneous diorite? (1) 10% (2) 30% (3) 60% (4) 90%

30. Which of the four rocks shown below probably formed by the slow cooling and solidification of magma deep within Earth?

1. Alternating bands of light and dark minerals

3. Glassy rock that breaks with shell-shaped fracture

2. Splits into thin layers. Made of tiny clay particles

4. Interlocking crystals of various colors

31. Which characteristic of an igneous rock provides the most information about how it formed? (1) color (2) streak (3) texture (4) hardness

Sedimentary Rocks.

Most **sedimentary rocks** are composed primarily of the weathered remains of other rocks. Sedimentary rocks usually form by the compression and cementing of particles of sediment. Grains of sediment are usually rounded by abrasion and deposited in layers. These characteristics will help you recognize most sedimentary rocks. Although sedimentary rocks are the most common rocks that you see at the surface, they generally exist as a relatively thin layer over metamorphic and igneous rocks, which are more abundant within Earth.

Characteristics. The most common group of sedimentary rocks are the **fragmental** (clastic) rocks, which are made up of different sized particles (see Figure 2-8). Shale is made of tiny clay particles that are not visible to the unaided eye. Sandstone has particles large enough to be visible and to give it a gritty feel. Con-

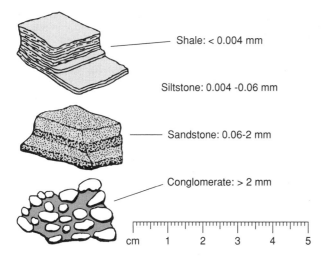

Shale: < 0.004 mm

Siltstone: 0.004 -0.06 mm

Sandstone: 0.06-2 mm

Conglomerate: > 2 mm

Figure 2-8. Clastic (fragmental) sedimentary rocks are classified by the size of their grains.

glomerate is composed of pebbles, cobbles, or boulders held together by natural cement.

There are two groups of sedimentary rocks that do not fit the characteristics discussed above. Coal and some forms of limestone result from the accumulation of plant and animal remains. For this reason, they are known as **organic** sedimentary rocks. **Fossils**, the remains of prehistoric life, are found almost exclusively in sedimentary rocks. Organic sedimentary rocks are especially rich in fossils.

Chemical sedimentary rocks are deposited by precipitation (settling) of materials from solution in seawater. This occurs during the evaporation of seawater and when chemical reactions in the water form insoluble compounds that settle. Although rock salt is the most common example of the **evaporite** rocks, there are others, such as gypsum. Figure 2-9 on page 32 shows how sedimentary rocks are classified.

QUESTIONS

32. Which of the following rock types often forms by precipitation from evaporating sea water? (1) gypsum (2) sandstone (3) basalt (4) shale

33. What property is used to classify a rock as shale, siltstone, sandstone or conglomerate? (1) the mineral composition (2) the shapes of the mineral crystals (3) the overall color of the rock (4) the size of the particles in the rock

34. How does rock salt form? (1) by crystallization of molten rock (2) by the cementing of cobbles and boulders (3) by heating and compression of other rocks (4) by the evaporation of sea water

35. According to the *Earth Science Reference Tables*, what kind of sedimentary rock may be composed of marine skeletons, or sea shell fragments cemented together? (1) limestone (2) rock salt (3) coal (4) siltstone

36. The accompanying diagram shows the actual size of a clastic (fragmental) sedimentary rock. According to the

Earth Science Reference Tables, what kind of rock is it? (1) conglomerate (2) sandstone (3) shale (4) siltstone

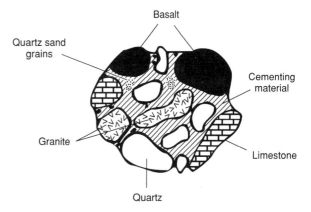

37. What can we conclude about the particles in this rock? (1) They must be the same age. (2) They formed in different ways. (3) They came from the same igneous rock. (4) They all contain the same minerals.

38. According to the *Earth Science Reference Tables*, sandstone can be composed entirely of sedimentary particles with a diameter of (1) 1/1000 (2) 1/10 cm (3) 1 cm (4) 10 cm

39. Where are sedimentary rocks usually found? (1) covering most of the continents (2) regions of recent volcanic activity (3) deep within the Earth's crust (4) next to igneous intrusions

40. Which process(es) change sediments into sedimentary rock? (1) melting (2) compression and cementing (3) extrusion and intrusion (4) metamorphism

41. Which feature provides the best evidence of the environment in which a rock was formed? (1) the overall color of the rock (2) the size of the rock sample (3) the texture of the rock (4) the thickness of the layers

42. Unlike sediments, sedimentary rocks often contain (1) rounded grains (2) layers (3) mineral cement (4) sorted particles

Directions: Base your answers to questions 43–44 on your knowledge of earth science and the *Earth Science Reference Tables*.

43. Some sedimentary rocks form as a direct result of (1) evaporation of seawater (2) recrystallization just before melting (3) solidification of melted rock (4) the weathering of solid rock

44. Rocks made directly from sediments usually contain (1) rounded particles in layers (2) hard, intergrown crystals (3) banded zones of minerals (4) distorted structures

Metamorphic Rocks   **Metamorphic rocks**
form when sedimentary and igneous rocks are changed by heat and/or pressure. Unlike sedimentary rocks, most metamorphic rocks have undergone significant changes caused by conditions deep within Earth. But, unlike igneous rocks, they never quite melted. Metamorphic rocks are the only kind of rock that forms directly from another rock.

INORGANIC LAND-DERIVED SEDIMENTARY ROCKS

TEXTURE	GRAIN SIZE	COMPOSITION	COMMENTS	ROCK NAME	MAP SYMBOL
Clastic (fragmental)	Sand, pebbles, cobbles, boulders	Mostly quartz, feldspar, clay minerals	Particles rounded and cemented by fine particles	Conglomerate	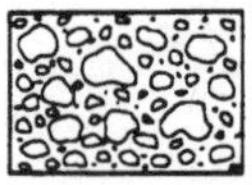
	Sand		Can be fine to coarse	Sandstone	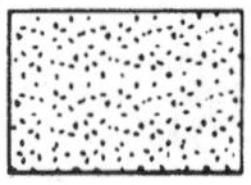
	Silt		Can be compact or easily split	Siltstone	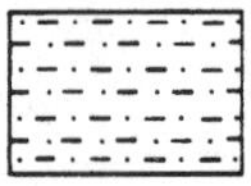
	Clay			Shale	

CHEMICALLY AND ORGANICALLY FORMED SEDIMENTARY ROCKS

TEXTURE	GRAIN SIZE	COMPOSITION	COMMENTS	ROCK NAME	MAP SYMBOL
Nonclastic	Coarse to fine	Calcite	Crystals from chemical precipitates (Incudes the evaporites)	Chemical Limestone	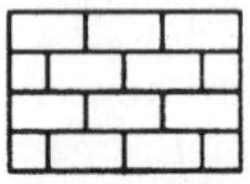
	All sizes	Mostly halite		Rock Salt	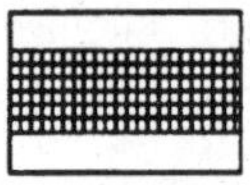
	All sizes	Gypsum		Rock Gypsum	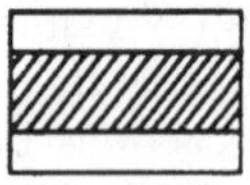
	All sizes	Dolomite	Changed from limestone by replacement	Dolostone	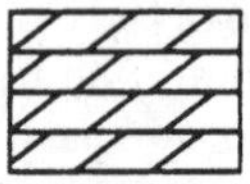
Organic	Microscopic to coarse (larger than 0.2 cm)	Calcite	Cemented shells, shell fragments, and skeletal remains	Fossil Limestone	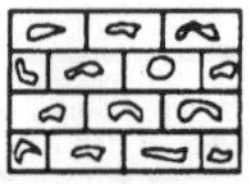
	All sizes	Carbon from plant remains	Black and nonporous	Coal	

Figure 2-9. Sedimentary rocks

The process of metamorphism may cause structures, such as layering, to become distorted or to disappear, it may cause new minerals to form, and/or crystals to grow. Metamorphism often results in the alignment of crystals, known as foliation. Schist is an example of a foliated rock. Metamorphism sometimes causes minerals to separate into light and dark layers, a property known as banding. Gneiss is an example of a rock that has light and dark bands. Figure 2-10 shows how these properties are used to classify and identify metamorphic rocks.

Most metamorphic rocks are formed deep (up to 20 km) within Earth. How do these rocks reach the surface where they can be seen? These rocks are pushed to the surface when mountains are formed. Forces within Earth move parts of the crust. This crustal movement causes mountains to be pushed up. The core of the mountains is made of metamorphic rock. In time, ero-

Scheme for Metamorphic Rock Identification

TEXTURE		GRAIN SIZE	COMPOSITION							TYPE OF METAMORPHISM	COMMENTS	ROCK NAME	MAP SYMBOL
FOLIATED	Slaty	Fine	CHLORITE	MICA						Regional	Low-grade metamorphism of shale	Slate	
	Schistose	Medium to coarse			QUARTZ	FELDSPAR	AMPHIBOLE	GARNET	PYROXENE		Medium-grade metamorphism; Mica crystals visible from metamorphism of feldspars and clay minerals	Schist	
	Gneissic	Coarse								(Heat and pressure increase with depth, folding, and faulting)	High-grade metamorphism; Mica has changed to feldspar	Gneiss	
NONFOLIATED		Fine	Carbonaceous								Metamorphism of plant remains and bituminous coal	Anthracite Coal	
		Coarse	Depends on conglomerate composition								Pebbles may be distorted or stretched; Often breaks through pebbles	Meta-conglomerate	
		Fine to coarse	Quartz							Thermal (including contact) or Regional	Metamorphism of sandstone	Quartzite	
			Calcite, Dolomite								Metamorphism of limestone or dolostone	Marble	
		Fine	Quartz, Plagioclase							Contact	Metamorphism of various rocks by contact with magma or lava	Hornfels	

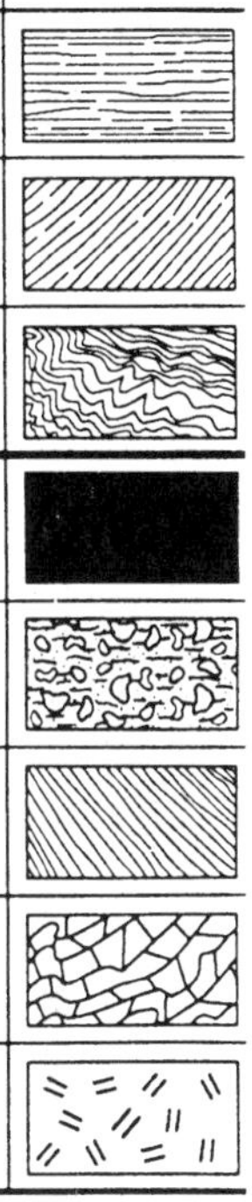

Figure 2-10. Scheme for metamorphic rock identification

sion wears down the mountains. This erosion may remove many kilometers of rock material, in the process exposing the deep metamorphic core of the mountains that once lay below Earth's surface.

The process by which rocks are transformed by pressure and heat deep within Earth is called regional metamorphism. The other process by which metamorphic rocks are formed is called contact metamorphism. In contact metamorphism, rocks are altered at or near Earth's surface as the result of contact with magma or lava. For example, when an igneous intrusion cuts through a layer of sandstone, the sandstone next to the hot, molten rock is baked. The crystal structure of the sandstone changes slightly, forming low grade quartzite. Because contact metamorphism does not involve the high temperatures and pressures found deep inside Earth, the rocks are usually not changed as much as they would be through regional metamorphism. Figure 2-11 shows the origins of the most common metamorphic rocks. Notice in Figures 2-11 and 2-12 (on page 34) how the type of metamorphic rock may change as a result of the intensity of metamorphism.

Classifying Rocks. A simplified scheme to classify rocks as igneous, sedimentary, or metamorphic is shown in Figure 2-13 on page 34. Clues given by their **texture** (the appearance and feel of the rock surfaces) help us identify these three kinds of rocks. Unfortunately, some rocks are difficult to classify because they do not clearly display these characteristics. For example, you might find it difficult to decide if a finely speckled gray rock is

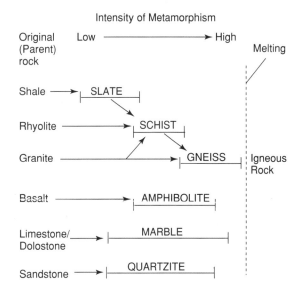

Figure 2-11. Origins of metamorphic rocks. This diagram shows the most common varieties of metamorphic rocks, as well as the original rock type before metamorphism. The "I-beam" below the rock names indicates the range of metamorphic change that forms any particular rock type. Please note that the conditions shown on the far right side of the diagram would melt the rock, resulting in magma, which could crystallize (solidify) to become igneous rock.

sandstone (sedimentary), low grade quartzite (metamorphic), or andesite (igneous). Still, this scheme is often useful in classifying rocks.

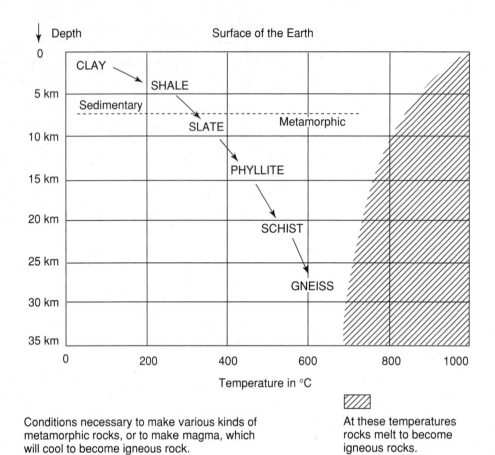

Depth

Surface of the Earth

Figure 2-12. A sequence of rock types shows the effect of increasingly deep burial.

Conditions necessary to make various kinds of metamorphic rocks, or to make magma, which will cool to become igneous rock.

At these temperatures rocks melt to become igneous rocks.

Because **igneous rocks** have formed from molten magma or lava, they are composed of intergrown crystals. Rapid cooling, however, can make the crystals too small to be visible. Igneous rocks are usually quite hard and dense, and layering is rare. Gas bubbles may give igneous rocks a frothy texture.

Most **sedimentary rocks** are composed of rounded fragments cemented in layers. In fine-grained rocks, the individual grains may be too small to be readily visible. Rocks made by chemical precipitation are composed of intergrown crystals, although these crystals are relatively soft. A rock that contains fossils is almost certainly a sedimentary rock.

Metamorphic rocks, like igneous rocks, are usually composed of intergrown crystals. But, like sedimentary rocks, they often show layering, banding, or foliation. The layers may be bent, or distorted.

Figure 2-13. A simplified way to classify rocks by means of their appearance

45. Metamorphic rocks are formed by (1) erosion of weathered rock (2) recrystalization of heated rock (3) cooling and solidification of magma (4) compression and cementing of sediment

46. How do metamorphic rocks differ from other rocks? Many metamorphic rocks (1) contain only one mineral (2) contain only dark, mafic minerals (3) show banding and distortion of structures (4) have an organic origin

47. According to the *Earth Science Reference Tables*, which of the following metamorphic rocks generally contains foliated crystals (crystals that have grown in the same direction)? (1) quartzite (2) schist (3) marble (4) meta-conglomerate

48. According to the *Earth Science Reference Tables*, which metamorphic rock generally contains the smallest crystals? (1) schist (2) gneiss (3) slate (4) metaconglomerate

49. Which of the following changes does *not* create a metamorphic rock? (1) growth of mineral crystals (2) intense heating without melting (3) compression within the Earth (4) melting and solidification

50. Which two rock types would probably be separated by a zone of metamorphic rock? (1) shale and basalt (2) limestone and soft coal (3) basalt and granite (4) sandstone and shale

51. According to the *Earth Science Reference Tables*, which rock in the diagram above, is shale? (1) A (2) B (3) C (4) D

52. How does metamorphic gneiss differ from igneous granite? (1) they contain very different minerals (2) the gneiss never quite melted (3) the granite has rounded grains (4) the granite shows thin layers.

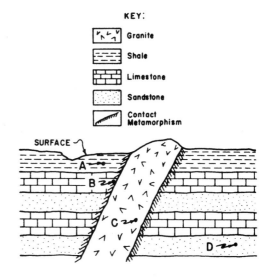

ROCK CYCLE

The **rock cycle** is a model of natural changes in rocks and rock material. Our planet has a limited mass. Although Earth receives a small amount of matter in the form of meteorites and a very small amount of our atmosphere is lost to outer space, our planet is basically a closed system. That is, the material of Earth can cycle through various forms, but the mass of Earth does not change. See Figure 2-14.

This diagram distinguishes between those processes that take place primarily at Earth's surface (external processes) and those that take place within Earth (internal processes). Internal processes, such as compression and heating, require the conditions of extreme temperature and pressure that occur deep underground.

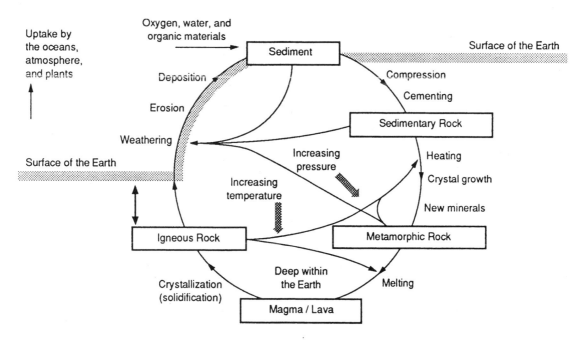

Figure 2-14. The rock cycle is a model that shows the changes that created the three principal rock types.

The rock cycle illustrates several important principles of geology. First, nearly all rocks are made from the remains of other rocks. (Coal and other organic sedimentary rocks are notable exceptions.) Second, rocks are classified on the basis of their origin. Finally, there are a variety of ways that rocks can change in response to changing conditions at the surface or within Earth.

If you follow the outside of the rock cycle diagram, you will see that sediments can be compressed and cemented to form sedimentary rocks. These rocks can then be changed by intense heat and/or pressure to become metamorphic rocks, which may be melted and recrystallized to make igneous rock. Weathering and erosion create sediments, and the cycle continues.

There is more than one path through the rock cycle. The arrows within the circle show that igneous rock can not only undergo weathering, erosion, and deposition to make sediment, but it can also be changed by heating, crystal growth, and the formation of new minerals to make a metamorphic rock. Alternately, it can be remelted to make molten rock, magma. Metamorphic rock can be melted and crystallized to become igneous rock, or weathered, eroded, and cemented into sedimentary rock. It can also be further altered by heat and pressure into new metamorphic rock.

Each rock type can remain relatively stable for long periods of time. Changes from one rock type to another may require thousands or even millions of years. Sometimes a rock may show evidence of more than one process or origin. For example, a conglomerate may be composed of cemented fragments of granite (igneous rock) and gneiss (metamorphic rock). Although conglomerate is a sedimentary rock, some of the rock fragments within it may be nonsedimentary.

QUESTIONS

Directions: Use the diagram below for Questions 53–58.

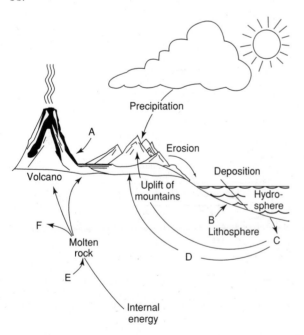

53. At which location on the diagram (bottom, left) is an igneous rock with small crystals or a glassy texture likely to form? (1) A (2) B (3) C (4) F

54. Which location is the most likely to produce a rock with a variety of hard, intergrown crystals and layers (foliation)? (1) A (2) B (3) E (4) D

55. Where are rocks composed of rounded particles cemented together likely to form? (1) A (2) F (3) C (4) E

56. As the rocks formed at C move toward D, how are the conditions likely to change? (1) heat and pressure will both decrease (2) heat and pressure will both increase (3) heat will increase, pressure will decrease (4) heat will decrease, pressure will increase

57. Fossils are the most likely to be found in the rocks at (1) A (2) D (3) C (4) F

58. A rock that cooled slowly at "F" and contains about 65% pyroxene should probably be classified as (1) granite (2) rhyolite (3) gabbro (4) basalt

59. According to the rock cycle diagram in the *Earth Science Reference Tables*, igneous rock *cannot* change directly into (1) sediment (2) metamorphic rock (3) magma (4) sedimentary rock

NATURAL RESOURCES

Natural resources are substances that come from Earth. Examples of geological resources of economic importance are shown in Table 2-3. As the need for these resources grows, there may come a time when they become scarce. Scarcity can cause the prices of these resources to increase, or it may influence us to find other substances to meet our needs. Recycling is also a way to help meet our needs and to save resources. In addition, recycling reduces the amount of trash that must be disposed of.

There are two types of natural resources: renewable and nonrenewable. **Renewable** resources can be replaced after they have been used. For example, trees are a renewable resource. After one crop of trees has been cut, another is planted. Fresh water is a renewable resource because rain refills the lakes and rivers. However, in the American southwest, surface and groundwater are being used more quickly than they can be replaced by the environment. Dwindling water supplies are unsettled political issues in these areas.

Table 2-3. Important Geological Resources		
Group	Minerals/ Products	Common Uses
Metals	Gold Copper	Jewelry, Coins, Dental Fillings Electrical Wiring, Plumbing, Coins
Non-Metals	Graphite Iron Ore Halite (rock salt) Garnet Feldspar	Lubricants, Pencil "Lead" Construction, Vehicles, Machinery Food, Chemicals, Melting Ice Abrasives, Jewelry Porcelain, Glass, Ceramics
Fossil Fuels	Coal Petroleum	Heating, Power Plants, Synthetics Fuels, Heating, Medicines, Plastics

Nonrenewable resources, after they are used, cannot be replenished for millions of years, if at all. The native metals, such as gold and copper, as well as the ores of metals, such as iron and aluminum, are considered nonrenewable resources. Although they are being formed in some locations, such as steam vents in the deep oceans, the rate of renewal is much slower than the rate at which they are taken from the ground.

The **fossil fuels**—coal, oil, and natural gas—were formed millions of years ago from the remains of ancient organisms. Fossil fuels are nonrenewable resources. In the past two centuries, these resources have been seriously depleted. In addition, our use of these fuels has accelerated in recent decades.

Although coal is the most abundant fossil fuel, scientists estimate that worldwide coal reserves will last only about 200 years. Supplies of crude oil, or petroleum, are being used up faster than new resources are being found. The United States imports much of the petroleum it uses. If enough oil cannot be imported, shortages develop. Figure 2-15 shows that the world's petroleum supply is not distributed equally. A small number of nations around the Persian Gulf control more than half the world's estimated reserves.

In addition to being used for fuel, petroleum is the source of the petrochemicals used to make plastics, synthetic fabrics, medicines, insecticides, fertilizers, and detergents, which are important to the global economy.

Alternative Energy Sources. Scientists are looking for other sources of energy to replace fossil fuels. One possible source of energy is the sun. Solar energy is plentiful and renewable. Solar energy can be used to provide heat, hot water, and to generate electricity. However, the amount of solar energy that reaches Earth varies with the time of day and the seasons. Today, using solar energy to produce electricity is possible, but it is

generally more expensive to produce electricity in this way than by using fossil fuels. Geothermal energy, from heat within Earth can be used to generate electricity, and produce heat and hot water. However, it is available only in certain areas, such as northern California and Iceland. Wind-driven generators are now used in many areas to provide electricity. These generators are practical only in areas where there are strong, steady winds. Nuclear energy is another possibility. It can be used to generate electricity without causing air pollution. The drawback to nuclear energy is the danger of a nuclear accident and of long-term storage of radioactive wastes.

QUESTIONS

60. Which of the following is a renewable resource? (1) fossil fuels (2) iron ore (3) solar energy (4) gold

61. Plastics, insecticides, and medicines are made from (1) solar power (2) petrochemicals (3) renewable resources (4) nuclear energy

62. Which of the following natural resources will be conserved if people use public transportation, smaller cars, and lower their thermostats in the winter? (1) native metals (2) metal ores (3) fossil fuels (4) all of them

63. If the United States could not import foreign petroleum products, which of the following might help us cope with the shortage? (1) build larger automobiles (2) reduce the price of airline tickets (3) build cars that are more fuel efficient (4) discontinue public transportation

64. Solar energy would *not* be a good alternative to fossil fuel in areas that have (1) variable winds (2) nuclear wastes (3) no wind (4) constant cloudy weather

---

The Scientist, Engineer, and Citizen

Devise guidelines to instruct mining companies that operate near your community to minimize the environmental damage resulting from both open-pit and below-ground extraction of minerals.

CHAPTER 2 REVIEW QUESTIONS

1. What two elements are the most common in the silicate minerals? (1) silicon and aluminum (2) oxygen and aluminum (3) iron and aluminum (4) oxygen and silicon

2. Which rocks would most likely be separated by a zone of metamorphic rock? (1) granite and limestone (2) sandstone and limestone (3) shale and sandstone (4) conglomerate and siltstone

3. According to the *Earth Science Reference Tables*, compared with basalt, granite is (1) darker in color (2) greater in density (3) more mafic in composition (4) more coarse-grained in texture

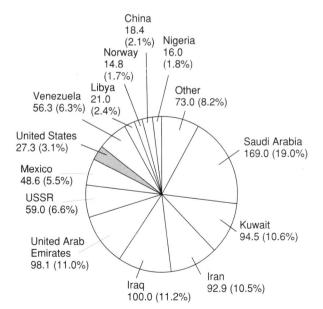

Figure 2-15. This pie graph shows that more than half of the world's estimated one trillion barrels of underground oil reserves are in the countries of the Persian Gulf.

4. Classifying rocks as igneous, sedimentary, or metamorphic is based upon differences in their (1) age (2) particle size (3) hardness (4) origin

5. What sedimentary rock would be formed from particles 2 to 4 centimeters in diameter cemented by a fine-grained matrix? (1) shale (2) sandstone (3) conglomerate (4) siltstone

6. What kinds of igneous rock have the same mineral composition? (1) rhyolite and granite (2) rhyolite and basalt (3) granite and gabbro (4) granite and basalt

7. Which of these four minerals is probably the most common within a relatively mafic sample of basalt? (1) plagioclase (2) biotite (3) pyroxene (4) hornblende

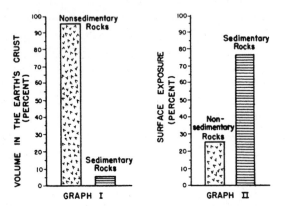

Directions: Base your answers to questions 8–11 on the graphs above and the *Earth Science Reference Tables*.

8. According to the graphs above, what portion of Earth's crust is composed of sedimentary rocks? (1) 5% (2) 25% (3) 75% (4) 95%

9. Which statement below is best supported by these two graphs? (1) The Earth's crust is mostly sedimentary rock. (2) Most rocks at Earth's surface are *not* sedimentary rock. (3) All rocks are composed of weathered and eroded remains of other rocks. (4) Sedimentary rocks are usually found at or near Earth's surface.

10. What is the most abundant element present in the rocks shown in Graph I? (1) nitrogen (2) oxygen (3) silicon (4) hydrogen

11. All of the rocks shown in Graph I contain (1) fossils (2) sediments (3) minerals (4) intergrown crystals

12. According to the *Earth Science Reference Tables*, what mineral is commonly found in granite, but not found in basalt? (1) quartz (2) plagioclase (3) olivine (4) hornblende

Directions: Use this diagram and the *Earth Science Reference Tables* to answer questions 13–19.

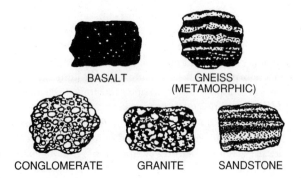

BASALT   GNEISS (METAMORPHIC)

CONGLOMERATE   GRANITE   SANDSTONE

13. Granite is composed of large crystals because it (1) is relatively high in density (2) is composed of felsic minerals (3) cooled slowly, deep underground (4) contains pebbles of various compositions

14. Which sample is composed of sedimentary particles from 0.006 cm to 0.2 cm in diameter that have been compressed and cemented together? (1) sandstone (2) gneiss (3) conglomerate (4) granite

15. Which rock was heated to a temperature near, but not above, the melting point? (1) conglomerate (2) gneiss (3) sandstone (4) granite

16. How does basalt form? (1) pressure and heat, just below melting (2) compaction and cementing (3) erosion and deposition (4) melting and solidification

17. Which of these samples is a coarse-grained igneous rock? (1) conglomerate (2) granite (3) sandstone (4) gneiss

18. All five of these rock samples contain (1) minerals (2) rounded particles (3) foliation (4) large crystals

19. Which sequence below best shows the environments in which these rocks formed, from those that formed near the surface, to those that formed the deepest within the Earth? (1) sandstone, gneiss, granite (2) gneiss, granite, sandstone (3) granite, gneiss, sandstone (4) gneiss, sandstone, granite

20. Which of the following minerals is the most dense?

MINERAL SAMPLES	MASS	VOLUME
Quartz	10 g	4 cm³
Feldspar	20 g	8 cm³
Galena	15 g	2 cm³
Biotite Mica	18 g	6 cm³

(1) quartz (2) feldspar (3) galena (4) biotite

The diagram below shows elements found in four common minerals. Use this diagram and the *Earth Science Reference Tables* to answer questions 21–24.

	O	Si	Al	Fe	Ca	Na	C
Quartz	X	X					
Feldspar	X	X	X		X	X	
Olivine	X	X		X	X		
Diamond							X

("X" means that the element is present)

21. According to the table above, which mineral is *not* a silicate? (1) quartz (2) diamond (3) olivine (4) feldspar

22. Which mineral contains the greatest variety of elements? (1) quartz (2) diamond (3) olivine (4) feldspar

23. Which of the following elements is the most abundant in the crust of Earth? (1) iron (2) silicon (3) oxygen (4) calcium

24. Which of these minerals is the *least* common in rocks around New York State? (1) quartz (2) diamond (3) feldspar (4) mica

25. How a rock was created can best be determined by observing the rock's (1) density (2) size (3) texture (4) chemical composition

26. A rock composed of intergrown crystals *must* be (1) sedimentary (2) igneous (3) metamorphic (4) any of these three

27. Which mineral property is most likely to change from sample to sample of the same mineral? (1) color (2) hardness (3) density (4) cleavage

28. How do most igneous rocks form? (1) erosion and deposition (2) melting and solidification (3) heat and pressure without melting (4) compaction and cementing

29. Which of the following is *not* a type of rock? (1) quartzite (2) feldspar (3) gneiss (4) conglomerate

30. Which of the following is *not* a mineral or a family of minerals? (1) feldspar (2) calcite (3) mica (4) sandstone

31. What is the most common mineral in rock salt? (1) feldspar (2) quartz (3) halite (4) silicon

32. Unlike the mineral quartz, calcite (1) is colorless (2) has a glassy luster (3) has a dark color (4) bubbles with acid

33. Most sedimentary rocks are formed by (1) uplifting and melting (2) compaction and cementing (3) eruption of volcanoes (4) changes deep within the Earth

34. Which of the following is usually a characteristic of nonsedimentary rocks? (1) crystals (2) fossils (3) layers (4) rounded grains

35. What rock is commonly composed of the remains of animal shells? (1) sandstone (2) granite (3) limestone (4) gneiss

36. Which type (or types) of rock is (are) usually heated as a part of its (their) formation? (1) sedimentary rocks only (2) sedimentary and igneous rocks (3) igneous rocks only (4) metamorphic and igneous rocks

37. What kind of metamorphic rock usually contains abundant mica crystals and a foliated texture? (1) schist (2) marble (3) slate (4) quartzite

38. Rocks are classified on the basis of (1) their density (2) their age in years (3) their shape (4) how they formed

39. Nearly all rocks contain (1) fossils (2) crystals (3) minerals (4) rounded grains

40. A renewable resource is one that cannot be used up because it is created nearly as fast as we use it. Which of the following resources is *not* renewable? (1) wind (2) petroleum (3) sunlight (4) groundwater

Directions: Base your answers to questions 41–44 on the diagram below that shows a profile view of a volcano and a variety of nearby rock types.

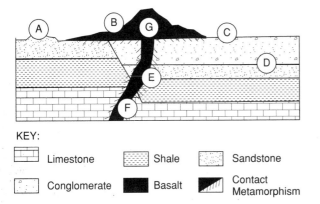

KEY:
☐ Limestone ☐ Shale ☐ Sandstone
☐ Conglomerate ■ Basalt ◢ Contact Metamorphism

41. At which location could you probably find a rock composed of very small intergrown crystals? (1) A (2) B (3) C (4) D

42. Where could you probably find quartzite? (1) A (2) B (3) D (4) E

43. The rock at B most likely contains (1) only quartz (2) quartz and hornblende (3) only pyroxene (4) pyroxene and plagioclase

44. At which location is a rock that contains weathered and recycled pebbles from older, former rocks? (1) B (2) C (3) F (4) G

45. According to the *Earth Science Reference Tables*, oxygen is the most abundant element near the Earth's surface within the (1) air (2) rocks (3) oceans (4) living materials

46. A chemically formed sedimentary rock composed of halite best describes a rock we know as (1) gypsum (2) limestone (3) rock salt (4) hard coal

FREE-RESPONSE QUESTIONS

(Answer the following questions on a separate sheet of paper.)

1. In one or more complete sentences, name a mineral, and list two properties that can be used to identify this particular mineral. (Do not use any properties that commonly change from sample to sample.) Be sure to give the specific properties of that mineral. For example, "You can tell by its weight" is *not* specific. "Weighs more than one kilogram" is specific.
(Complete sentence(s), +1; Mineral name, +1; Correct properties, +1 & +1)

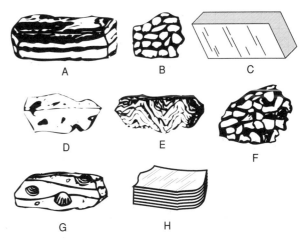

2. Of the eight diagrams above, two represent sedimentary rocks. List the letters of each of the sedimentary rock samples, and tell what feature of each identifies it as a sedimentary rock. The same reason may not be used twice. For example, letter A represents a metamorphic rock (gneiss) because it shows metamorphic banding: light and dark layers. Use one or more complete sentences.
(At least one correct sample letter, +1; Each reason, +1)

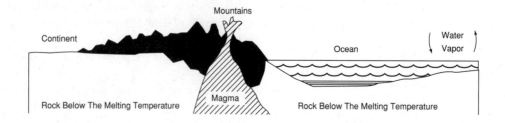

3. The diagram above represents a profile view of a part of Earth's crust. Describe the location where

(a) sedimentary rocks may now be forming,

(b) coarse-grained igneous rocks may now be forming,

(c) metamorphic rocks may be forming.

(+1 for each location)

4. In one or more complete sentences, name one mineral resource that is important to our daily lives, tell how that mineral is changed so that we can make use of it, and give an example of how we use it.

(Complete sentence(s), +1; Mineral name, +1; How it is changed, +1; How we use it, +1)

5. According to the table Selected Mineral and Energy Resources, for which of these mineral resources is the United States **most** dependent upon other countries? Name the mineral and explain why in a complete sentence.

(Mineral, +1; Sentence, +1)

6. Using the information in Selected Mineral and Energy Resources, state two (2) reasons why gold is more valuable than halite. (Use one or more complete sentences.)

(Each reason, +1; Sentence(s), +1)

7. Explain how we know if one mineral is harder than another. Don't just name the test, be sure to explain what you would have to do. Assume that all you have is the two mineral samples. Please keep your answer brief. (Use one or more complete sentences.)

(Procedure, +1 or +2; Sentence(s), +1)

8. Use this circle to make a pie chart of the approximate mineral composition of the igneous rock basalt.

(Readable Pie Graph, +1; Number of Minerals, +1; Relative Percentages, +1)

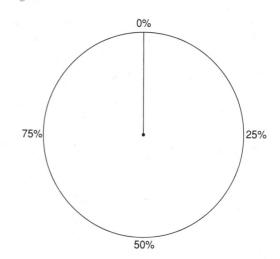

MINERAL NAME	% OF BASALT

Selected Mineral and Energy Resources			
Group	Mineral	Uses	Occurrence (USA & Foreign)
Native Elements			
	Gold	Investment, Electrical Conductors, Dental fillings	California, South Africa, Russia
	Copper	Electrical Wiring, Plumbing, Coins	Michigan, Chile, Arizona
	Graphite	Lubricants, Pencil "lead"	New York, Ceylon
	Diamond	(Form of Carbon) Gems, Abrasives, Phono Needles	South Africa, Russia
Mineral Compounds & Mixtures			
	Hematite	(Ore of Iron) Construction, Motor Vehicles	Michigan, New York (worldwide)
	Halite	Food Additive, Melting of ice, Chemicals	New York, Louisiana (worldwide)
	Garnet	Abrasive (sandpaper), January birthstone	New York, Madagascar, India
	Feldspar	Porcelain, Glass, Ceramics	New York (worldwide)
Fuels			
	Coal	Heating, Transportation, Synthetic Chemicals	Pennsylvania (worldwide)
	Petroleum	Fuel, Plastics, Synthetic Materials, Medicines	Texas, Arabia (worldwide)

CHAPTER 3 The Dynamic Crust

WHAT CAUSES EARTHQUAKES?

An **earthquake** is any vibrating, shaking, or rapid motion of Earth's crust. Most earthquakes occur when stress builds along a zone of weakness or a break in the rock known as a **fault**. See Figure 3-1. When the stress exceeds the ability of the crust to resist breaking, the crust shifts and energy is released suddenly. The energy radiates in all directions in the form of vibrations. The place underground where the break occurs is the **focus** of the earthquake. The **epicenter** is the location at Earth's surface just above the focus. When the vibrations reach the surface, we feel them as an earthquake, first at the epicenter and then at greater distances from the epicenter. The features of an earthquake are shown in Figure 3-2.

Measuring Earthquakes.
There are two types of measurement applied to earthquakes: magnitude and intensity scales. Scales of **intensity**, such as Mercalli scales, are based upon the reports of people who experienced the earthquake and observed the amount of destruction. A simplified scale of Mercalli intensities is shown in Table 3-1 on page 42. Intensity scales do not measure the energy level of an earthquake, but they do indicate its human impact. The intensity at which an earthquake is felt depends on the observer's distance from the epicenter and the ability of the ground to transmit this energy. With the widespread use of seismometers, you might think that intensity scales are becoming obsolete. However, because there is a limited number of seismic instruments and the uncertain nature of Earth materials through which the earthquake waves travel, it is often difficult to locate the epicenter of an earthquake. Geologists still use Mercalli reports to measure seismic events and to locate the epicenters of earthquakes.

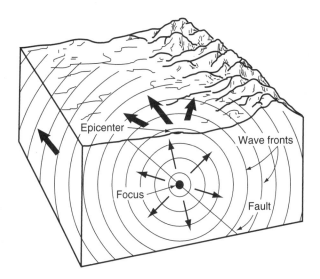

Figure 3-2. Ground motion radiates from the focus of an earthquake in energy waves.

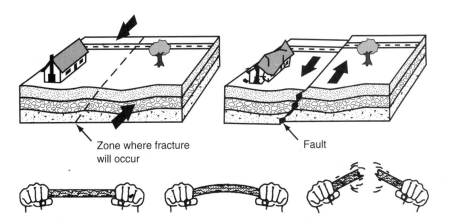

Figure 3-1. When stress exceeds the strength of Earth's crust, rocks break along a zone of weakness and move. Sudden shifting along the fault releases the energy that you can feel as an earthquake.

Table 3-1. A Simplified Scheme for Measuring Earthquakes

Mercalli Intensity	Observed Effects and Experiences	Number per Year World Wide	Estimated Magnitude
I or II	May not be felt, but can be recorded by sensitive seismometers.	~one million	2
V to VI	Felt by most people. Some dishes and windows broken.	~tens of thousands	4
VII to VIII	Difficult to stand up. Collapse of structures that are not reinforced.	~one hundred	6
X to XII	Waves visible on ground. Damage to buildings may be total.	~one every five years	8

The most reliable measures of earthquakes are made with **seismographs**. As shown in Figure 3-3, these instruments operate on the principle that a heavy weight suspended on a spring tends to remain steady while the ground shakes. A pen is attached to the weight. During an earthquake, the pen remains stationary while the drum shakes. The pen makes tracings on the paper attached to the revolving drum. Technological advances have led to electronic instruments that can record a wide range of frequencies and magnitudes. Seismographic records of earthquakes have enabled geologists to establish **magnitude** scales, such as those pioneered by Charles Richter and others. It is important to note that magnitude scales are logarithmic. That is, each increase of one unit means a ten-fold increase in shaking. Therefore, a magnitude 6 earthquake has 10 times as much shaking as a magnitude 5 event and 100 times more shaking than a magnitude 4 event.

LOCATING EARTHQUAKES

When an earthquake occurs, the energy of the quake radiates in waves away from the focus as shown in Figure 3-2. These waves can be grouped into three categories. **P-waves** travel the fastest. In addition to standing for Primary, "P" also stands for push-pull, which describes the ground motion as these waves pass. The vibration of a P-wave is like the motion of a spring when it is alternately pulled tighter and then released.

The second category is **S-waves**. "S" stands for Secondary or side-to-side. (Actually, S-waves vibrate in all directions perpendicular to the direction of travel.) S-wave motion is like the wave that travels down a rope when one end is moved quickly from side-to-side. S-waves travel more slowly than P-waves. See Figure 3-4.

The third category of seismic waves is the surface waves. These waves include both push-pull and side-to-

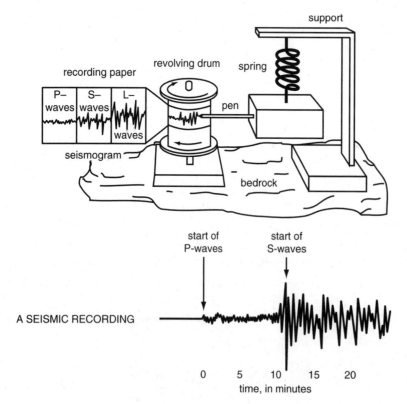

Figure 3-3. Traditional seismographs record shaking of the ground with a large mass suspended on a spring. However, the most modern instruments use electronic devices to generate a digital output. The instrument should be capable of showing movement over a wide range of frequencies and many orders of magnitude.

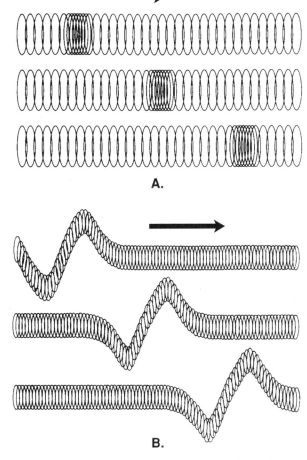

A.

B.

Figure 3-4. As P-waves travel outward from the earthquake focus, they cause the rock to vibrate forward and back, parallel to the direction of motion, like sound waves. (A) But S-waves vibrate at an angle of 90° to the direction of motion, like light waves. (B)

side motion. Surface waves cause the most damage as they travel along Earth's surface.

The Epicenter.
The seismograph records the magnitude of an earthquake and the time the seismic waves arrive. **Seismologists** (scientists who study earthquakes) use the difference in the speeds of P- and S-waves to locate the epicenters of earthquakes. The *Travel Time Graph* found in the *Earth Science Reference Tables* shows how long it takes P- and S-waves to travel through Earth. Scientists know that as the seismic waves travel outward from the focus, the time delay between the P-waves and S-waves increases.

Finding Your Distance From an Earthquake Epicenter. To calculate your distance from an earthquake epicenter, proceed as follows:

1. Subtract the arrival time of the P-waves from the arrival time of the S-waves. (This can be expressed in minutes and seconds, such as 06:40.) See Figure 3-5A.

2. On the clean edge of a sheet of paper, make two marks to show that interval along the travel-time scale

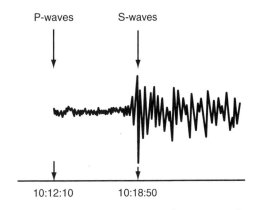

Figure 3-5A. A 6-minute, 40-second separation between P- and S-waves.

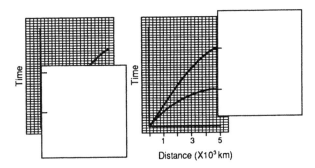

Figure 3-5B. The distance to the epicenter of an earthquake can be determined if we know the time difference between the arrival of P-waves and S-waves.

on the vertical axis of the *Time Travel Graph*. See Figure 3-5B.

3. Keeping the edge of the paper vertical, slide the marks on the edge of your paper along the P- and S-curves of the travel-time scale until the marks coincide with both curves. See Figure 3-5B.

4. Follow the marked edge of your paper down to the horizontal axis to find the distance to the epicenter.

This procedure has not yet located the epicenter, but it has established the distance from the recording station to the epicenter. If a circle with a radius equal to that distance is drawn around the recording station, the epicenter should be located somewhere along that circle. To find the exact location, follow the procedure above to find the distance from the epicenter to three seismic recording stations. Draw circles around each of these stations at the proper distances. The epicenter is the point at which the *three* circles intersect. See Figure 3-6 on page 44. (In practice, the circles seldom intersect at a single point. More often, they make a small triangle. The epicenter's location is at the center of that triangle.)

The Origin Time of an Earthquake.
An earthquake's waves are detected at later times by observers at greater distances from its epicenter. Each observer may know immediately when he or she feels the

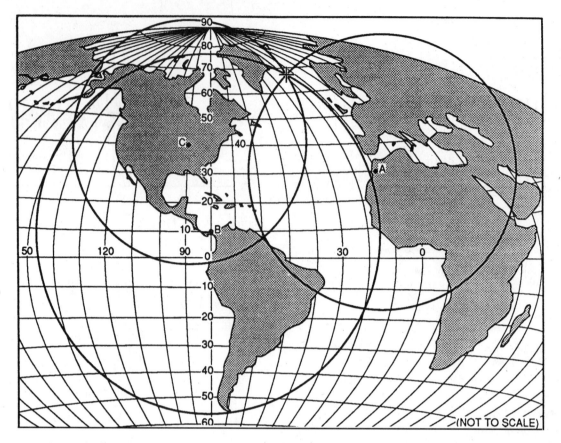

Figure 3-6. The location of an epicenter can be determined if we know the distances from three seismic recording stations. This epicenter is in Iceland, in the North Atlantic.

vibrations, but may not know when the earthquake occurred at the epicenter.

To find the **origin time**, a seismologist needs to know the time at which the earthquake was first recorded at the station, that is, the arrival time of the P-waves and the amount of time that the waves took to get there (the travel time). If we know the distance to the epicenter (as determined in the section above), the travel time can be determined from the *Earthquake S-wave & P-Wave Time Travel Graph* in the *Earth Science Reference Tables*. For example, if the epicenter is 4000 kilometers away, the travel time for P-waves is 7 minutes. Thus, if the earthquake was recorded at a station at 2:25 PM (14:25:00) and the P-waves took 7 minutes to get there (travel time), then the earthquake must have actually happened 7 minutes earlier, at 2:18 PM (14:18:00).

(2) the depth of the earthquake focus (3) the geographic location of the epicenter (4) the distance to the epicenter

3. Which graph below best shows the difference in arrival times for P- and S-waves?

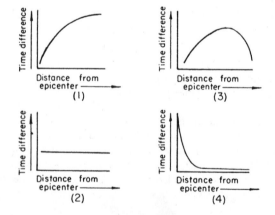

4. How far can S-waves travel in 3 minutes? (1) 700 km (2) 1400 km (3) 5700 km (4) 10,000 km

5. If the P-wave from an earthquake arrives 5 minutes, 30 seconds before the S-wave, how far away is the earthquake epicenter? (1) 1000 km (2) 2000 km (3) 3000 km (4) 4000 km

6. If a P-wave arrives 4 minutes after an earthquake occurs at the epicenter, how far away is the epicenter? (1) 1000 km (2) 2000 km (3) 7000 km (4) 10,000 km

QUESTIONS

1. As the distance from an earthquake epicenter increases, the time between P-wave arrival and S-wave arrival will (1) decrease (2) increase (3) remain the same

2. Which of the following can be determined by knowing only the arrival times of both P- and S-waves at a single recording station? (1) the direction to the earthquake

Directions: Use this table to answer questions 7, 8, and 9.

Seismic Station	P-wave Travel Time
A	8 min 20 sec
B	0 min 31 sec
C	12 min 18 sec
D	3 min 20 sec

7. Which station is the closest to the epicenter? (1) A (2) B (3) C (4) D

8. If the P-wave arrived at station D at 09:25:10, what was the origin time of the earthquake, at the epicenter? (1) 06:04:50 (2) 06:05:00 (3) 09:21:50 (4) 09:22:50

9. How far from the epicenter was Station D? (1) 900 km (2) 1600 km (3) 2000 km (4) 5100 km

10. An earthquake occurred at 05:00:00. When would the first P-waves arrive at a seismic recording station 3000 kilometers away? (1) 05:01:40 (2) 05:04:30 (3) 05:05:40 (4) 05:10:15

11. What type of earthquake wave is usually received first at a recording station 2000 km from the epicenter? (1) A-waves (2) L-waves (3) P-waves (4) S-waves

Directions: Use this map to answer questions 12–16.

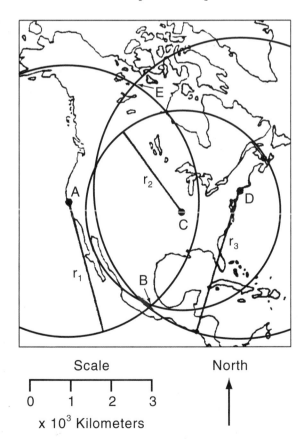

Scale

0   1   2   3

x 10³ Kilometers

North

12. Which letter shows the location of the epicenter? (1) E (2) B (3) C (4) D

13. Where was this earthquake felt first? (1) A (2) E (3) C (4) D

14. Which location is best shown by the seismogram below?

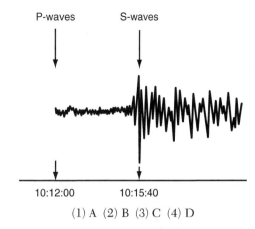

P-waves   S-waves

10:12:00   10:15:40

(1) A (2) B (3) C (4) D

15. How long did it take for the P-waves to reach location E, 5000 kilometers from the earthquake? (1) 10 min (2) 8 min, 20 sec (3) 15 min, 30 sec (4) 25 min

16. Which event happened first? (1) arrival of P-waves at A (2) arrival of S-waves at A (3) arrival of P-waves at C (4) arrival of S-waves at C

EARTH'S LAYERS

Have you ever had an X-ray or a CAT-scan? Doctors use these techniques to "see" inside your body without having to perform surgery. Just as physicians need to know what is inside the human body, geologists want to know what is going on inside Earth. They cannot use X-rays or CAT-scans to see into Earth. Although it is possible to dig fairly deep into the crust, it is impossible to journey to the center of Earth. Scientists have discovered that earthquake waves penetrate Earth. The study of these waves provides scientists with valuable information about the structure of the interior of our planet.

The Crust.   The **crust**, the outermost layer of our planet, varies from about 5 kilometers of thickness under the oceans to about 60 kilometers under some mountain ranges on the continents. The composition of the crust is reasonably well known from observations at the surface and from mines and bore holes. In most places a thin layer of sedimentary rocks covers the mostly granitelike (**granitic**) rocks of the **continental crust**. The **oceanic crust**, under the layers of marine sediments, is composed mostly of darker and denser rocks similar to basalt (**basaltic**).

The Mantle.   Although we have explored the whole surface of Earth and have traveled thousands of kilometers into space, we have barely penetrated the ground beneath our feet. The deepest drill holes are about 10 kilometers, a mere $\frac{1}{10}$ of 1% of Earth's diameter. The solid layers of Earth and increasing heat and pressure within Earth have prevented direct observations of its interior. By using observations within the upper layers of Earth, however, we have inferred information about its interior.

As earthquake waves travel toward Earth's center, they reach a layer in which their speed suddenly increases. The Yugoslavian geophysicist Andrija Mohorovičić, who discovered this change, postulated that it marked an interface, or boundary, between the rocks of the crust and a denser layer. This interface is called the **Moho**, or the Mohoroičić discontinuity. The layer below the Moho is Earth's **mantle**.

The mantle, extending to a depth of about 2900 kilometers, includes most of Earth's volume. Scientists have inferred its composition from a variety of observations:

• Based on measurements of Earth's curvature, we can readily calculate the volume of our planet. The mass of the earth has been determined from measurements of gravitational attraction. From these figures, scientists have calculated the average density of Earth to be about $5\frac{1}{2}$ times the density of water. That's about twice the density of most rocks found at Earth's surface.

• Earthquake waves travel faster in the mantle than they do in the crust.

• The composition of magmas from deep within Earth includes a high proportion of the dense, mafic minerals.

• A large portion of the **meteorites** that fall to Earth are composed of the mafic minerals on the far right side of the *Scheme for Igneous Rock Identification* in the *Earth Science Reference Tables*. Scientists believe that these meteorites are the remains of the material from which Earth formed billions of years ago. If they are, they should show an overall composition similar to that of Earth.

All these observations suggest that the mantle is composed mostly of the dense, dark mafic minerals olivine and pyroxene. See Figure 3-7.

The Core.

The deepest layers of Earth are known as the *outer* and *inner cores*. The composition of these layers is thought to be a mixture of iron and nickel. These elements are abundant in some meteorites, and they are relatively dense. It is logical that these densest materials would sink into Earth's center.

The **outer core** is thought to be a liquid because S-waves are unable to pass through the outer core. The **inner core** seems to be a solid. Although the outer core and the inner core are both composed of iron and nickel, the higher pressures at the center of Earth cause the inner portion of the core to be a solid. The solid

state of the inner core is inferred from the speed of P-waves, which travel relatively fast through it. The *Inferred Properties of the Earth's Interior* found in the *Earth Science Reference Tables* summarizes scientists' ideas about Earth's interior.

Earthquake Shadow Zones.

When a major earthquake occurs, both P-waves and S-waves are received over most of Earth. The part of Earth opposite the side where the earthquake occurs receives P-waves, but no S-waves. This is because S-waves cannot penetrate the liquid outer core. Surrounding this "P-wave only" zone is a region where neither P- nor S-waves are received. Refraction (bending) of the waves at the mantle-core boundary causes this ring-shaped region known as the *shadow zone*. It extends from 102° to 143° from the epicenter. See Figure 3-8.

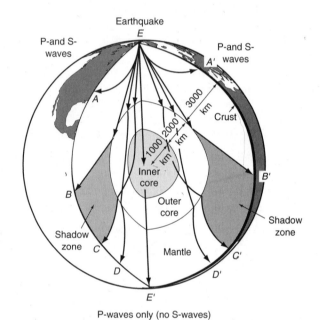

Figure 3-8. The layers of Earth have been defined based upon the passage of earthquake energy waves. The core and the mantle allow both P- and S-waves to pass. The outer core, being a liquid, will not pass S-waves. Refraction (bending) of the waves at the mantle-core boundary causes a shadow zone where neither P- nor S-waves are received.

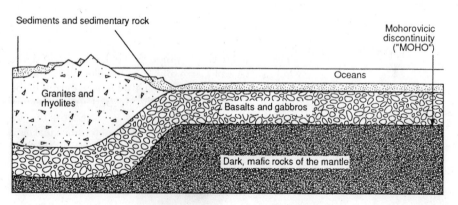

Figure 3-7. The continents and the ocean basins. Under the granitic rocks of the continents and the basaltic rocks of the ocean basins is Earth's mantle layer. The mantle is probably composed of mafic minerals rich in iron and magnesium.

17. On the diagram below, X marks the position of an earthquake. What seismic waves would be recorded at location Y? (1) only P-waves (2) only S-waves (3) both P-waves and S-waves (4) neither P-waves, nor S-waves

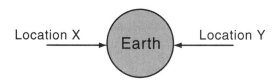

Location X → Earth ← Location Y

18. How far apart will the first P-waves and first S-waves be if an earthquake is 1800 km away? (1) 3 min (2) 3 min, 40 sec (3) 5 min (4) 5 min, 20 sec

19. Which of the following gives the layers of Earth in order of increasing density? (1) crust, mantle, outer core, inner core (2) crust, mantle, inner core, outer core (3) inner core, outer core, crust, mantle (4) outer core, inner core, mantle, crust

20. Theories about Earth's core are supported by meteorites composed of (1) oxygen and silicon (2) aluminum and iron (3) aluminum and oxygen (4) iron and nickel

21. According to the *Earth Science Reference Tables*, which of the following factors increase with depth within Earth? (1) density, temperature and pressure (2) not density, temperature or pressure (3) density and temperature, not pressure (4) density, but not temperature or pressure

Directions: Base your answer to questions 22 through 23 on your knowledge of earth science, the *Earth Science Reference Tables*, and the diagram below. The diagram represents a cross section of Earth showing the paths of earthquake waves from a single earthquake source. Seismograph stations are located on Earth's surface at points *A* through *F*, and they are all located in the same time zone.

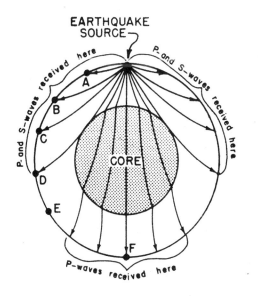

EARTHQUAKE SOURCE

P and S-waves received here

P- and S-waves received here

CORE

P-waves received here

22. At which station is the difference in time between the arrival of P- and S-waves the greatest? (1) A (2) B (3) C (4) D

23. According to the *Earth Science Reference Tables* in which part of Earth does the temperature change at the greatest rate with depth? (1) the inner core (2) the outer core (3) the mantle (4) the crust

24. How do scientists know that the outer core of Earth is a liquid? (1) S-waves cannot travel through the outer core. (2) The outer core is too cool to be a solid. (3) Many earthquakes occur within the outer core. (4) All liquids are more dense than solids.

25. According to the *Earth Science Reference Tables*, in what part of Earth is the actual temperature above the melting temperature? (1) outer core (2) inner core (3) crust (4) mantle

EARTHQUAKES AND VOLCANOES

Earthquakes and volcanoes are not distributed randomly over Earth. Most of them occur in zones of crustal activity, where crustal deformation and mountain building take place. For example, a surprisingly large number of the world's volcanoes and seismic events occur around the edges of the Pacific Ocean, in a region called the "**Ring of Fire**." See Figure 3-9 on page 48. Countries, such as Japan, and states on the western coast of the United States, such as California, are on the Ring of Fire. These areas are damaged frequently by earthquakes and volcanoes. In fact, the greatest natural disasters in human history have been two earthquakes in China, each of which is thought to have caused more than half a million deaths. See Table 3-2 on page 48.

Seismic Hazards.

Earthquakes cause damage in several ways. Of course, there is the damage caused by shaking. Buildings and bridges may collapse, or be damaged beyond repair. Movement of the crust can damage roads and railroad tracks. Earthquakes in or near oceans often cause large waves, called **tsunamis**. When these waves reach land, they can cause terrible damage. Fire is also a danger in earthquakes. Gas lines can rupture; the gas may be ignited by sparks from downed power lines. In addition, water pipes may be broken, which makes fighting fires difficult. The shaking of the ground can also cause landslides in areas where there are soft sediments.

In areas that experience earthquakes frequently, governments have developed building codes that call for the reinforcement of bridges and buildings. In addition to making these structures able to withstand moderate quakes, these precautions make it less likely that people will be injured by falling debris. Figure 3-10 on page 49 is a seismic risk map for the United States.

Volcanic Hazards.

When volcanoes erupt they may spew hot lava, hot ash, and/or toxic gases. The lava and ash can bury cities, and the toxic fumes can suffocate people.

Volcanoes can also be helpful. Some of the most fertile soil is composed of weathered volcanic material.

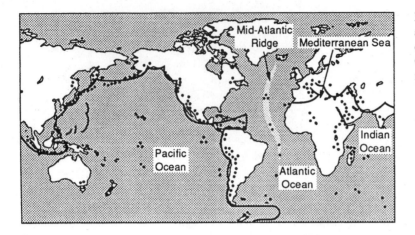

Figure 3-9. Earthquakes, active volcanoes, and regions of mountain building generally occupy distinct linear zones of crustal activity. One such zone is the "Ring of Fire" that surrounds the Pacific Ocean.

Table 3-2. **Selected Historic Seismic Events**

Location	Date	Magnitude	Notes
Shensi, China	1556	Unknown	Worst natural disaster known. 830,000 deaths
New Madrid, MO	1812	~8 (est.)	Few deaths due to sparse settlement. Flow of Mississippi River briefly reversed.
San Francisco, CA	1906	~8.3 (est.)	Most damage caused by uncontrolled fires. Water lines broken.
Massena, NY	1944	~6 (est.)	Largest in NY state. Chimneys destroyed, water lines broken.
Lebu, Chile	1960	9.6	Largest event measured with seismographs. In Pacific Ocean.
Anchorage, AK	1964	9.3	Extensive tsunami. Damage to buildings extensive. 131 deaths.
Haicheng, China	1975	7.5	Predicted by scientists. City evacuated. Only ~130 deaths.
Tengshan, China	1976	7.6	Prediction fails. Worst modern natural disaster. ~650,000 deaths.
Mexico City, Mexico	1985	8.1	Worst damage in city built on fill far from the epicenter. ~9000 deaths.
Westchester Co., NY	1985	4.0	No damage reported. 1/923,521 the energy of the 1985 Mexico event.
Northridge, CA	1994	6.7	$10 billion in damages. 61 deaths.
Kobe, Japan	1995	7.2	Destroyed the port built on landfill. 5,500 deaths.
Izmit, Turkey	1999	7.4	More than 12,000 dead and 34,000 injured. Lateral offsets of 2.5 m (9 feet). Largest event in a modern, industrialized area since San Francisco in 1906 and Tokyo in 1923.

The Hawaiian Islands were built by volcanoes. And some volcanoes are used as sources of geothermal energy.

We need to understand that forces of nature, including earthquakes, tornadoes, and other natural events, athough disastrous in the short term, are important parts of Earth's cycles. For example, earthquakes are a part of mountain building.

QUESTIONS

26. The place within Earth where an earthquake originates is called the (1) epicenter (2) focus (3) zenith (4) moho

27. The place on the surface of Earth directly above the point at which an earthquake originates is called the (1) moho (2) focus (3) epicenter (4) zenith

28. During the past 100 years, earthquakes have taken place most frequently (1) in the interior of continental areas (2) in the polar regions (3) along the rim of the Pacific Ocean (4) along the Atlantic Ocean coastlines

29. A zone of weakness or a break in Earth's crust is known as the (1) earthquake (2) focus (3) volcano (4) fault

30. According to the Richter scale, an earthquake that measures 4 has how many times more shaking than a quake measuring 3? (1) 1 (2) 10 (3) 100 (4) 1000

31. Two different cities experience earthquakes with a magnitude of 5.5 on the Richter scale. However, on the Modified Mercalli Intensity Scale, the earthquake was rated V in one city and VII in the other city. What is the best explanation for this difference? (1) one city is nearer to the equator, the other is near a pole (2) the earthquake in one city occurred at 8 PM and the other occurred at

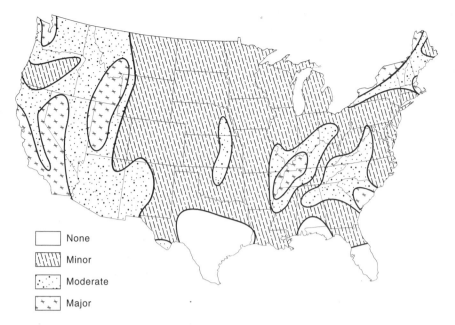

Figure 3-10. Most predictions of earthquake hazard are based upon historical records. Although earthquakes are less common in the Central and Eastern United States than they are along the Pacific Coast, there have been major earthquakes in all three regions.

4 AM. (3) one city is built on bedrock while the other is built on loose sediments (4) one city is in a drier climate zone than the other

32. Geologists use seismographs to (1) measure earthquake magnitude (2) measure earthquake intensity (3) predict earthquakes (4) find volcanoes

33. What kind of waves do not travel through liquids? (1) P-waves (2) S-waves (3) both (4) neither

34. What geologic structure is shown in this diagram? (1) tilted strata (2) a fault (3) a fold (4) a tsunami

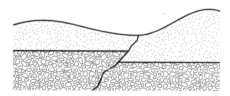

35. Where does most present-day faulting of rock occur? (1) in regions of glacial activity (2) in the interior areas of continents (3) at locations with many lakes (4) at interfaces between moving parts of the crust

36. Useful information regarding the composition of the interior of Earth can be derived from earthquakes because earthquake waves (1) release materials from within Earth (2) travel through Earth at a constant velocity (3) travel at different rates through different materials (4) change radioactive decay rates of rocks

37. Which graph best shows the relationship between volcanic activity and the number of earthquakes in an area?

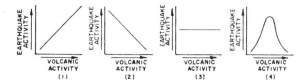

CONTINENTAL DRIFT

In 1912, Alfred Wegener (VEG' en er), a German meteorologist and astronomer, proposed that in the distant past Earth's continents were all joined as a single landmass. He said that the continents have separated and collided as they have moved over Earth's surface for millions of years. Wegener cited several forms of evidence for his theory.

Ever since accurate maps had correctly shown the eastern and western shores of the Atlantic Ocean, people had noticed that the shoreline of the Americas would fit remarkably well with the shores of Europe and Africa. Wegener proposed that this was more than a coincidence. He suggested that this jigsaw puzzle fit was the result of the opening of the Atlantic Ocean, which broke apart an ancient supercontinent Wegener named Pangaea. Figure 3-11 on page 50 shows a modern interpretation of the break-up of Pangaea.

Wegener also noted that if these land areas were brought back together, the move would line up ancient mountain ranges, similar continental rock formations and evidence of ancient glaciers (scratched and polished bedrock surfaces) as shown in Figure 3-12 on page 50. There were even similar fossils on both sides of the Atlantic that would be brought together by the re-assembly of Pangaea. Wegener called his idea of moving landmasses "continental drift."

Wegener's proposal was not accepted by most geologists because they could not understand what would cause the continents to "plow" through the ocean basins. For over 50 years, continental drift was generally considered a creative, but unlikely, theory. But exploration of the world's oceans based on technology developed in World War II revealed surprising features on the ocean bottoms.

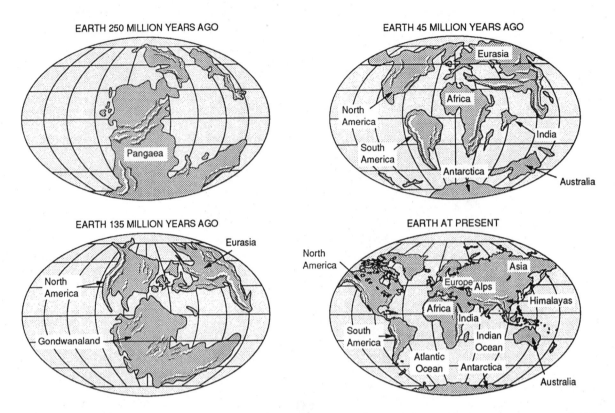

Figure 3-11. The Atlantic Ocean was born when the great continent of Pangaea began to split apart approximately 200 million years ago. While this was happening, Australia and India were moving north from the south polar region to their present positions.

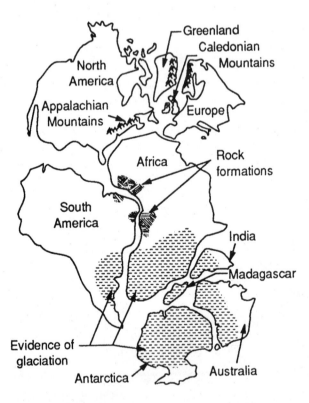

Figure 3-12. When the continents are reassembled to form the ancient continent of Pangaea, glacial features, rock formations, and mountain ranges come into contact from both sides of the Atlantic Ocean.

Evidence from the Oceans.

The evidence that convinced most scientists to accept Wegener's ideas emerged in the 1950s. At that time, oceanographers used sonar to measure the shape of ocean bottoms, as they also retrieved samples from the ocean bottoms. Both fossils and the analysis of radioactive materials showed the age of the oceanic crust increases with increasing distance from the mid-ocean ridges. It appeared that some oceans were growing wider from the middle.

Another form of evidence of the age-distance relationship was discovered by scientists using magnetic measurements. The scientists found stripes of rock with normal magnetic polarity alternating with stripes that had reversed polarity. These **patterns of magnetic polarity** resulted from molten rock coming to the surface at ridges. While the rock was still molten, the iron particles in it aligned with the magnetic field of Earth. When the rock hardened, it kept that alignment forming a permanent record of Earth's magnetic field at the time the new oceanic crust was formed. When scientists realized that north and south magnetic poles reverse at intervals of roughly 100,000 years, they understood that they were looking at diverging and slow-moving sections of ocean crust. Parallel stripes of magnetism on both sides of the ridges preserve a record of many reversals of Earth's magnetic field in the geologic past. Scientists recognized that oceanic crust is being created at the mid-ocean ridges and being swallowed back into Earth at the ocean trenches. Figure 3-13 shows how the

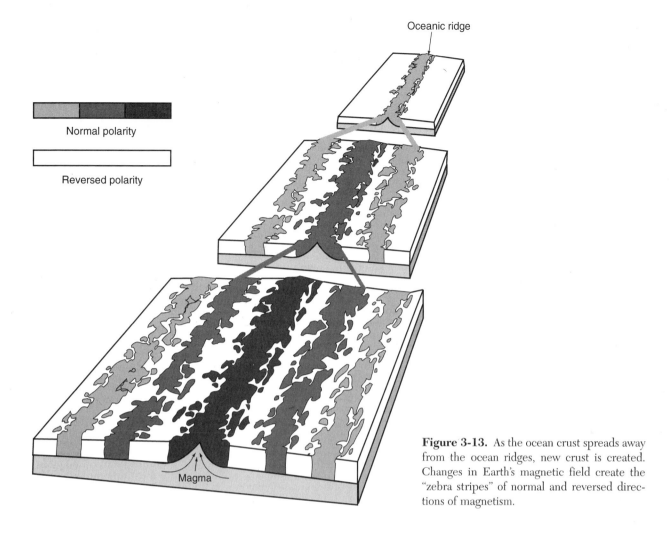

Oceanic ridge

Normal polarity

Reversed polarity

Magma

Figure 3-13. As the ocean crust spreads away from the ocean ridges, new crust is created. Changes in Earth's magnetic field create the "zebra stripes" of normal and reversed directions of magnetism.

ocean floor is created by divergence at the ocean ridges. This is called sea-floor spreading.

Plate Tectonics.

Continuing observations on the continents and under the oceans have been integrated into the unified theory of **plate tectonics**. (**Tectonics** refers to large-scale deformation of Earth's crust.) According to this theory, the surface of Earth is composed of about a dozen major rigid, moving crustal plates and several smaller plates. These plates contain areas of light continental rock as well as the dense oceanic bottoms. For example, the western Atlantic Ocean and the North American continent occupy a single plate. See Figure 3-14 on page 52.

Plate Boundaries. The lines along which plates meet and interact are called plate boundaries. As plates move, crustal change—volcanoes, earthquakes, and mountain building—occur, mostly along these boundaries. At the western edge of South America, the South American plate collides with the Pacific plate. As a result of this collision, the Andes Mountains are rising as the crust crumples. See Figure 3-15 on page 52. These converging plates form a **convergent boundary**. **Subduction** occurs when an oceanic plate, made of rela-

tively dense basalt, dives beneath a lighter continental plate, composed of granitic rocks. Subduction forms the ocean **trenches**. Ocean trenches are linear fractures that are the deepest parts of the oceans and are also where ocean-plate convergence is occurring. On the other hand, the collision of two continental plates, which resist subduction, leads to folding, faulting, and mountain building.

Where plates slide past one another, they meet at a **transform boundary**. The San Andreas Fault, which is responsible for many earthquakes in California, is a transform boundary. Here the Pacific plate is moving northward with respect to the North American plate.

The third kind of plate boundary is called the **divergent boundary**. This type of boundary is found at the **mid-ocean ridges** where upwelling material creates new crust that moves away from the ridge in both directions somewhat like twin conveyor belts. A divergent boundary is also known as a **rift**.

In general, the direction of plate movement is away from the ocean ridges and toward the trenches. At a few centimeters per year, this may seem very slow. But when we look at the millions of years of Earth's history, as shown in Figure 3-11, the land masses have moved great distances through geologic history.

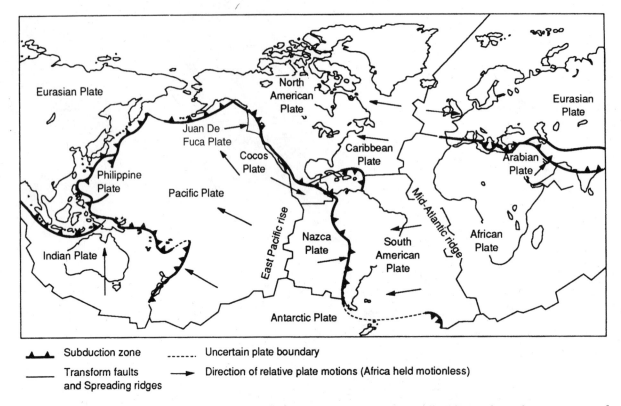

Figure 3-14. Earth's crust is composed of about a dozen major plates and many smaller plates. These plates move toward each other at convergent boundaries, move away from each other at divergent boundaries, and shift past each other at transform boundaries.

Although we are not able to observe convection currents deep within our planet, we can observe their effects at the surface. In various places, crustal plates move past each other, separate, or collide. We see that zones of crustal activity are associated with earthquakes, volcanoes, and the slower forces of mountain building. These events are part of a global system of energy flow.

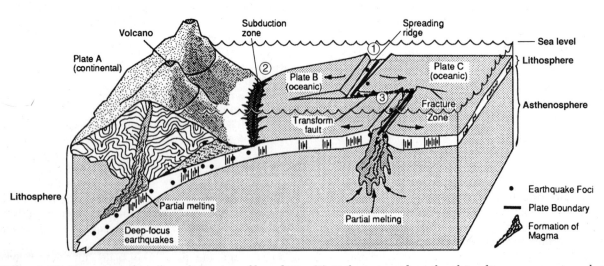

Figure 3-15. The crustal plates form three types of boundaries. (1) At the ocean ridges, the plates diverge as new ocean bottom is created at the rift zones. The mid-Atlantic ridge is a rift boundary. (2) Where two plates converge and collide, an ocean trench (when at least one plate is an ocean) or a mountain range (at least one plate is a continent) is usually the result. The Andes Mountains, Himalayan Mountains, and Aleutian Trench were created by colliding plates. (3) When the plates shift past each other, a transform fault, such as the San Andreas fault that runs most of the length of California, is the result.

38. The theory of plate tectonics does *not* explain (1) the match of rocks now many kilometers apart (2) the melting of recent continental glaciers (3) the apparent fit of continental edges (4) tropical fossils found in Antarctica

39. Which diagram below best shows a profile of the Atlantic Ocean (with considerable vertical exaggeration)?

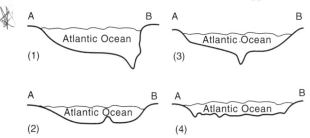

Directions: Base your answers to questions 40–44 on your knowledge of earth science, *The Earth Science Reference Tables*, and the diagram at bottom of page. The diagram represents the present positions of Africa and South America.

40. Which Precambrian rock unit in South America is probably the same type of rock and age as rock unit F in Africa? (1) Unit A (2) Unit B (3) Unit C (4) Unit D

41. What feature of the Atlantic Ocean was created when these two continents drifted apart? (1) the North Magnetic Pole (2) The South Magnetic Pole (3) the Pacific Ocean (4) the Mid-Atlantic Ridge

42. Which diagram below best shows the direction that Africa is now drifting with respect to South America?

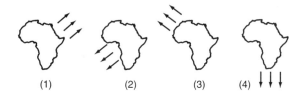

43. Compared with the age of the rocks in these two continents, the rocks of the ocean floor between them is (1) younger (2) older (3) the same

44. According to the *Earth Science Reference Tables*, when did Africa and South America split into two separate continents as shown in question 42? (1) before the Cambrian Period (2) during the Carboniferous Period (3) during the Triassic Period (4) after the Cretaceous Period

45. According to the *Earth Science Reference Tables*, which of the following locations is the site of a convergent plate boundary? (1) the mid-Atlantic ridge (2) the Aleutian trench (3) the Atlantic-Indian ridge (4) the Pacific/North American plate boundary

46. Which provides the best evidence of ocean floor spreading? (1) Volcanoes appear at random spread over the ocean floor. (2) Sandstone and limestone can be found both in South Africa and in Europe. (3) Rocks of the ocean ridges are younger than those of the nearby sea floor. (4) Deep earthquakes occur below the ocean ridges, but not around the continents.

47. Fossils of shark's teeth found high in the mountains support the idea of (1) crustal subsidence (2) continental glaciers (3) ocean floor spreading (4) crustal uplift

What Drives the Tectonic Plates?

The magnetic pattern of the ocean floor helped scientists understand what drives ocean-floor spreading. Within planet Earth, there is a great deal of heat. People who work in the diamond mines of South Africa know that the deeper you go in the mines, the hotter it gets. Very deep wells also confirm that Earth's temperature increases with depth. Heat always flows from places of high heat to areas of lower heat. In the case of Earth, this means from the center toward the surface.

Heat flows in three ways. Earth receives solar energy by **radiation**, but radiation can only flow through the vacuum of space and through transparent materials, such as air and glass. Since our planet is not transparent, heat cannot travel through it by radiation. **Conduction**

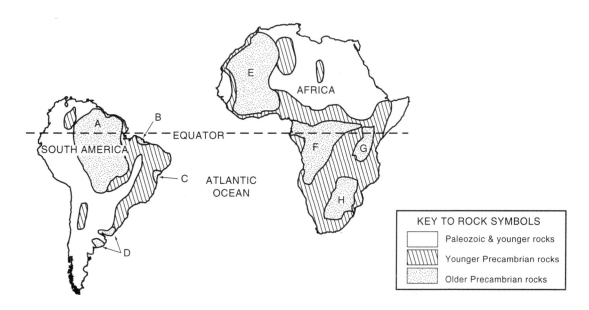

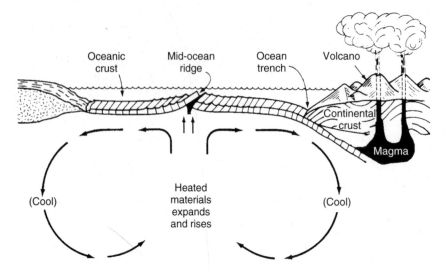

Figure 3-16. Convection currents within Earth enable heat to escape from Earth's interior. These currents create and expand the ocean bottoms, and they carry the continents as passive "rafts" of lighter rock.

allows energy to flow through solids, but it is a very slow process. On the other hand, **convection** distributes heat through fluids. Most materials expand when they are heated, which makes them less dense. Materials that are less dense tend to rise while denser materials sink. These differences in density, caused by heating, set up **convection cells** in fluids.

Although the rock of the mantle would probably crack if you hit it hard with a hammer, under the conditions of extreme heat and pressure found within Earth, this rock is a fluid, and it is able to flow very slowly. Crustal plates move because they are driven by convection cells circulating within the mantle. The rigid portion of the plates includes Earth's crust as well as a small part of the upper mantle. This rigid layer is known as the **lithosphere**. The plates float on a partially molten portion of the mantle called the **asthenosphere**. Convection cells bring material to the surface at the ocean ridges and pull it back into Earth at the trenches. Figure 3-16 shows how heated material rises toward the

surface and diverges from the ocean ridge forming new ocean floor.

How Do Plate Motions Shape Earth's Crust?
It may be helpful to think of Earth's surface as the top of a conveyor belt, similar to the one the cashier in the supermarket uses to move your groceries. Therefore, rift zones can be thought of as places where two conveyor belts (plates) rise to the surface and spread apart, or *diverge*. Although Earth's plates move at a rate of just a few centimeters a year, over millions of years they cover great distances. The subduction zones are places where the ocean crust is drawn back into the mantle. The oceanic crust, which is mostly basalt, is dense enough to move downward. But the continents, which are made of lighter rocks such as granite, resist subduction. When a continent moves into a subduction zone, it usually crumples without being drawn downward. This process causes the most active

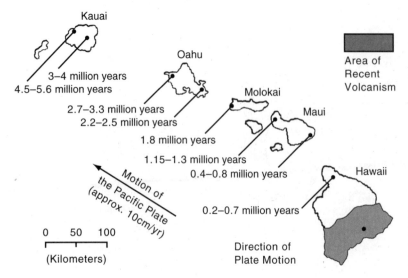

Figure 3-17. The progressive age of volcanic activity in the Hawaiian Islands shows the slow movement of the Pacific plate over a hot spot deep within Earth.

volcanic regions and the highest mountains in the world, for example the Andes of South America and the Himalayas of Asia.

In several places, hot plumes of magma pierce the crust. As a crustal plate moves over this source of magma, volcanoes form at the **hot spot**. This movement of a plate leads to the formation of a chain of volcanoes of differing ages. The most dramatic example of this is probably the Hawaiian Islands. The Big Island of Hawaii has several active volcanoes. It is the youngest island that rises above the ocean in the chain. As you move westward toward Kauai, the age of the islands increases. Kauai formed about 4 to 5 million years ago. See Figure 3-17. What looks like a progression of volcanic activity through time toward the southeast actually shows the slow movement of the Pacific plate toward the north-west. As the plate moves, a relatively stationary source of magma forms volcanoes that have created a chain of volcanic islands and submerged volcanoes thousands of kilometers long.

QUESTIONS

48. In the past 100,000 years the distance between South America and Africa has (1) decreased (2) increased (3) remained the same

49. According to the *Inferred Position of Earth Landmasses* information shown in the *Earth Science Reference Tables*, on what other landmass would you most likely find fossil remains of the late Paleozoic reptile called Mesosaurus shown below?

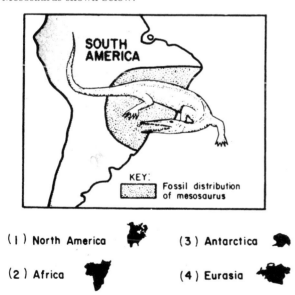

KEY:
Fossil distribution of mesosaurus

(1) North America

(3) Antarctica

(2) Africa

(4) Eurasia

50. Which statement best supports the theory that all the continents were once a single landmass? (1) Rocks of the ocean ridges are older than those of the adjacent sea floor. (2) Rock and fossil correlation can be made where the continents appear to fit together. (3) Marine fossils can be found at high elevations above sea level on all continents. (4) Great thicknesses of shallow-water sediments are found at interior locations on some continents.

51. Igneous materials found along oceanic ridges contain magnetic iron particles that show reversal of magnetic orientation. This is evidence that (1) volcanic activity has occurred constantly throughout history (2) Earth's magnetic poles have exchanged their positions (3) igneous materials are always formed beneath oceans (4) Earth's crust does not move

52. Which is the best evidence supporting the concept of ocean floor spreading? (1) Earthquakes occur at greater depths beneath oceans than beneath continents. (2) Sandstones and limestones can be found both in North America and Europe. (3) Volcanoes appear at random within the oceanic crust. (4) Igneous rocks along the mid-oceanic ridges are younger than those farther from the ridges.

Directions: Base your answers to questions 53 through 55 on your knowledge of earth science and on the diagram below. The diagram shows an enlargement of the mid-Atlantic ridge and surrounding area in its position with respect to the continents. Magnetic polarity bands of igneous rock parallel to the ridge are illustrated according to the key.

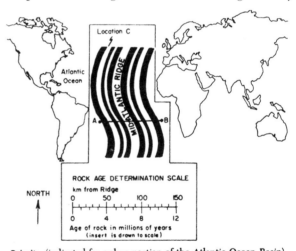

Polarity (indicated for only a portion of the Atlantic Ocean Basin)

Normal —The magnetic minerals in these rocks indicate magnetic north as it is today.

Reverse —The magnetic minerals in these rocks indicate magnetic north where magnetic south is today.

53. Ocean floor rock found 20 kilometers west of the ocean ridge would have an approximate age of (1) 1.6 million years (2) 3.0 million years (3) 15 million years (4) 30 million years

54. What are two characteristics of ocean floor rock found at location C? (1) normal polarity, continental composition (2) normal polarity, oceanic composition (3) reverse polarity, continental composition (4) reverse polarity, oceanic composition

55. Along the line from position A to position B, the comparative age of the rock (1) continuously decreases from A to B (2) continuously increases from A to B (3) decreases from A to the mid-Atlantic ridge and then increases to B (4) increases from A to the mid-Atlantic ridge and then decreases to B

56. Which of the cross-sectional diagrams below best represents a model for the movement of rock material below the crust along the mid-Atlantic ridge?

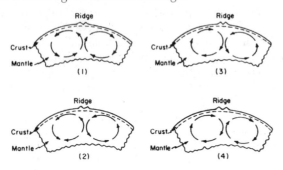

The Scientist, Engineer, and Citizen

Produce an engineering report that identifies earthquake hazards in and around your school building, and recommend ways to reduce those hazards. Your recommendations should include an emergency preparedness plan for people to follow in case of a major seismic event, as well as structural and placement changes in the school building and school grounds that could save lives and property.

Include estimates of how much money would be saved by using your recommendations as well as the estimated cost of following your recommendations. (Your teacher or your school administrators may be able to help you establish the costs of construction to repair or replace a damaged school building.)

CHAPTER 3 REVIEW QUESTIONS

Directions: Base your answers to questions 1 through 3 on the *Earth Science Reference Tables*, the diagram below, and your knowledge of earth science. The diagram represents three cross sections of Earth at different locations to a depth of 50 kilometers below sea level. The measurements given with each cross section indicate the thickness and the density of the layers.

1. In which group are the layers of Earth arranged in order of increasing average density? (1) mantle, crust, ocean water (2) crust, mantle, ocean water (3) ocean water, mantle, crust (4) ocean water, crust, mantle

2. Compared with the oceanic crust, the continental crust is (1) thinner and less dense (2) thinner and more dense (3) thicker and less dense (4) thicker and more dense

3. The division of Earth's interior into crust and mantle, as shown in the diagram, is based primarily on the study of (1) radioactive dating (2) seismic waves (3) volcanic eruptions (4) gravity measurements

4. Fossils of organisms that lived in shallow water can be found in horizontal sedimentary rock layers at great ocean depths. This fact is generally interpreted by most Earth scientists as evidence that (1) the cold water deep in the ocean kills shallow-water organisms (2) sunlight once penetrated to the deepest parts of the ocean (3) organisms that live in deep water evolved from species that once lived in shallow water (4) sections of Earth's crust have changed their elevations relative to sea level

5. Which diagram below shows the least evidence of movement of Earth's crust?

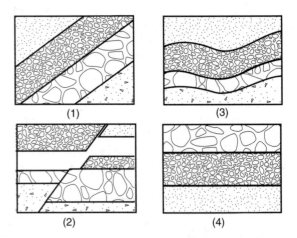

6. How can we best explain why fossils of organisms that live in the ocean are now found high in some mountain regions? (1) The fossils were dropped by the birds that ate the marine animals. (2) Marine organisms lived in the mountains in the geologic past. (3) The seas were several kilometers deeper in the past. (4) The rocks in the mountains have been pushed up from below.

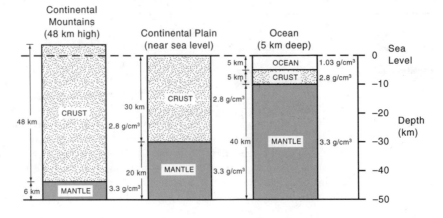

7. A sandstone layer is tilted at a steep angle. What probably caused this tilting? (1) The sediments that formed this sandstone layer were originally deposited at a steep angle. (2) This sandstone layer has changed position due to crustal movement. (3) This sandstone layer has recrystallized due to contact metamorphism. (4) Nearly all sandstone layers are formed from wind deposited sands.

8. Landing a seismograph on the moon has allowed us to tell if the moon has (1) liquid water (2) an atmosphere (3) radioactivity (4) crustal movements

9. How much larger is an earthquake of Richter magnitude 6, than another earthquake of magnitude 4? (1) 100 times larger (2) 20 times larger (3) twice as large (4) 50% larger

10. Which statement best represents how earthquake waves travel through Earth? (1) P-waves will pass through solids, but not liquids (2) P-waves will pass through liquids, but not solids (3) S-waves will pass through solids, but not liquids (4) S-waves will pass through liquids, but not solids

11. Which of the following features found in an outcrop is *not* evidence of crustal change? (1) folded layers of sedimentary rock (2) faulted strata of sediments (3) tilted layers of rock (4) flat sedimentary strata

12. Which is the chief cause of earthquakes in California? (1) cavern collapse (2) volcanic activity (3) folding (4) faulting

13. Which best describes a major characteristic of both volcanoes and earthquakes? (1) They are centered at the poles. (2) They are located in the same geographic areas. (3) They are related to the formation of glaciers. (4) They are restricted to the Southern Hemisphere.

14. Earthquakes generally occur (1) in belts (2) uniformly over the earth (3) only under the oceans (4) mostly in North America

15. Base your answer to the following question on your knowledge of earth science and the diagrams below.

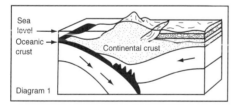

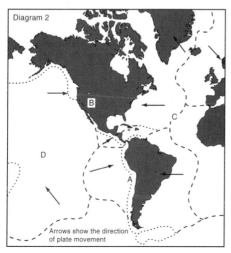

At which location in diagram 2 would the plate boundary shown in diagram 1 most likely be found? (1) A (2) B (3) C (4) D

Directions: Base your answers to questions 16 through 20 on your knowledge of earth science and the two diagrams given which are used to help explain the theory of continental drift.

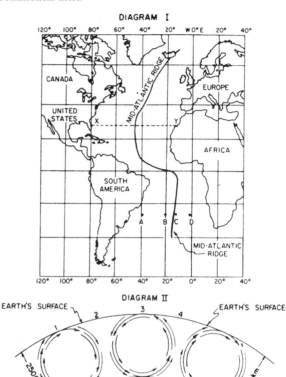

Diagram I represents a map of a portion of Earth showing the relative position of the Mid-Atlantic ridge. Points *A* through *D* are locations in the ocean and points X and Y are locations on the continents.

Diagram II represents a portion of Earth's interior with a model of probable convection cells. Locations 1 through 4 are at Earth's surface.

16. Which graph best represents the most likely pattern of the heat flow along line XY?

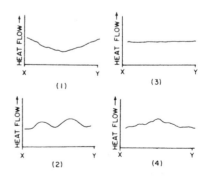

17. According to the theory of continental drift, which locations in Diagram I would most likely have the best correlation of rock, mineral, and fossil evidence? (1) the eastern coast of the United States and the southern coast

of Africa (2) Central Canada and Central Europe (3) the eastern coast of South America and the Western coast of Africa (4) the Central United States and Central South America

18. A ship obtains a sample of igneous bedrock from each of the positions A, B, C, and D. Which rock sample would probably be the oldest? (1) A (2) B (3) C (4) D

19. Which location in Diagram II would correspond to the position of the Mid-Atlantic ridge in Diagram I? (1) location 1 (2) location 2 (3) location 3 (4) location 4

20. Diagram II refers to convection cells which probably exist in the (1) crust (2) mantle (3) outer core (4) inner core

Directions: Use the diagram below and your knowledge of earth science to answer questions 21–27.

21. What is the approximate velocity of P-waves at a depth of 1000 km? (1) 4 km/s (2) 6 km/s (3) 8 km/s (4) 10 km/s

22. Why is the speed of S-waves not shown at depths of 4000 km and 6000 km? (1) S-waves are not strong enough to reach those depths (2) P-waves absorb S-waves inside Earth (3) S-waves cannot travel through a liquid (4) S-waves cannot travel through a solid

23. The records of just two seismic stations allow us to determine the distance from each recording station to the epicenter of an earthquake. Those two stations alone probably enable us to locate this epicenter as (1) a single point (2) one of two points (3) one of three points (4) somewhere on a circle

24. As earthquake waves travel through Earth at a depth of 2500 km, how far ahead of the S-waves would the P-waves be after 1 second? (1) 3 km (2) 6 km (3) 8 km (4) 14 km

25. According to the *Earth Science Reference Tables*, which levels are within Earth's mantle? (1) Level A only (2) Level C only (3) Levels C and D (4) Levels D and E

26. According to the *Earth Science Reference Tables*, what is the approximate density of the rock at level D? (1) 2.5 g/cm³ (2) 4.5 g/cm³ (3) 10 g/cm³ (4) 12 g/cm³

27. Which graph below best shows the relationship between pressure and depth within the Earth?

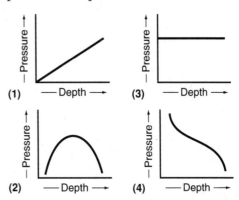

28. How can we best explain shallow water marine fossils now found high in the mountains? (1) Crustal uplift has pushed the rocks up. (2) The oceans were once twice as deep as they are now. (3) Major earthquakes caused the crust to sink. (4) These organisms formerly lived on land.

29. The fact that igneous rocks increase in age with distance from the ocean ridges shows that (1) the ocean floor is unchanging (2) the ocean ridges are sinking (3) volcanoes are only found on land (4) the ocean is spreading apart at the ridges

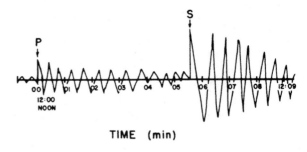

TIME (min)

30. What is the distance from the seismic station that recorded the information above to the epicenter of the earthquake? (1) 1500 km (2) 2500 km (3) 4000 km (4) 6000 km

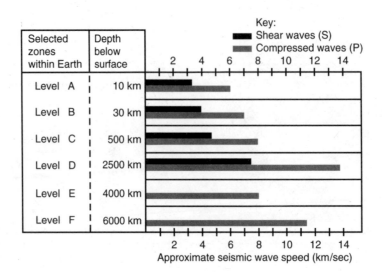

Station	Travel-Time Difference
A	4 min. 32 sec.
B	3 min. 52 sec.
C	3 min. 10 sec.
D	4 min. 17 sec.

31. Which of the four seismic stations in the table above is the greatest distance from the epicenter? (1) A (2) B (3) C (4) D

32. At which location is the crust of Earth probably the thickest? (1) ocean ridge (2) continental shelf (3) deep ocean basin (4) mountain ranges

33. Convection within Earth's mantle is thought to be caused by (1) Earth's rotation (2) escaping heat (3) hot air currents (4) weather conditions

34. Which is suggested by the occurrence of higher than average temperature below the surface of Earth in the area of the mid-Atlantic ridge? (1) the existence of convection cells in the mantle (2) the presence of heat due to orographic effect (3) a high concentration of magnetism in the mantle (4) the existence of a thinner crust under mountains

35. A large belt of mountain ranges and volcanoes surrounds the Pacific Ocean. Which events are most closely associated with these mountains and volcanoes? (1) hurricanes (2) sandstorms (3) tornadoes (4) earthquakes

36. The accompanying diagram shows a cross-sectional view of Earth's interior. The motion represented by the arrows indicates that Earth's mantle (1) has properties of a fluid (2) is composed of solid metamorphic rocks (3) is not affected by the heat from Earth's core (4) is more dense than the core

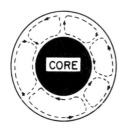

FREE-RESPONSE QUESTIONS

(Answer the following questions on a separate sheet of paper.)

1. In one or more complete sentences, briefly explain one type of evidence that supports the theory of plate tectonics. (Complete sentence, +1; Correct evidence, +1)

2. The diagram below shows a coastal region that has frequent and large earthquakes. Indicate the most probable earthquake caused danger to homes constructed at each of the three locations shown. (You may not use the same danger for more than one location.) (Each correct response, +1)

3. If you wanted to provide evidence that bedrock can be moved, what kinds of crustal features could you show? Draw a labeled diagram that illustrates at least two (2) bedrock features that indicate crustal motion. Explain why each indicated movement of Earth's crust. (Each correct response, +1; Legible diagram, +1)

4. Why do fossils of marine organisms that are found on mountains indicate that the rocks have moved? (Complete sentence, +1; Correct reasoning, +1)

5. Make an annotated (labeled) drawing that someone could use to construct a simple seismometer. (Weight, +1; Freedom of move movement, +1; Clearly labeled, +1)

6. In the next 50 years, how likely are we to have destructive earthquakes in New York state. Explain your answer. (Reasoning, +1; Complete sentence, +1)

Questions 7 through 10 may require the use of information in the *Earth Science Reference Tables.*

7. How do geologists locate earthquake epicenters? Please number the steps (1, 2, 3, and so on). (Complete sequence, up to +3)

8. We think of rock as a solid. If we hit a rock with a hammer, it shatters. So how can solid rocks flow within Earth's mantle to cause the "drifting" of the continents? (Your response must refer to the mantle as a solid, which, for the most part, it is.) Answer in one or more complete sentences. (Reason, +1; Complete sentence(s), +1)

9. Seismologists point out that if we had a large earthquake in the New York City area, many people could be killed by man-made structures. Why haven't New York City's buildings and other structures been built to withstand large earthquakes? (Please name just one reason.) (Reason, +1)

10. What are the chances of earthquake damage in the county in which you live? Support your opinions with facts. (Partial response, +1; Complete response, +2; Complete sentences, +1)

Use the map of New York State at the top of page 60 to answer questions 11–13.

11. Write an "X" on the map at the most likely location of the epicenter of this earthquake. (+1)

12. Use the map to construct six (6) isoseismals (isolines of equal intensity) that cover New York State. (Use an interval of one Mercalli intensity unit.) Please end your isolines just past the boundaries of New York State. (+1)

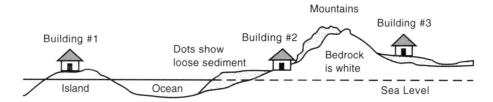

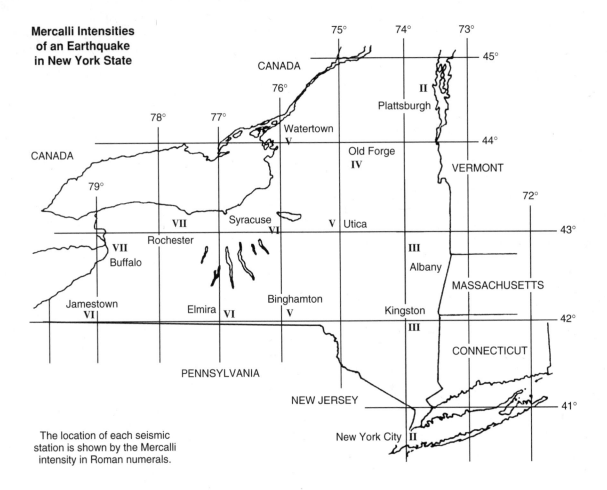

Mercalli Intensities of an Earthquake in New York State

The location of each seismic station is shown by the Mercalli intensity in Roman numerals.

13. What is the approximate latitude of Syracuse, NY? (Angle and direction) (+1)

14. If an earthquake epicenter is 2000 kilometers away from you and the first P-wave is detected at 14:10:10, at what time will the first S-wave arrive? (+1)

15. What do we mean when we say that the Richter scale of earthquake magnitude is a logarithmic scale rather than a linear scale? Please answer in one or more complete sentences. (Response, +1; Sentence, +1)

Use the accompanying map of the world to answer questions 16–17.

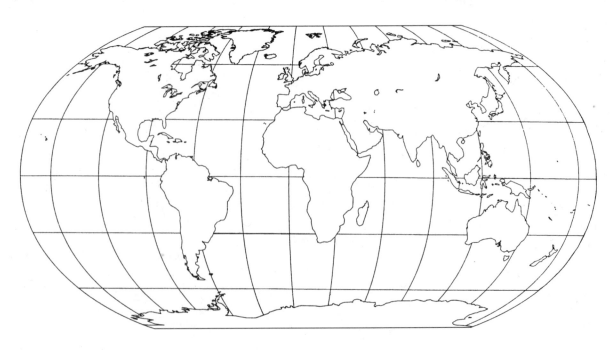

16. Write a dark "X" on the map at the bottom of page 60 to show a location that has an unusually high risk of major earthquakes. You will need to use your *Earth Science Reference Tables.*
(Location, +1)

17. List the latitude and longitude of the location shown by your X. Be sure to list both angle and direction.

Latitude _____ Longitude _____
(Latitude, +1; Longitude, +1 (± 10°))

18. Make a neat diagram to show a person familiar with building things from common materials like metal and wood how to make a working seismograph. The builder has no background in seismology. Label the most important parts of the instrument according to what they must do. Keep your design simple and neat.
(Parts Clear, +1; Functionality, +1)

19. In a single complete sentence, briefly state one form of natural evidence visible on Earth to support the theory of Plate Tectonics. (Nothing artificial) Please be brief.
(Evidence, +1; Sentence, +1)

The diagram below is a map of the Hawaiian Islands, where the Pacific Plate is moving over a hot spot below Earth's crust. All of these islands are volcanoes that have grown above sea level. The ages of the lava flows that created some islands are shown in parentheses in millions of years. Use this diagram to answer questions 20–22.

20. Draw an arrow on the map to show the relative motion of the Pacific Plate.
(Correct placement, +1)

21. Calculate the approximate rate in cm/year (± 50%) at which the Pacific Plate is moving in the space below. Use a distance measure that spans at least half the horizontal length of the map. Start by writing this formula: (Hint: 1 km = 100,000 cm)

$$\text{Rate} = \frac{\text{Distance}}{\text{Time}}$$

(Formula, +1; Values, +1; Answer, +1; Units, +1)

22. What two (2) ways would the oceanic rocks of the Hawaiian Islands look unlike the rocks you would be likely to find in most of the rest of the United States?
(Reasons, +1 each)

23. Describe a feature that we could observe in the field to show evidence that Earth's plates are in motion. Name the feature and tell where we could see it. Do *not* use the Hawaiian Islands as your location. Use one or more complete sentences.
(Feature, +1; Location, +1; Complete sentences, +1)

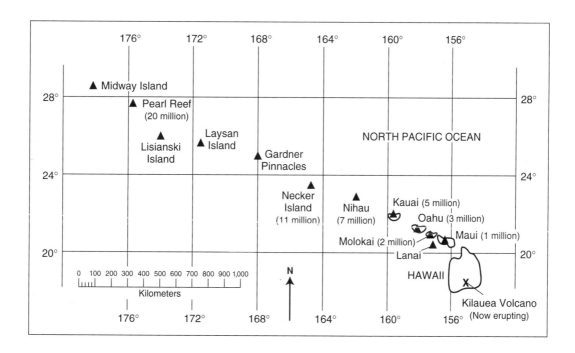

CHAPTER 4 Weathering, Erosion, Deposition, and Landscapes

WHY DO ROCKS WEATHER?

When rock that was formed within Earth's crust is uplifted and exposed to wind, water, and biological processes, it usually undergoes changes in its observable properties and composition. The breakdown of rock due to physical or chemical changes is called **weathering**. See Figure 4-1.

Physical Weathering.

Physical weathering changes the size and/or shape of a rock—for example, by breaking it into smaller pieces—without changing the rock's chemical composition. **Frost action** is an important agent of physical weathering in climates that experience seasonal temperature changes alternately above and below 0°C. In weathering by frost action, water seeps into cracks in rocks. The water expands as it freezes and makes the cracks in the rock a little larger. When the ice melts and the resulting liquid water evaporates, the rock is left more porous than before. Over a period of time, the alternate freezing and melting of the water in the cracks will cause the rock to crumble.

Plant roots that grow in the cracks of rocks and animals that burrow beneath the ground are important agents of physical weathering. As a plant grows, its roots expand in the crevices of a rock and gradually push the rock apart. When animals burrow, they constantly expose new rock surfaces to weathering.

When rock particles are carried along by a stream, they bump and rub against one another and the streambed. Collisions such as these wear down rock particles by a form of physical weathering known as **abrasion**. Wind, moving ice, and gravity are also agents of abrasion.

Some rock minerals are harder than others. Quartz (silicon dioxide) and feldspars (complex aluminum silicates) resist physical weathering. But softer minerals, such as micas (hydrated aluminum silicates), are quickly broken apart by physical weathering.

Chemical Weathering.

Most rocks deep within Earth's crust remain stable under the conditions in which they were formed. However, when these rocks are uplifted to the surface and exposed to the atmosphere and hydrosphere, they often undergo **chemical weathering**. Chemical weathering changes the chemical composition of rock, thereby forming new substances. Chemical weathering breaks down rock by changing the rock's chemical composition. For example, when feldspar is uplifted to Earth's surface, it weathers to clay. As chemical weathering occurs, the compounds that make up feldspar react with water and form new substances. See Figure 4-2.

The rusting of a nail is another example of chemical weathering. Iron rusts in the presence of moisture. The iron atoms combine with oxygen atoms to form rust (iron oxide).

Chemical weathering requires heat energy and often water to bring about chemical changes. Thus chemical weathering takes place more rapidly in warm, moist climates. See Figure 4-3.

Some minerals are more resistant to chemical weathering than others. Quartz, a common mineral in beach sand, is relatively stable and resistant to chemical weathering. However, olivine, a mineral that is common deep within Earth, quickly weathers to clay when it is exposed to the atmosphere and hydrosphere. Limestone is a very hard rock that resists physical weathering until it is decomposed by exposure to acids. For example, rainwater that absorbs carbon dioxide from the at-

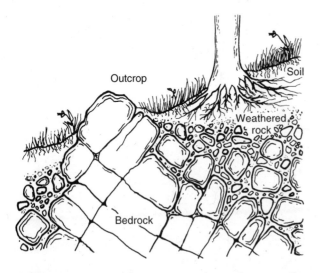

Figure 4-1. Most weathering occurs when rock is exposed to surface processes.

62

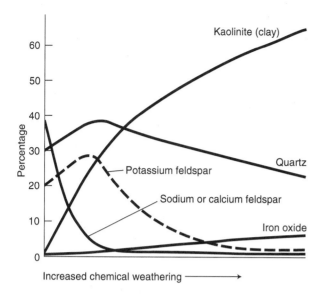

Figure 4-2. Chemical weathering of granite. As granite weathers, feldspars decrease in abundance as the amounts of clay minerals and iron oxide increase.

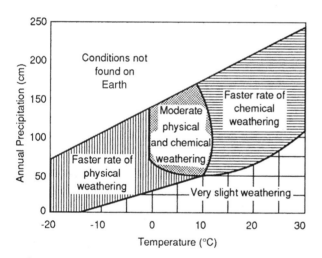

Figure 4-3. Weathering and climate. The type of rock weathering largely depends on the local climate. In general, chemical weathering dominates in warm moist climates, while cooler climates favor physical weathering (especially frost action).

mosphere becomes slightly acidic. The emission of atmospheric pollutants, such as the oxides of sulfur and nitrogen, can make rainwater unnaturally acidic. When acids, such as carbonic, nitric, and sulfuric, are released in the form of acid precipitation, they are able to change hard rocks like limestone into a soft residue.

QUESTIONS

Directions: Base your answers to questions 1–6 on the following table and your knowledge of earth science.

Mass of Rock Samples Remaining (grams)

Rock Shaking Time (min)	Shale A	Marble B	Rock Salt C	Limestone D
0	200	200	200	200
5	160	200	120	200
10	125	200	60	195
15	100	190	20	170
20	75	180	0	150
25	55	175	0	135
30	50	175	0	125

1. Which of the following best explains why there was a different amount of each rock sample remaining after 30 minutes of shaking? (1) each one had a different container (2) each rock had a different composition (3) some were shaken longer than others (4) some had more initial mass than others.

2. Which graph below best shows how the amount of rock sample A changed through time?

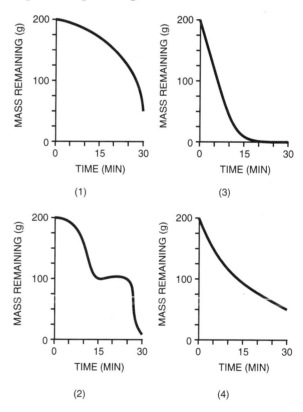

3. Which rock type was the most resistant to abrasion? (1) A (2) B (3) C (4) D

4. What portion of Rock A was left after 30 minutes? (1) 25% (2) 30% (3) 50% (4) 160%

5. This experiment was a measure of rock (1) growth (2) aging (3) erosion (4) weathering

6. How would the rock particles at the end of the experiment compare with the original samples? The rock particles remaining would be (1) more angular (2) larger (3) more rounded (4) softer

7. Chemical weathering is often dominant in climates that are (1) warm and dry (2) warm and moist (3) cold and dry (4) cold and moist

8. Which substance has the greatest effect on the rate at which rocks weather? (1) nitrogen (2) water (3) hydrogen (4) argon

9. Which property of a rock probably has the least effect on the rate at which it weathers? (1) exposure to the atmosphere (2) geologic age (3) mineral composition (4) surface area

10. What is the most important kind of physical weathering in high mountain areas? (1) abrasion by wind (2) oxidation and rusting (3) frost wedging (4) dissolving into solution

11. Iron changes to iron oxide when it is exposed to the atmosphere. This is an example of (1) water erosion (2) physical weathering (3) wind erosion (4) chemical weathering

12. Over time, a rock breaks up into small pieces without any change in its composition. This is an example of (1) chemical weathering (2) elemental weathering (3) density change (4) physical weathering

13. Physical weathering is the most active (1) in a tropical rain forest (2) deep within the earth (3) in a fast moving mountain stream (4) along the bottom of a large ocean

14. In what season is chemical weathering likely to be more active than physical weathering (1) winter (2) spring (3) summer (4) fall

15. What word most nearly means the same as the word weathering? (1) breakdown (2) transportation (3) growth (4) gravity

16. Frost action breaks rock apart because (1) rocks contract when they become very cold (2) chemical weathering is faster in cold weather (3) frost forms from water vapor by condensation (4) water expands when it freezes

HOW DO SOILS FORM?

Soil is the mixture of weathered rock and organic remains that usually covers bedrock. The nature of a soil depends upon the rocks from which it weathered and

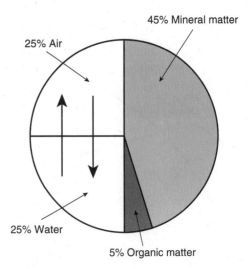

Figure 4-4. Soil composition by volume. The best soils for plant growth contain a mixture of weathered minerals and organic material. The proportions of air and water in the pores depend upon recent weather conditions.

the local climate. Under natural conditions, both physical and chemical weathering processes are usually involved in the development of soils. Physical weathering breaks solid rock into small particles. Chemical weathering changes hard minerals into softer forms. Plants and animals add organic materials in the form of waste products and dead organisms. The decay of organic remains produces organic acids which accelerate chemical weathering. Burrowing animals, such as earthworms, insects, and rodents, help circulate air and water through the soil and mix mineral and organic remains. See Figure 4-4.

The weathering of soil produces layers known as soil horizons. See Figure 4-5. The top layer is usually the best layer for growing crops because it is rich in dark-colored organic remains called humus, although some important minerals may have been transported deeper into the soil by groundwater infiltration. This make the layer below mineral enriched. The lowest layer of the

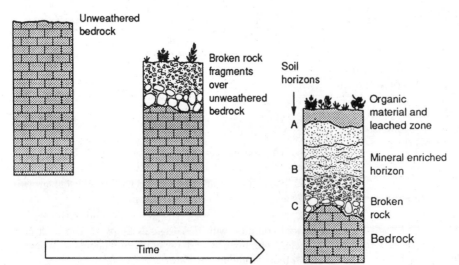

Figure 4-5. The development of soil horizons. Weathering, leaching, and organic processes gradually change exposed bedrock into mature soil.

soil is generally composed of broken-up bedrock, which may grade into solid bedrock.

Most of the soils of New York State do not show the complete development of these horizons. Continental glaciers that repeatedly invaded New York from the north stripped the soils from where they originally formed and moved them southward. The most recent withdrawal of continental ice sheets was only about 10,000 to 20,000 years ago. As a result, the lowest soil horizon (broken bedrock) is generally missing, and weathered soil sits directly on top of a hard, smoothed bedrock surface.

Soil is a resource that must be protected. It takes between 100 and 400 years for one centimeter of topsoil to form. Human technology has contributed to the loss of soil. For example, construction and mining projects have moved great quantities of rock and soil from their original locations. By destroying plant cover, and by poor farming and forestry practices, soil is left exposed and unprotected. The exposed soil is quickly carried away by running water and wind.

Salt used to remove ice from roads in winter is washed into the soil at the side of the road. If the concentration of salt in the soil is high enough, plants will not be able to grow there. Without plants to hold the soil in place, it will be carried away by wind and rain.

QUESTIONS

Directions: Base your answers to question 17 on the diagram below and your knowledge of earth science.

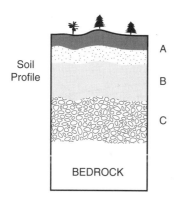

Soil Profile

A

B

C

BEDROCK

17. Which layer in the diagram above contains the most organic material? (1) A (2) B (3) C (4) the bedrock

18. The composition of soil that has formed in place is mostly determined by the local (1) agent of erosion (2) age of the bedrock (3) slope of the land (4) minerals in the bedrock

19. What makes the best soil for growing most crops? (1) solid bedrock (2) organic remains without any weathered rock (3) organic remains mixed with weathered rock (4) broken-up rock without organic material

20. How is soil created from rock? (1) physical weathering without chemical weathering (2) chemical weathering without physical weathering (3) erosion without weathering (4) weathering without erosion

21. Which two processes have been the most important in the formation of our soils? (1) weathering and biological events (2) leaching and evapotranspiration (3) evaporation and condensation (4) erosion and sublimation

22. The chemical composition of a residual soil in a certain area is determined by the (1) method by which the soil was transported to the area (2) slope of the land and the particle size of the soil (3) length of time since the last crustal movement in the area occurred (4) minerals in the bedrock beneath the soil and the climate of the area

23. Which change would cause the topsoil in New York State to increase in thickness? (1) an increase in slope (2) an increase in biologic activity (3) a decrease in rainfall (4) a decrease in air temperature

HOW ARE WEATHERED MATERIALS TRANSPORTED?

Rocks that have been broken into fragments, regardless of their size, are called **sediments**. The mineral composition or other characteristics of sediments may be unlike the properties of the underlying bedrock. In such a case, the sediments have been created elsewhere and then transported from their place of origin. **Erosion** involves the transporting of sediments away from their place of origin and the depositing of them elsewhere.

Most forms of erosion are driven by the force of gravity. For example, rock on a cliff that is weakened by weathering is pulled by gravity to fall to the bottom of the cliff. Piles of talus accumulate at the bottom of a cliff where continued erosion, perhaps aided by wind or water, move the sediment downslope, away from the cliff.

Erosion by Water.
Running water transports sediments in several ways. The smallest particles are carried in solution. These particles are so small they cannot be filtered out of the water. Sediments in suspension can be taken out with filters, but they are too small to settle on their own. (A cloud is a mass of tiny water droplets or ice crystals held in suspension in the atmosphere.) The largest and most dense particles are rolled or bounced along the streambed. Particles of low density, especially organic remains, are carried along the surface by flotation. See Figure 4-6 on page 66.

Running water is the chief agent of erosion in moist areas. Each year, the streams and rivers of the world carry millions of tons of sediment downstream and into the oceans. The relationship of transported particle size to water velocity is shown in Figure 4-7 on page 66. The graph shows that the water velocity needed to transport particles of sediment is chiefly a function of the size of the particles. Particles in solution and suspension can be carried by slow-moving water. But particles rolled along the bottom of the stream require faster stream velocities. A convenient method to estimate the velocity of a stream is to observe the size of the sedimentary particles that have been carried along the bottom of the stream. Faster streams contain larger particles of

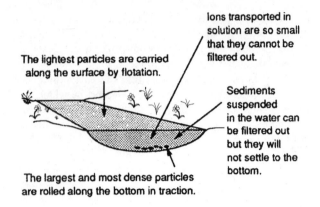

The lightest particles are carried along the surface by flotation.

Ions transported in solution are so small that they cannot be filtered out.

Sediments suspended in the water can be filtered out but they will not settle to the bottom.

The largest and most dense particles are rolled along the bottom in traction.

Figure 4-6. Erosion of sedimentary particles by streams

sediment. Slow-moving streams can transport only the smaller sedimentary particles.

The Velocity of Streams.   The velocity of a stream is controlled by the slope and the amount of water flowing in the stream (**discharge**). As the stream gradient increases, so does the velocity of the water flowing in the stream. Velocity is also increased by an increase in the quantity of water flowing in the stream. Most of the erosion caused by running water takes place when streams are in flood, because of an increase in both the quantity of water and the velocity of the floodwaters.

The speed of a stream is a balance between the force of gravity pulling the water downhill and the frictional forces slowing the stream. Water usually flows the fastest near the center of the stream away from the stream banks and the streambed. There is even a small amount of friction with the air above the water, so the fastest flow is commonly found at midstream just below the surface. See Figure 4-8.

Streams with broad, flat valleys often develop S-shaped curves called meanders. At the bends in the stream, the fastest-flowing water swings to the outside of the bends, causing erosion along the outer bank of

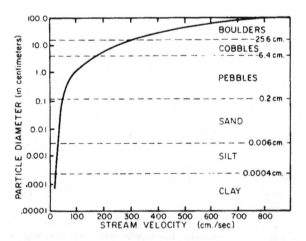

Figure 4-7. There is a direct relationship between the velocity of a stream and the size of the particles it can transport. Large grains of sediment can only be eroded by fast-moving water. This generalized graph shows the water velocity needed to maintain, but not start movement.

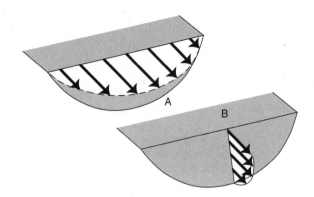

Figure 4-8. The velocity of a stream is a balance between gravity pulling the water downhill and friction with the banks of the stream and the streambed. There is even a small amount of friction with the air above the stream. Therefore, streams have the greatest velocity near the center of the stream, just below the surface. Diagram A shows that the greatest velocity is near the center of the stream, and diagram B shows that the greatest velocity is just below the top surface.

the meanders. See Figure 4-9. The slowest moving water stays to the inside of the bends, causing deposition along the inner bank of the meanders.

Erosion by Wind.

Another agent of erosion is wind. It can pick up loose rock materials, such as sand, silt, and clay, and carry them away. Wind erosion occurs mainly in dry areas, such as deserts, and beaches, where there is little plant life to hold soil in place. Wind also erodes by abrasion. In this process, sand blown by the wind breaks down material on a rock's surface. For example, the windblown sand in a desert often grinds rocks into angular shapes called ventifacts. See Figure 4-10.

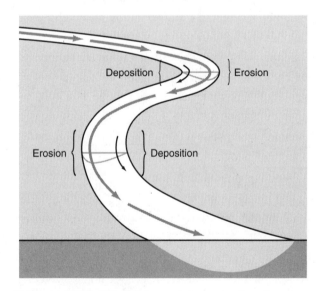

Figure 4-9. Erosion and deposition in meanders. In stream bends, inertia swings the fastest water to the outsides of the meanders as shown by the dark lines above. Due to differences in the velocity of the water, streams change their courses by eroding the banks along the outsides of the bends and depositing sediment on the insides.

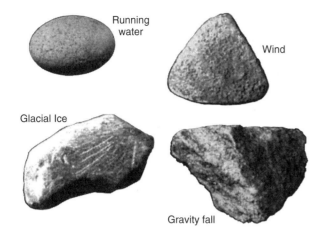

Running water

Wind

Glacial Ice

Gravity fall

Figure 4-10. Characteristics of particles eroded by different agents. Each agent of erosion produces its own characteristic shape and texture in rocks. Rocks tumbled in running water are round and smooth. Glacial rocks are partly rounded with scratches (striations). Wind-eroded rocks (ventifacts) are smooth and angular with pitted surfaces. Talus rocks (from rock falls) are rough and angular and may show some fresh and some weathered surfaces.

Erosion by Ice.
During the winter, most of North America receives precipitation as snow. If more snow accumulates in the winter than melts in the summer, the snow on the bottom turns to ice. If it becomes thick enough, its weight will cause it to move under the pull of gravity. A **glacier** is a large mass of moving ice. As a glacier moves, it carries, pushes, and drags loose rock material. The glacier, with pieces of rock embedded in its ice, acts like a huge abrasion system; it smooths, striates (scratches), and grooves bedrock. When the ice melts, unsorted rocks and boulders are left scattered around on hilltops and the sides of valleys.

A continental glacier deepens and widens valleys parallel to its movement. It grinds down the hills, leaving them polished and rounded. As a valley glacier moves, it scours away the rock to make a U-shaped glacial valley in which the valley walls may be nearly vertical. (Valleys eroded by streams are more often V-shaped with narrow valley floors.)

In some ways, valley glaciers are like streams and rivers, but glaciers move much slower. The ice may advance less than a meter a day, but, like streams, the ice in a valley glacier moves the fastest near the center of the flowing ice. Unlike water deposits, sediment left by melting glacial ice usually contains clay, sand, cobbles, and boulders mixed together. These **unsorted deposits** left by glacial ice are often found in ridges and mounds.

Four periods of continental glaciation in the past two million years have moved most of the soils of New York from their original locations and deposited them farther to the south. In New York, as elsewhere, transported soils are more common than residual soils. The Pleistocene (10,000 to 2 million years ago) ice sheets that covered mountains as well as valleys in New York State has left mountaintops that are rounded off and bedrock that is polished, grooved, and striated.

Agents of Erosion.
Each agent of erosion causes characteristic changes in the particles that it carries. Sedimentary particles carried by a stream are usually rounded and polished as a result of being tumbled about in the stream's current. Rocks transported by a glacier are usually partially rounded by abrasion and are often scratched (striated) on a flattened face as a result of being dragged along the bottom of the glacier. Rough and angular particles deposited at the base of a cliff usually indicate that gravity alone is responsible for transporting the rock a short distance. In this case, the rock particles often have some freshly exposed surfaces, as well as older surfaces that are more weathered. As different surfaces of a wind-worn rock are exposed to wind erosion, the rock develops smooth, flat surfaces, or facets, with distinct edges. These angular rocks are called ventifacts. Windworn rocks are often pitted where softer minerals have been scoured by the wind. See Figure 4-10.

QUESTIONS

24. Four identical rocks dropped into a stream and were washed downstream. Which of the rocks below was probably transported the least distance.

(1) (2) (3) (4)

25. Which of the following is most likely to be carried by flotation in a stream? (1) a branch of a tree (2) a large boulder (3) crystals of salt (4) grains of sand

26. Which factor usually has the greatest effect on stream erosion? (1) (liquid) water temperature (2) stream gradient (3) direction of flow (4) fish population

27. The diagram below shows a profile view of a large, straight portion of a stream. Which letter best shows where the water is probably the fastest? (1) a (2) b (3) c (4) d

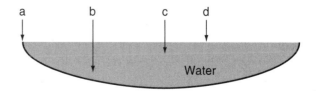

28. For which movement of earth materials is gravity not the main force? (1) sediment flowing in a stream (2) boulders carried by a glacier (3) snow tumbling in an avalanche (4) water evaporating from an ocean

29. This diagram shows a stream bend. Where is there probably the most erosion now occurring? (1) a (2) b (3) c (4) d

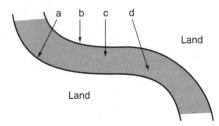

Directions: Base your answers to questions 30 through 32 on the following diagram and your knowledge of earth science.

30. The diagram below shows a stream meander. Which letters show the locations most likely to be experiencing stream erosion?

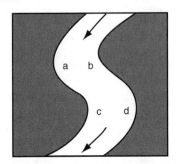

(1) a & b (2) b & c (3) c & d (4) d & a

31. Which diagram below best shows a bottom profile of the stream above along a-b?

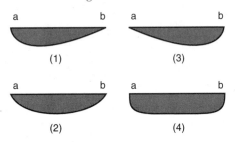

32. What change in this stream would cause the velocity of the water to increase? (1) an increase in atmospheric pressure (2) an increase in the water discharge (3) a decrease in slope (4) a decrease in water temperature

33. According to the *Earth Science Reference Tables*, what stream velocity could transport pebbles, but not cobbles? (1) 10 cm/s (2) 100 cm/s (3) 250 cm/s (4) 800 cm/s

34. As the gradient of a stream increases, the ability of the stream to carry sediment (1) decreases (2) increases (3) remains the same

35. A hard kind of cobble that is very round and smooth was most likely transported by (1) gravity acting alone (2) a glacier (3) the wind (4) a stream

36. A major toxic chemical spill occurs near Albany, New York. If this dangerous chemical is very soluble in water, what location is most likely to be in danger in a week or two? (1) Utica (west of Albany) (2) New York City (south of Albany) (3) Plattsburgh (north of Albany) (4) Buffalo (along Lake Erie)

WHAT IS DEPOSITION?

When an agent of erosion deposits, or lays down, particles and fragments of earth materials (sediments), the process is called **deposition**. Deposition is also called *sedimentation*. Agents of erosion, such as water, ice, and wind, are also agents of deposition. Most deposition actually takes place in water.

Factors That Affect Deposition.
The rate at which sediments are deposited depends upon the size, shape, and density of the sediment particles and the speed of the transporting medium.

Particle Size. The settling rate of particles is affected by particle size. Smaller particles, such as clay and silt, settle more slowly than cobbles and boulders. Very small particles (up to 0.001 mm in size), may remain in solution or suspension indefinitely. These particles of minerals normally do not settle out of a water solution unless the solution becomes *saturated*. For example, in some parts of the Persian Gulf, evaporation leaves the remaining water so rich in salt that the water becomes saturated. It can hold no more salt in solution. If more water evaporates, some of the salt must settle to the bottom of the ocean. The salt crystals that form and settle out of solution are called precipitates, and the process is called precipitation.

Particle Shape. The shape of sedimentary particles also affects how quickly they settle. Friction between water and the surfaces of particles slows down settling. Therefore, flat, angular, and irregularly shaped particles that have more surface area than smooth, rounded particles settle more slowly.

Particle Density. The density of particles also affects their settling rates. Among particles of the same average size and shape, denser particles settle faster, whereas less dense particles require more time for settling. See Figure 4-11.

Settling Rate and Settling Time. There is an inverse relationship that exists between the rate of set-

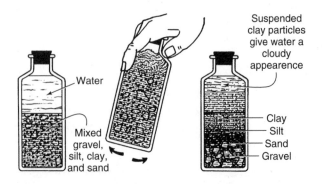

Figure 4-11. When a jar of water and sediments of mixed sizes is shaken, the largest, roundest, and most dense particles tend to settle to the bottom. The gradual change in sediment size from bottom to top is known as graded bedding.

tling and the settling time. Sediments that settle at a faster rate require less time. Thus, as the rate of settling increases, the settling time decreases.

Sorting of Sediments.

The velocity of a transporting medium plays a major role in determining when the deposition of particles will occur. Deposition is usually initiated by a reduction in the velocity of a transporting medium. For example, when a stream enters a large body of water, such as an ocean, the stream's velocity is reduced as it mixes with the ocean water. Particles of sediment begin to settle out. The largest, roundest, and densest particles are deposited first near the ocean's shoreline, while the smallest, flattest, and least dense particles are carried farthest from shore. The separation of particles, in this case, is called **horizontal sorting**. See Figure 4-12.

When particles sort out from bottom to top in a layer, it is called **vertical sorting**. During vertical sorting, the roundest, largest, and densest particles settle at the bottom of a layer, while the flattest, smallest, and least dense particles settle at the top of a layer. Vertical sorting may occur when a landslide suddenly dumps a variety of particle sizes into still water.

A series of depositional events, such as a succession of underwater landslides in deep water, can cause a type of vertical sorting known as graded bedding. For example, the first landslide causes a large volume of sediments to move down an underwater slope. The sediments sort vertically—large particles giving way gradually to smaller and smaller particles from the bottom to the top. This is the first graded bed. Another landslide produces another graded bed. An abrupt change in the particle size—from very fine sediments to a layer of very coarse sediments—separates one graded bed from another. Each graded bed represents a period of deposition or a single, distinct depositional event, such as one landslide. See Figure 4-13.

Deposition in Streams.

Most streams have some sections where the water runs quickly and other places where the water moves more slowly. Deposition in the slower sections of the stream can create charac-

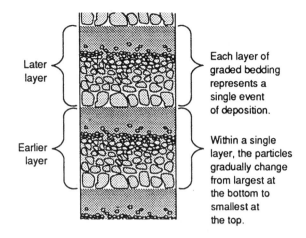

Figure 4-13. Vertical sorting in graded bedding. Layers of graded bedding represent a series of depositional events.

teristic features. For example, the sediment can form sand bars. Some rivers used for transportation or shipping cargo must be dredged in their slower sections to keep the river deep enough so that boats can pass.

Where a river or stream enters a lake or ocean the water slows down and drops its load of sediment in a fan-shaped deposit. This deposit is called a delta because it resembles the Greek letter "delta" (Δ), an ancestor of our letter "D." The land around New Orleans, Louisiana, was deposited as the Mississippi River slowed down upon reaching the Gulf of Mexico. The Mississippi delta includes thousands of square miles of river sediments.

Deposition by Wind.

Like running water, wind generally sorts its sediments by size. Hills of wind-blown sand called dunes can be seen in some beach areas as well as in certain desert regions. (Most desert areas, however, are dominated by poorly sorted, rocky soils that have been deposited by streams in flash floods after rare but intense downpours.) Within a sand dune we can often observe different layers of sand-sized particles. The finer particles have been blown away by the wind while larger rocks cannot be moved in by the wind. Layers that meet at different angles, a feature known as cross bedding, are common in windborne sediments.

Deposition by Gravity.

When gravity acts alone as the agent of erosion, the sediments deposited are not sorted. Therefore, at the base of a cliff where pieces of weathered rock have fallen, you will find pieces of many different sizes.

Deposition by Glaciers.

Deposition by glaciers occurs when a glacier melts and sediments are released. Glacial deposits are fairly easy to identify. **Glacial erratics** are large rocks that have been transported by glacial ice without being broken into small particles. They are often found high above stream

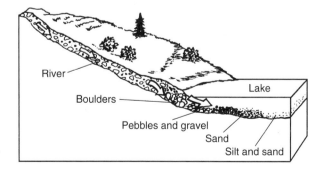

Figure 4-12. Horizontal sorting at the end of a stream. As a stream enters a lake or ocean the larger particles are deposited first. The smaller sediments can be carried a greater distance from shore.

valleys, which shows that they could not have been deposited by running water. Particle rounding and striations (scratches) also indicate transport by glaciers. Erratics commonly differ in composition from the bedrock on which they rest.

Glacial sediments can be classified into two kinds of deposits. Material that is deposited directly by moving ice contains a wide range of particle sizes without sorting or layering. Sediments deposited by streams of meltwater, on the other hand, usually contain layers in which sediments are sorted by particle size. When we see ice age sediments we can usually tell whether they were laid down by the advancing ice or moved into place by meltwater. This classification is done on the basis of layering and sorting in the sediments, especially when viewed in profile.

QUESTIONS

37. Which profile below best represents a series of three pulses (events) of deposition in deep water?

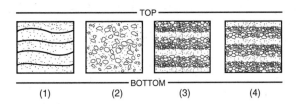

38. A hill of unsorted sediments of mixed grain sizes was probably deposited by (1) ice (2) wind (3) water (4) frost action

39. The diagram below represents a top view of a river emptying into an ocean bay. *A-B* is a reference line along the bottom of the bay. Which characteristic would most likely decrease along the reference line from A to B? (1) the amount of salt in solution (2) the size of the sediments (3) the density of the water (4) the depth of the water

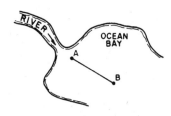

40. The rate at which particles are deposited by a stream is least affected by the (1) size and shape of the particles (2) velocity of the stream (3) stream's elevation above sea level (4) density of the particles

41. If all other factors remain constant, as the particle size of sediments increases from fine sand to coarse sand, the time necessary for settling in still water will probably (1) decrease (2) increase (3) remain the same

42. A large glass cylinder containing a mixture of sediments of the same density and water is shaken. Which drawing below best represents the result after settling?

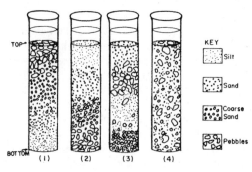

43. Which graph best represents the general relationship between particle density and settling rate in still water?

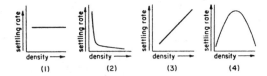

44. Flat-shaped particles may settle more slowly in a fluid than spherical particles that have the same mass and volume because the flat particles have (1) less weight (2) more potential energy (3) a lower density (4) more resistance due to shape

45. When the velocity of a stream decreases, there will most likely be an increase in (1) downcutting by the stream (2) deposition by the stream (3) the size of the particles carried in suspension by the stream (4) the amount of material carried in solution by the stream

Directions: Base your answers to questions 46 through 49 on the following four graphs and your knowledge of earth science.

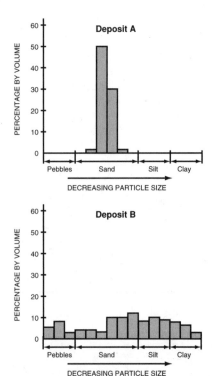

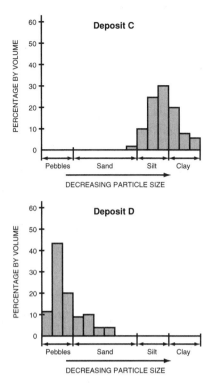

The graphs show four different samples of sediment that were laid down by wind, glaciers, a slow-moving river, and a rapid river. Each graph shows the percentage by volume of particles of various sizes.

46. Which deposit is best sorted into particles of a particular grain size? (1) A (2) B (3) C (4) D

47. What was the total portion of sand in deposit D? (1) 8% (2) 10% (3) 25% (4) 50%

48. Which deposit was probably taken from material that was laid down directly by a glacier? (1) A (2) B (3) C (4) D

49. Which deposit had the most particles that would stay in suspension in water for the longest time? (1) A (2) B (3) C (4) D

Directions: Base your answers to questions 50 through 53 on the *Earth Science Reference Tables*, the information provided in the diagram, and your knowledge of earth science.

50. Which graph best represents the effect of particle size on settling time if the particle densities are the same?

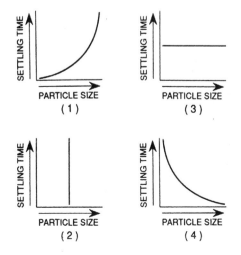

51. All three sediments in diagram I are placed in the cylinder with water, the mixture is shaken, and the particles are allowed to settle. Which diagram best represents the order in which the particles settled?

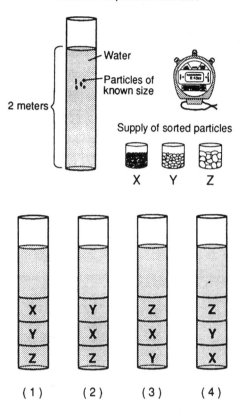

52. The stream shown in diagram II is carrying a mixture of sediments into the ocean. Which sediment will probably be carried farthest into the ocean by stream current? (1) silt (2) clay (3) pebbles (4) sand

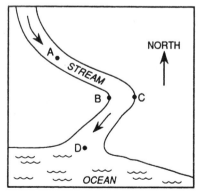

53. What is the minimum stream velocity needed to maintain the movement of a rock with a diameter of 25.6 centimeters? (1) 100 cm/s (2) 150 cm/s (3) 200 cm/s (4) 300 cm/s

NEW YORK AND THE ICE AGES

Glaciers are accumulations of snow and ice large enough to survive the summer melt. In present day New York, the climate is too warm to support glaciers, even in the highest mountains. However, as recently as 20,000 years ago, most of New York State was covered by a great continental ice sheet. This was during the last of the four ice ages that occurred in North America during the past two million years. Recent studies of past ocean temperatures have shown that ice ages were not restricted to just the past two million years. See Figures 4-14 and 4-15.

If ice forms under the weight of accumulating layers of snow, it will begin to flow downhill, away from its thickest accumulation, at rates ranging from a few centimeters to several meters per day. **Alpine glaciers**, also known as valley glaciers, occur in mountain regions, and may carve out U-shaped valleys with their moving ice. **Continental glaciers**, also known as ice sheets, are the type of glacier responsible for most of the glacial features found throughout New York State. The sculpting that is caused by a glacier is not formed directly by ice rubbing against rock. Rather, it is the rock carried within the glacier or dragged under its flowing ice that causes most glacial erosion.

As the ice sheet advanced over New York during the ice ages, it acted like sandpaper, grinding the jagged edges from the mountains and smoothing hard bedrock surfaces (**glacial polish**). Rocks within the glacier also left parallel grooves and scratches in the bedrock, forming **striations**. The Finger Lakes, shown in Figure 4-16, were created in western New York State as the advancing ice deeply scoured former north-south river valleys. In addition to creating features through erosion,

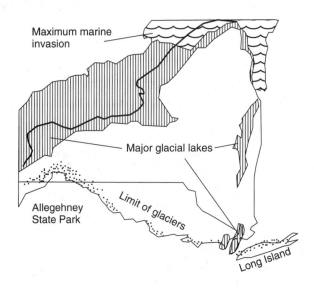

Figure 4-15. Nearly all of New York State was covered by glacial ice. Some areas held large glacial lakes as the ice front melted northward.

the ice sheets also created features through deposition of unsorted glacial sediment (till). Accumulations of rock and soil that built up in front of the flowing ice formed **drumlins** as the ice moved up and over these hills of sediment. Where the ice front stopped its southward advance, piles of unsorted soil and rock became terminal **moraines**, such as those that form the twin forks of Long Island (see Figure 4-17). Terminal moraines also dammed the valleys that became the Finger Lakes, creating the lakes, and forcing the water to flow north toward Lake Ontario. Low spots in the

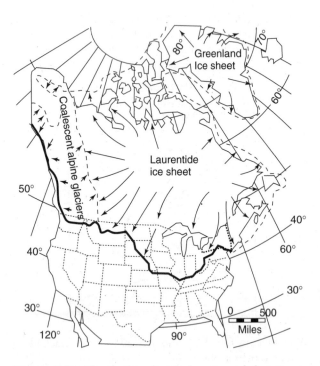

Figure 4-14. The southern limits of continental glaciation in North America.

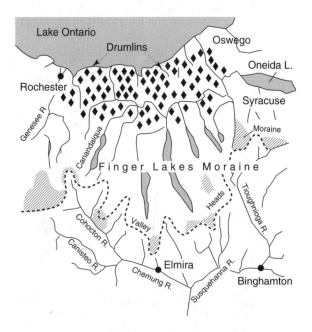

Figure 4-16. Glacial feature of the Finger Lakes region include the glacially scoured north-south valleys, several moraines, and a large drumlin field.

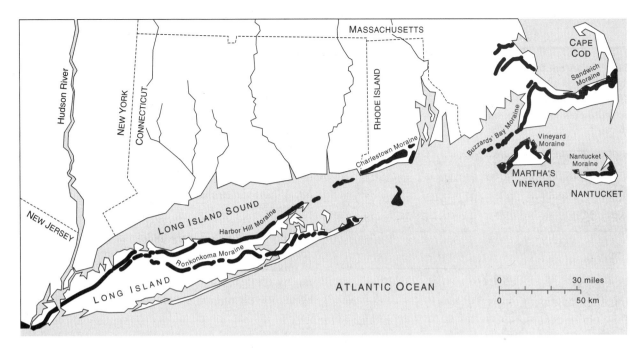

Figure 4-17. Long Island and nearby coastal New England are part of a series of terminal moraines.

glacial deposits and places where large, buried ice blocks melted left dry depressions called **kettles** and ponds called **kettle lakes**.

It is important to note that the glaciers that covered New York State continuously flowed southward. It was only when the rate of melting back was greater than the southward flow that the glaciers began to retreat. Figure 4-18 shows some of the features that can be seen throughout New York State as a result of the ice ages.

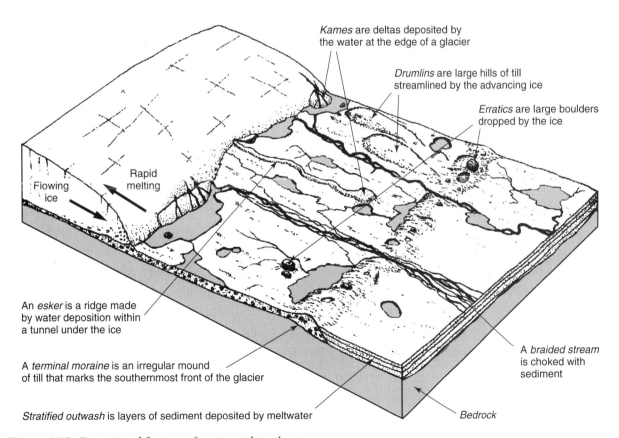

Kames are deltas deposited by the water at the edge of a glacier

Drumlins are large hills of till streamlined by the advancing ice

Erratics are large boulders dropped by the ice

Rapid melting

Flowing ice

An *esker* is a ridge made by water deposition within a tunnel under the ice

A *terminal moraine* is an irregular mound of till that marks the southernmost front of the glacier

Stratified outwash is layers of sediment deposited by meltwater

A *braided stream* is choked with sediment

Bedrock

Figure 4-18. Depositional features of continental ice sheets

Weathering, Erosion, Deposition, and Landscapes

54. A valley cut by a glacier is usually (1) A-shaped (2) V-shaped (3) U-shaped (4) W-shaped

55. Which diagram below best illustrates a cross section of sediments that were transported and deposited by a glacier?

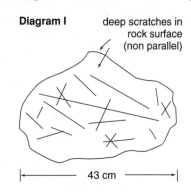

(1)　　　　(3)

(2)　　　　(4)

Diagram I (below) shows the appearance of rocks picked up at various deposit locations as shown in Diagram II.

Diagram I　deep scratches in rock surface (non parallel)

⊢——— 43 cm ———⊣

Diagram II

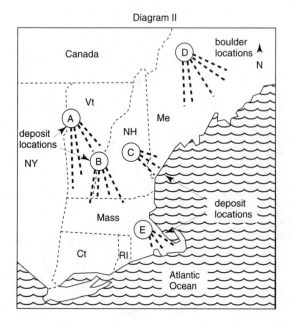

Letters A through E show the places where these rock types have been found in the bedrock.

56. The agent that eroded and then deposited these rocks probably came from the (1) northwest (2) northeast (3) southwest (4) southeast

57. What was the probable cause of the scratches in these rocks? (1) erosion by running water (2) pitting by wind-blown particles (3) splitting caused by frost (4) movement of the boulder over bedrock

58. How much larger is the real rock than the diagram? (1) 5 times (2) 10 times (3) 30 times (4) 100 times

59. What characteristic was probably common to the sedimentary deposits that contained all of these boulders? (1) They are all composed of a single type of rock. (2) They are all found at the ends of large rivers. (3) They are all found in piles of unsorted sediments. (4) They were all eroded from source region A.

60. These boulders were probably eroded and deposited by (1) ice (2) running water (3) wind (4) gravity acting alone

61. Which of the four rocks shown below was probably deposited by a glacier?

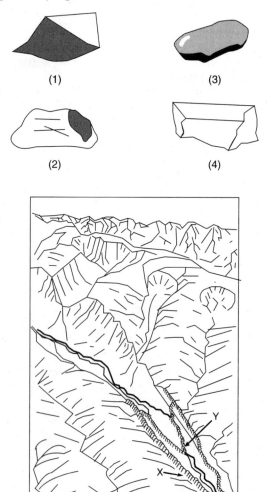

(1)　　　　(3)

(2)　　　　(4)

62. The ridges labeled X and Y on the diagram above were probably deposited by (1) running water (2) moving ice (3) wind currents (4) landslides

63. When a valley glacier erodes a valley, the valley is likely to become (1) more rounded and deeper (2) more angular and deeper (3) more rounded and shallower (4) more angular and shallower

64. The diagram below represents a section of the Earth's crust.

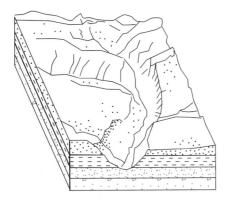

This surface landscape was most likely caused by (1) folding of the crust (2) sinking of rock layers (3) erosion by valley glaciers (4) deposition of stream sediments

THE OCEANS AND COSTAL PROCESSES

As you can see in Figure 4-19, seawater covers almost 71% of our planet. The oceans are also very deep, with an average depth of about 4 kilometers (3 miles). The deepest part of the Pacific Ocean could submerge the world's tallest mountain (Mount Everest) with another mile of ocean above its peak.

Most of the sediments deposited on land or in freshwater will later be eroded and deposited in the ocean. That's one reason why most fossils found in sedimentary rocks are the remains of marine organisms. Some of the sediment carried in solution to the oceans consists of simple compounds called salts. As Figure 4-20 shows, these salts are primarily made up of common table salt (sodium chloride), but a variety of other salts are also present in lesser concentrations. Where evaporation of ocean water causes the salts to become too concentrated to stay in solution, they are precipitated as sediment.

The edges of the oceans are places of rapid change caused by the action of waves and longshore currents. Although ocean waves may appear to be carrying water along, water does not actually flow with the waves. Instead, the surface water usually circulates in little circles or ellipses (ovals) as the wave passes. The waves actually carry energy, which is released as the waves break along

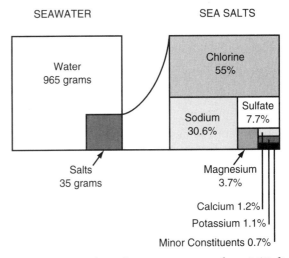

Figure 4-20. One liter of seawater contains about 3.5% dissolved solids. Sodium chloride (table salt) is the most common compound, but calcium and potassium compounds are also abundant.

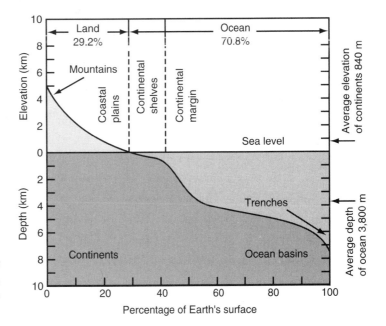

Figure 4-19. This diagram shows that most of Earth (70.8%) is covered by oceans. It also shows that the most common elevation of the geosphere is below sea level.

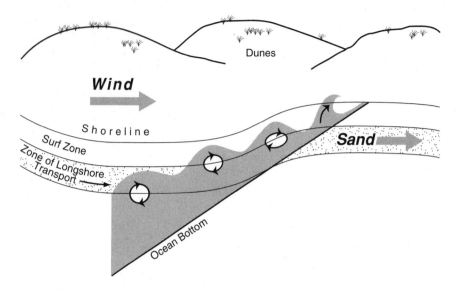

Figure 4-21. Longshore transport. This diagram illustrates what happens when the wind approaches the shore at an angle. The arrows show how the water moves when waves pass. As the waves near the shore, they "feel bottom," which makes the lower part of the wave slow. When the top of the wave gets too far ahead of the lower part, the wave breaks on the shore and deposits sand. Backwash returns the water to the ocean, washing sand off the beach. At the same time, the longshore current carries sand parallel to the beach. The motion of the sand forms a zigzag pattern, moved back and forth by the waves and down the beach by the wind.

the shore. This energy can change the sediments along the beach. Beach sediments are rounded and reduced in size by abrasion as the energy in the breaking waves causes the particles to rub against one another. In addition, the energy in the waves can also change the shoreline. Sand is often transported along the beach just outside the breaking waves in the zone of longshore transport. See Figure 4-21.

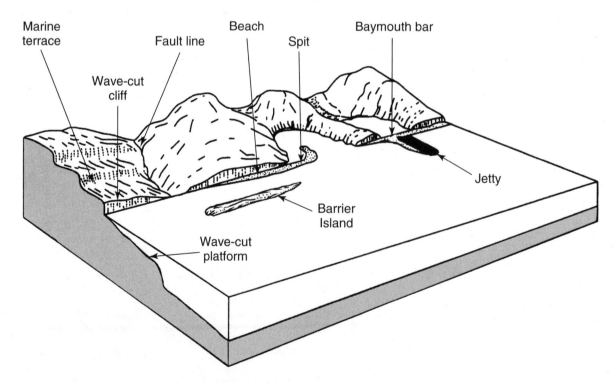

Figure 4-22. As waves erode back the land, longshore transport deposits sand in beaches, coastal sand bars, and barrier islands.

This movement of sand along the shore build the characteristic features of ocean shorelines, including sand bars, barrier islands, and sand spits, as shown in Figure 4-22. Migrating sand bars can form these features above the water's surface as well as forming underwater sandbars that run parallel to shore.

We sometimes build structures along the shore like breakwaters, which shelter boats from the main force of the waves, and jetties (see Figure 4-22), which are meant to hold sand on a beach. However, such efforts to control the force of the waves often create other problems, such as speeding up undesirable beach erosion somewhere else along the shore, or causing unwanted deposition within a harbor. Many progressive oceanfront communities are beginning to understand that beaches come and go in natural cycles, and are learning to plan for these changes. Some enlightened towns now forbid the building of homes or other permanent structures along the shore or even in the sand dunes behind the beach.

QUESTIONS

65. What portion of Earth is covered by the oceans? (1) 5% (2) 30% (3) 55% (4) 71%

Directions: Base your answers to questions 66–69 on the diagram below and your knowledge of earth science.

Dissolved Salts in Ocean Water

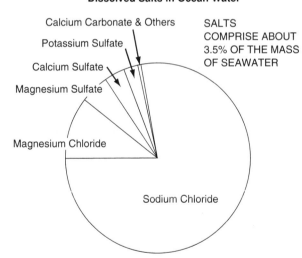

66. Table salt is the most common chemical in seawater. What is the chemical name for table salt? (1) sodium chloride (2) magnesium chloride (3) magnesium sulfate (4) calcium carbonate

67. What is the approximate portion of magnesium chloride in ocean salt? (1) 1% (2) 10% (3) 35% (4) 50%

68. Approximately how much salt (of mixed composition) would you expect to find in one liter (1 kilogram) of ocean water? (1) 0.35 grams (2) 35 grams (3) 350 grams (4) 3.5 kilograms

69. Which resource could be extracted from a given amount of seawater in the greatest quantity? (1) limestone (2) gold (3) iron (4) magnesium

Directions: Base your answer to questions 70–72 on the graph below and your knowledge of earth science.

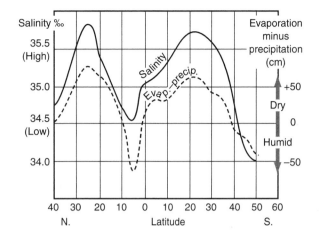

70. According to the graph, what process causes ocean water to become more salty? (1) inflow from rivers (2) wind-driven currents (3) precipitation (4) evaporation

71. Based upon this graph, the salinity of the oceans at the North and South Poles is probably (1) relatively high (2) relatively low (3) variable with the seasons (4) unpredictable

72. At what latitude is precipitation relatively abundant? (1) 25° North (2) 5° North (3) 15° South (4) 30° South

73. Calculate the gradient between two points located on the continental slope. The first point is 200 meters below sea level and the second point is at a depth of 1,850 meters. The distance between the two points is 2.0 kilometers. (1) 12 m/km (2) 825 m/km (3) 3 km/m (4) 3 m/km

74. Approximately how deep are the oceans? (1) They are just about a mile, at their deepest. (2) They are about as deep as they are wide. (3) Oceans are deeper than the elevations of the tallest mountains on land (4) We have not yet found ways to measure the deepest parts of the oceans.

75. What causes the ocean bottoms to change through time? (1) deposition, only (2) erosion, only (3) erosion, deposition, and plate motions (4) the orbital and rotational motions of Earth

76. Which of the following usually causes the transport of sand in the surf zone along the shore? (1) the wind (2) river currents that enter the ocean (3) gravity (4) Earth's magnetic field

77. Why do waves break as they reach the beach? (1) The waves slow down as they come ashore. (2) The waves speed up as they come ashore. (3) Increasing salinity makes the waves break. (4) Waves do not break.

78. Most natural ocean beaches reach a condition in which they do not appear to change from year to year. How can we best characterize their condition? (1) Deposition dominates over erosion. (2) Erosion dominates over deposition. (3) Erosion and deposition are in equilibrium. (4) Neither erosion nor deposition is occurring.

79. Which of the following statements best describes ocean waves? (1) The water near the surface travels forward along with the wave. (2) Waves carry energy. (3) Air caught in the depressions between waves is carried along with the wave. (4) Waves allow large fish to move with them, without any effort by the fish.

WHAT IS A LANDSCAPE?

A **landscape** is a region on Earth's surface in which physical features, such as hills, valleys, and streams, are related by a common origin. The shape (**topography**) and composition of the landscape are determined by the climate, the local bedrock, geologic structures, and human activities. Landscapes may reveal the interaction between the natural and human history of a region.

Landscape Regions.
Most landscape regions can be classified as mountains, plateaus, or plains. See Figure 4-23. Each has its own geologic structures and topographic relief. Topographic **relief** is the change in elevation between the highest and the lowest places.

Mountain landscapes have the greatest relief between the highest peaks and the deepest valleys. A great

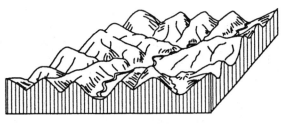
Mountain landscape

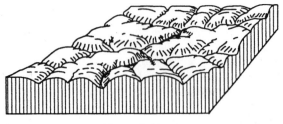
Plateau landscape

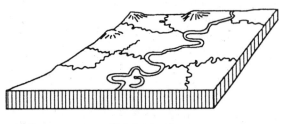
Plain landscape

Figure 4-23. Landscapes are generally classified on the basis of topographic relief. A variety of structures and variable rock types with large changes in elevation make mountain landscapes the most complex. The lower elevations of plateaus and plains may be a function of how long they have been eroded or a function of their uniform or horizontal rock layers.

variety of rock types, often including igneous and metamorphic rocks (as well as folded and faulted sedimentary rock), are common in mountain landscapes. These structures result from the tectonic forces within Earth that push up mountains. Mountains are especially common where converging tectonic plates collide. Stream gradients are high, and the fast moving streams quickly erode deep valleys between the mountain peaks. In landscapes such as the Rockies, the Alps, and the Himalayas, much of the land is on steep mountain slopes.

Plateau landscapes are often relatively flat or rolling uplands in which streams have cut deep valleys. Plateaus are commonly underlain by flat layers of sedimentary rock. The Colorado Plateau near the Grand Canyon of northern Arizona is a good example. Although plateaus usually have less topographic relief than mountains, they have more relief than plains.

Plains have the least topographic relief. Although they may contain a few small hills, plains are generally flat and at a low elevation. Plains are commonly underlain by flat layers of sedimentary rock. Most of Florida and the agricultural areas of the midwest exhibit plains topography.

Large areas, such as North America, and even smaller areas, such as New York State, can be divided into various landscape regions. See Figure 4-24. Each landscape region has its own characteristic hillslopes, drainage patterns, and soil associations.

The Influence of Climate.
Landscapes in moist climates are generally rounded, while those in arid climates are characterized by sharp angles and steeper slopes, as shown in Figure 4-25. Moisture plays an important part in chemical weathering. Humid climates promote the development of mature soils with a good balance of minerals and humus (organic remains of plants and animals). While you might think that these soils would be quickly eroded by the streams in a moist climate, this does not happen. Abundant rainfall throughout the year supports the growth of plant cover. Plant cover protects the soil from rapid runoff and erosion and produces the rounded slopes characteristic of humid climates. The moist climate also maintains many small streams that flow through most of the year.

Arid (dry) climates generally produce thin soils with little humus. Physical weathering, particularly frost action in the colder months, is a dominant form of weathering. This kind of weathering tends to form soils with large and angular grains. There is little fine-grained material to fill the pores and retard rapid and deep infiltration of precipitation. Only specialized desert plants can survive the long periods between rainstorms. While rain is infrequent in desert regions, it often comes down very hard when it does rain. With little plant cover to protect the soil, sediment is readily carried away in time of rainfall. Large areas of exposed bedrock and steep rock faces are the result. Most of the small streams remain dry, except immediately after the widely scattered storms. You may be surprised to know that within the United States, the regions of most rapid stream erosion are the desert areas where rainfall is infrequent.

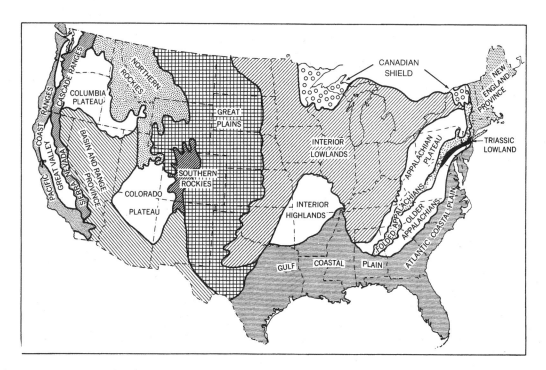

Figure 4-24. Landscape regions of the United States. Major landscape regions are large areas with common rock structure and surface topography. Plains and plateaus have horizontal rock structure while mountains have nonhorizontal structure. Plateaus have higher elevations than do plains.

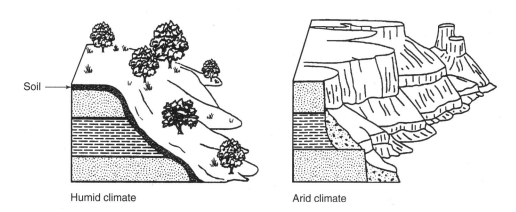

Figure 4-25. Landscapes in humid climates and arid climates. In humid climates, the slopes are not usually as steep as they are in arid climates. This is because a moist climate promotes a protective cover of vegetation.

Thus, the amount and distribution of rainfall influence the landscape features. These include the angle of hillslopes, the number of permanent streams, the vegetative cover, and the nature of the soil.

The interfaces (boundaries) between landscape regions are often remarkably distinct. East of Denver, Colorado, are the gently rolling Great Plains. The plains landscape ends suddenly just west of Denver, where the Rocky Mountains begin. This abrupt change in landscape is a result of a change from the horizontal sedimentary rocks of the plains to the complex folds and faults of the mountain landscape. In fact, most land-scape regions end rather suddenly; thus it is often easy to locate the boundaries between landscapes.

HOW DO GEOLOGIC FACTORS INFLUENCE THE LANDSCAPE?

Even in the same climate, locations with different rock types or different structures can develop very different landscape features.

Rocks that are hard and resist weathering and erosion are called competent rocks. Competent rocks form the

Weathering, Erosion, Deposition, and Landscapes

higher portions of a landscape—the plateaus, mountains, and **escarpments** (cliffs). The softer rocks and rocks that have been fractured usually underlie valleys and other low areas.

Softer rock erodes faster than competent rock. If all the exposed bedrock on a hillslope has about the same degree of competence, the slopes will be worn down fairly evenly. If the layers of the hillslope differ in competence, the softer rocks will wear away faster, giving the hillslope an uneven or stepped appearance. The more competent layers will form the steepest slopes and cliffs.

Streams generally follow zones of weakness, such as less competent rock, faults, and joints. Faults and joints particularly influence the stream patterns in mountainous areas of a single rock type.

Landscape Affects Drainage Patterns.

If two very different rock types occur in the same area, the harder rock will form the hills and ridges. Erosion of the weaker rock type will make the major valleys. Therefore, streams will tend to follow zones of weaker rock. This knowledge, coupled with your understanding that water flows downhill, should help you to identify stream patterns associated with geologic features. Figure 4-26 shows some of the drainage patterns that develop in different bedrock structures.

Landscapes of New York State.

New York State can be divided into several distinct landscape areas. See Figure 4-27.

The *St. Lawrence/Champlain Lowlands*, New York's northernmost region, is a low-lying plain along the St. Lawrence River and Lake Champlain. This lowland region partially encircles the Adirondack Mountains. The bedrock is predominantly layers of sedimentary rock that gently slope away from the Adirondacks.

The *Appalachian Uplands* are New York's largest landscape region. This region is underlain by mostly flat layers of sedimentary rocks that were laid down in a shallow, sinking ocean basin hundreds of millions of years ago. The land was later pushed up over 1,000 meters to form a plateau and is cut into by many streams. The Catskills, near the eastern end of this region, reach over 1 kilometer above sea level. The **Finger Lakes**, near the center of this region, were formed when glaciers moved into existing north-south valleys, widening and deepening them. As the glacier melted back, it deposited till that blocked natural outlets to the south, thus making long north-south lakes. Within New York State, the Appalachian Plateau has been divided into the Catskills and the Allegheny Plateau.

The *Erie-Ontario Lowlands* lie south of these two great lakes. Although a plains landscape, these lowlands have many hills composed of unsorted glacial till. Layered sediments left by meltwater from the continental glaciers are also common. Good soils which were deposited and mixed by glaciers, and a climate moderated by the Great Lakes, make this an important agricultural area.

The *Adirondack Highlands* in the northeast are New York's only true mountain landscape. The ancient metamorphic and igneous rocks of this region were pushed up in the middle to form a dome. Most of these rocks are very hard and resistant to erosion. Major valleys commonly run northeast-southwest along joint and fault structures. New York's highest point, Mount

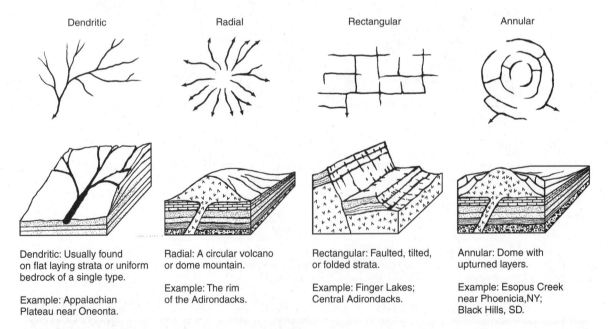

| Dendritic | Radial | Rectangular | Annular |

Dendritic: Usually found on flat laying strata or uniform bedrock of a single type.

Example: Appalachian Plateau near Oneonta.

Radial: A circular volcano or dome mountain.

Example: The rim of the Adirondacks.

Rectangular: Faulted, tilted, or folded strata.

Example: Finger Lakes; Central Adirondacks.

Annular: Dome with upturned layers.

Example: Esopus Creek near Phoenicia,NY; Black Hills, SD.

Figure 4-26. Stream drainage patterns and possible associated geological structures. (1) On flat-lying layers of uniform composition, without zones of weakness, a branching, *dendritic pattern* will form. (2) On a volcano or rounded hill (dome) with little difference in rock competence, a *radial pattern* will form. (3) Joints or faults produce a rectangular or *trellis pattern*. Tellis drainage is often found in areas where rock layers with differing competence have been folded or tilted and eroded to form ridges. (4) If there are great differences in rock competence, an *annular pattern* of concentric circles will probably form.

Reviewing Earth Science: Chapter 4

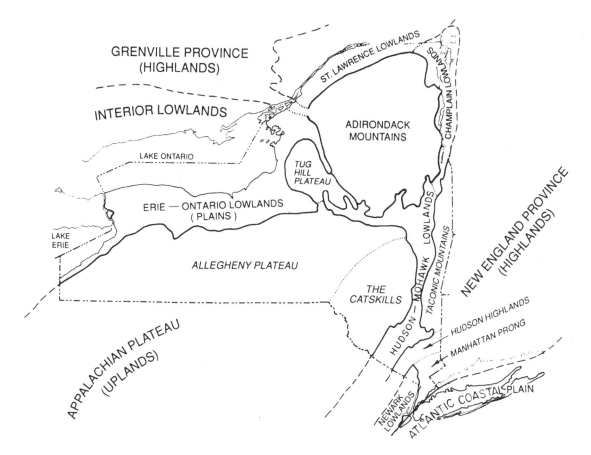

Figure 4-27. Generalized landscape regions of New York State

Marcy (at 1628 meters above sea level), is within this region. The lower areas of these highlands are filled with lakes, ponds, and swamps, many of which were formed by glacial deposits.

The *Tug Hill Plateau* is a small region of elevated sedimentary layers near the eastern end of Lake Ontario. The Tug Hill region is a small part of the Appalachian Plateau. Poor drainage (caused by glacial deposits) and abundant winter snowfall make this one of the least-inhabited and least-used areas of the state.

The *Hudson-Mohawk Lowlands* (plains) follow a zone of easily eroded limestones and shales. The Mohawk river valley, which provided water-level access to the interior of America, was especially important as a trade route in the development of New York in the 1700s and 1800s. Consequently, many towns and cities were established in this region.

The *New England Highlands*, a region of intensely folded and faulted metamorphic rocks, include the Taconic Mountains along the eastern boundary of the state. The entire area was covered by the last continental glacier, which left rounded hills and a variety of glacial and meltwater deposits. In its southern portion, the highlands split into two prongs. One extends westward toward New Jersey as the Hudson Highlands. The other section extends to the south through Westchester and into the Bronx and Manhattan.

The *Triassic Lowlands* are a section of sandstones and shales deposited in a fault basin between the lower portions of the New England Highlands and the Hudson River. The region is geologically younger than the surrounding highlands.

The *Atlantic Coastal Lowlands*, made up of Staten Island and Long Island, form a coastal plain largely composed of glacial sediments. Along the north shore and the center of Long Island are two terminal moraines left by the last great glacier that covered the state during the Pleistocene Epoch. The land south of these moraines is composed of sorted material washed out of glaciers. This relatively flat area south of the terminal moraines is an **outwash plain**. It is underlain by layers of sandy sediment deposited by streams flowing out of the glaciers. Landforms of glacial origin, such as *kettles* (where buried ice blocks may have melted) and *kames* (where glacial streams slowed down to deposit deltas as they entered calm water at the edge of the glacier), are common on Long Island.

Human Activities Affect Landscapes.

Farming and construction projects can accelerate erosion and affect landscape development. Farmers and engineers must be guided in planning their projects by appropriate conservation practices. For example, contour plowing is practiced on farms that have hilly areas. Contour plowing curves around a hill, rather than plowing up and down the hillside. This practice helps keep the soil from being washed away. Strip mining removes

Weathering, Erosion, Deposition, and Landscapes

81

the layers of soil to extract the minerals found in the bedrock. Rather than leaving a scar on the landscape when the mining operation is finished, engineers can grade the land, replace the soil, and plant plants to hold the soil in place. It is now estimated that more rock and soil is moved by humans than by all rivers combined.

QUESTIONS

80. In what type of climate does chemical weathering usually dominate over physical weathering? (1) cold and dry (2) cold and moist (3) warm and dry (4) warm and moist

81. If a landscape is in equilibrium, the surface elevations will be generally (1) decreasing (2) increasing (3) remaining the same

82. According to the *Earth Science Reference Tables*, which type of landscape region is located at 44° 30' North, 74° 30' West? (1) plateau (2) coastal lowlands (3) plains (4) mountains

83. Which part of New York State has been the most changed by wave erosion in the past 200 years? (1) the Atlantic Coastal Plain (2) the Hudson-Mohawk Lowlands (3) the St. Lawrence Lowlands (4) the Triassic Lowlands

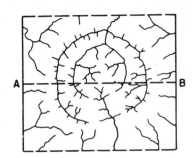

84. Which of the geologic cross sections below would be likely to underlie the drainage pattern shown above?

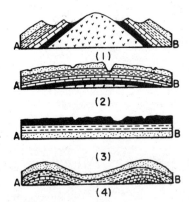

85. According to the *Earth Science Reference Tables*, which landscape region of New York contains mostly bedrock of Devonian age? (1) Adirondack Highlands (2) Atlantic Coastal Lowlands (3) Appalachian/Allegheny Plateau (4) Tug Hill Plateau

86. The landscape below developed in an arid climate.

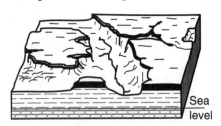

If erosion had taken place in a humid climate, which of the four diagrams below best shows how the landscape would have then looked?

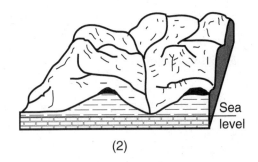

(1)

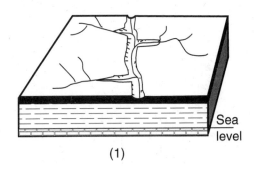

(2)

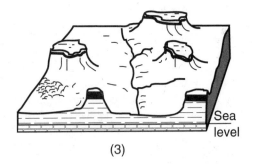

(3)

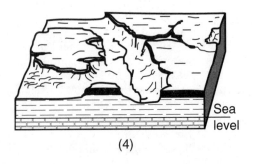

(4)

---

87. On the profile view of a cliff below, which kind of rock seems to be the most resistant to weathering? (1) shale (2) conglomerate (3) limestone (4) sandstone

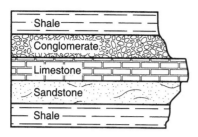

88. According to the *Earth Science Reference Tables*, which landscape region separates the Adirondack Mountains from the Catskill Mountains? (1) Taconic Mountains (2) Long Island (3) Hudson-Mohawk Lowlands (4) Lake Champlain Lowlands

89. According to the *Earth Science Reference Tables*, in which landscape region is Ithaca, New York? (1) Appalachian/Allegheny Plateau (2) Adirondack Mountains (3) Catskill Mountains (4) St. Lawrence Lowlands

90. The diagram that follows shows a cross section of a bedrock outcrop in New York State underlain by sedimentary rock. What caused the differences in the gradient of this slope? (1) changes in ages of the rock layers (2) the variable thickness of the rock layers (3) changes in the tilt of the rock layers (4) the variable resistance of the rock layers

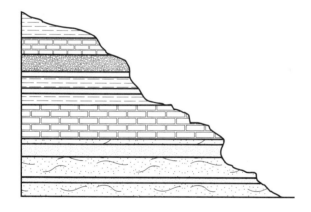

91. What two factors have the greatest influence on the development of a natural landscape? (1) air pressure and wind speed (2) local climate and geology (3) population and longitude (4) evapotranspiration and cloud cover

92. The landscape below is a result of (1) faulting (2) folding (3) changes in rock type (4) changes in climate

93. Observing hillslopes, stream patterns, and bedrock structures would help identify (1) magnetic north (2) earthquake epicenters (3) fossils (4) landscape regions

94. According to the *Earth Science Reference Tables*, how do the Catskills differ from the Adirondacks? (1) The

Adirondacks have milder winters. (2) The Adirondacks are composed mostly of metamorphic bedrock. (3) The Catskills do not have any vegetation. (4) The highest mountains of the Catskills are higher above sea level.

95. Which feature helps to identify a landscape that has been developed mostly by stream action? (1) marine terraces well above sea level (2) sand dunes and other coastal deposits (3) "V" shaped valleys and little soil (4) parallel hills and unsorted sediments

96. Which landscape region of New York is composed of low hills of unsorted sediments of Cretaceous and Pleistocene age? (1) the Hudson-Mohawk Lowlands (2) the Atlantic Coastal Plain (3) the Champlain Lowlands (4) the Erie-Ontario Lowlands

97. In a landscape where erosion is dominant over uplifting forces (1) high mountains will be very common (2) the mountains will be growing higher (3) the mountains will be worn away (4) the landscape will not change

98. Gentle slopes and rounded mountains are most often the result of (1) shifting of fault blocks (2) the age of the bedrock (3) conditions of climate (4) volcanoes and meteorites

99. Which drainage pattern shown below is the most likely to develop in a region of uniform bedrock without folding or faulting?

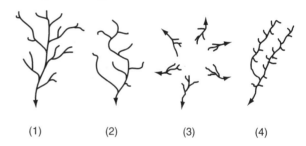

(1)   (2)   (3)   (4)

100. Which region of New York State has the greatest topographic relief? (1) the Hudson-Mohawk Lowlands (2) the Atlantic Coastal Plain (3) the Appalachian Plateau (4) the Adirondack Mountains

101. Which factor is likely to cause changes in the local landscape in a very brief portion of geologic time? (1) human activities (2) changes in climate (3) chemical weathering (4) physical weathering

102. We can best identify boundaries between landscape regions by observing (1) changes in stream discharge through time (2) changes in rock structure and elevation (3) average annual precipitation (4) national borders on political maps

---

The Scientist, Engineer, and Citizen

Soil erosion is one of the most serious threats to environmental quality in many agricultural areas. Report on the damage already done by soil erosion, various measures to preserve local soils and the economic impact of the measures you suggest.

1. As a rock is transported downstream in a swift river, how is it likely to change? (1) It becomes smaller and more angular. (2) It becomes smaller and more rounded. (3) It becomes larger and more angular. (4) It becomes larger and more rounded.

2. Which factor is most likely to affect the amount of erosion done by a stream? (1) the direction of flow (2) the elevation (3) the water temperature (4) the gradient

3. Which graph best shows the relationship between the largest size of particles that a stream can transport and the velocity of the stream?

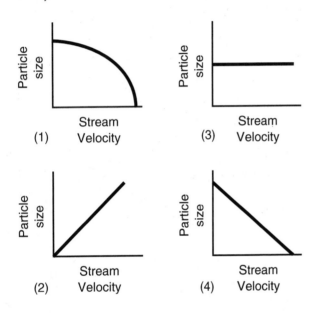

4. Which of the following is an example of a physical change? (1) abrasion of sediment in a stream (2) rusting of iron in a damp place (3) burning of wood in a forest fire (4) limestone dissolving in acid

5. In what part of a stream is the water usually flowing the fastest? (1) in the center near the bottom (2) in the center near the surface (3) a few centimeters from the edge (4) at the very edge of the stream

6. Which of the following changes will make a stream flow faster? (1) a decrease in gradient (2) flowing into a lake (3) freezing from top to bottom (4) an increase in water discharge

7. What force is responsible for the movement of water in a stream? (1) the wind (2) heat energy (3) gravity (4) magnetic force

8. Which is responsible for the most erosion in the United States in the past 100 years? (1) glaciers (2) streams (3) the wind (4) gravity acting alone

9. How are the least dense particles carried by a stream? (1) by rolling along the bottom (2) in solution (3) by flotation (4) in suspension

10. The diagram to the right shows a stream flowing in the direction of the arrows. Which drawing below best shows the cross-sectional (profile) shape of the stream along line X-Y?

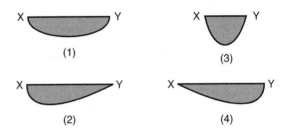

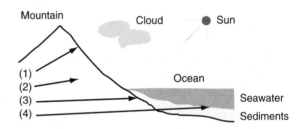

11. Physical weathering by frost tends to be the greatest in a climate that is (1) always warm and moist (2) always warm and dry (3) moist with great changes in temperature (4) dry with great changes in temperature

12. According to the *Earth Science Reference Tables*, how fast must water be moving to erode pebbles, but not cobbles? (1) 10 centimeters per second (2) 100 centimeters per second (3) 1000 centimeters per second (4) 10,000 centimeters per second

13. The diagram below shows an ocean and mountain landscape in profile view. Where is weathering probably happening the fastest?

14. What are most soils made from? (1) unweathered rock (2) only organic remains (3) a mixture of air and unweathered rock (4) weathered rock and organic remains

15. The depth of a soil is likely to be greater if (1) the soil formed over a long period of time (2) it formed from a rock that weathers very little (3) the soil formed on a steep mountain slope (4) it is quickly eroded by wind and rain

16. A stream carries a variety of rock particles into a calm lake. Which particles are most likely to be deposited near shore at the end of the stream? (That is, which will not be carried far out into the calm water?) (1) the largest particles (2) the smallest particles (3) particles carried by flotation (4) particles carried in solution

17. Which of the following agents of erosion usually deposits sediments that are not sorted by size? (1) wind (2) streams and rivers (3) glaciers (4) glacial melt water

18. According to the *Earth Science Reference Tables*, what type of landscape is found in New York along the south shore of Lake Ontario? (1) plains (2) plateau (3) mountains (4) continental shelf

19. Which drainage pattern shown below would develop along the slope of a steep volcano?

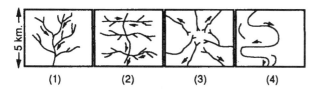

(1)   (2)   (3)   (4)

20. The variety of landscapes we see in New York State is a result of local differences in (1) geologic features (2) climate (3) solar energy (4) rainfall

21. What kind of landscape usually has the greatest range of topographic relief (elevation)? (1) plains (2) plateaus (3) rolling hills (4) mountains

22. When was most of New York State covered by large ice sheets? (1) only once, early in Earth's history (2) only once, in the recent geologic past (3) many times throughout Earth's history (4) not in the past, but probably in the future

23. At which position in the stream meander shown below is erosion probably dominant over deposition?

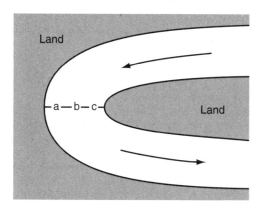

(1) a (2) b (3) c

24. Which diagram below best shows a top to bottom profile of the stream along a-b-c?

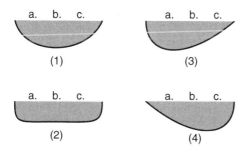

(1)   (2)   (3)   (4)

25. If there were a flood at this location, the speed of water flowing in the stream would probably (1) decrease (2) increase (3) remain the same

26. What event, that occurred over 10,000 years ago, had a great effect on the soils of New York State? (1) a great flood on the Hudson River (2) advance of continental glaciers (3) lowering of sea level by hundreds of meters (4) a drought, followed by intense dust storms

27. Where is abrasion the dominant form of weathering? (1) along the beach (2) at a rocky mountaintop (3) deep in the soil (4) in water-filled rock cracks

28. Shown below are three stages in the development of a soil. What is the proper order for these diagrams?

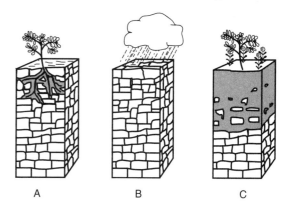

A   B   C

(1) A-B-C (2) C-B-A (3) C-A-B (4) B-A-C

29. Which of the following changes is a chemical change? (1) rusting of iron ore (2) splitting of rocks by ice (3) abrasion of rock as it is washed downstream (4) sand grains worn down by wave action

30. Which group of words has nearly the same meaning as "weathering?" (1) rain, snow, erosion, and wind (2) erosion, moving, and deposition (3) temperature, pressure, and humidity (4) breakdown, rusting, and abrasion

31. The agent of erosion active in New York State 10,000 years ago was (1) standing water (2) glaciers (3) the wind (4) gravity acting alone

32. In what month is chemical weathering usually most active in New York State? (1) January (2) May (3) July (4) October

33. Which of the diagrams below best shows a typical soil profile?

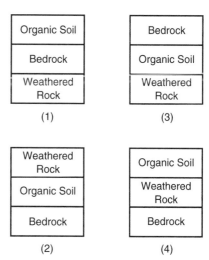

(1)   (3)   (2)   (4)

34. According to the *Earth Science Reference Tables*, the glaciers that shaped the landscape of New York State occurred at approximately the same time as the (1) formation of the Taconic Mountains (2) development of humans

(3) appearance of the first sharks (4) extinction of the trilobites

35. Why is most of New York State no longer covered by large ice sheets? (1) There is no longer enough ice. (2) The climate is now too cold. (3) The climate is too warm. (4) There is too much freshwater.

36. The diagram below represents the cross section of a soil deposit from a hill in central New York State.

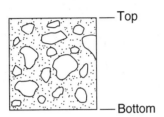

The deposition was most likely caused by (1) a glacier (2) a windstorm (3) a stream entering a lake (4) wave action along a beach

37. Unsorted sediments are commonly deposited by (1) moving ice (2) wind (3) running water (4) ocean currents

Directions: Base your answers to questions 38 through 42 on the map below and your knowledge of earth science. The map shows the southernmost advance of four major stages of continental glaciation in the central United States. White areas represent land once covered by glacial ice. The general direction of ice movement was from north to south.

38. The landforms that mark the terminal glacial boundaries are made up of (1) residual soil particles resting on a flat plain (2) rounded grains in a sand dune (3) layered clay particles on a flat plain (4) unsorted sediments in low, irregular hills

39. Which state was partly or completely covered by glacial ice during all four stages of ice advance? (1) Iowa (2) Kentucky (3) Kansas (4) Missouri

40. In the state of Kansas, the average distance between the Nebraskan Stage ice boundary and the Kansan Stage ice boundary is approximately (1) 40 km (2) 180 km (3) 90 km (4) 300 km

41. What evidence found on the former ice-covered areas would best show the direction of continental glacial movement? (1) resistant, folded metamorphic bedrock (2) high-temperature igneous and volcanic bedrock (3) bedrock with parallel scratches and grooves (4) bedrock containing fossils of animals that lived in cold water

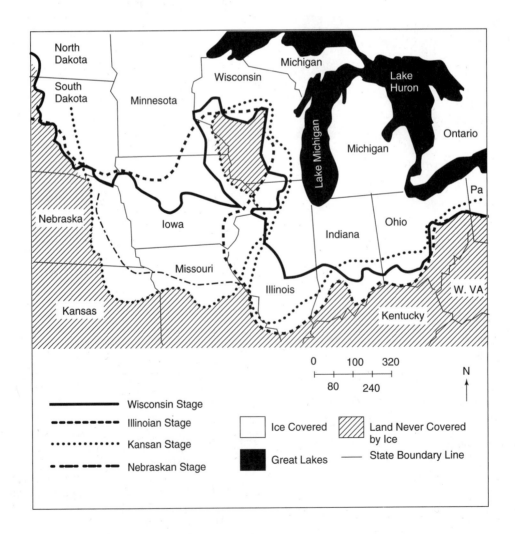

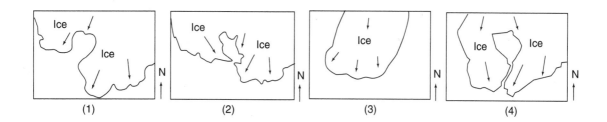

(1)   (2)   (3)   (4)

42. Which map above best represents the southernmost advance of the continental ice sheet during the Wisconsinan Stage?

FREE-RESPONSE QUESTIONS

(Answer the following questions on a separate sheet of paper.)

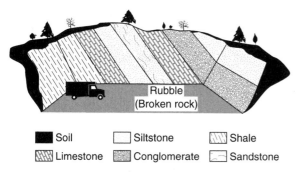

Rubble (Broken rock)

■ Soil   □ Siltstone   ◩ Shale
▨ Limestone   ▨ Conglomerate   ▱ Sandstone

1. Congratulations! You have inherited a rock quarry that has been cut into a hill, as shown directly above. The quarry is used to supply building stone. Your first order has come from a customer who wants the highest quality stone: the one that will wear the least and last the longest. Based upon the diagram, which kind of stone will best suit your needs?

Explain your choice in one or more complete sentences.
(Rock type, +1; Reasoning, +1; Sentence, +1)

2. How and why do landscapes (landforms) in moist areas, like New York State, differ from those in dry areas, like the desert of the southwest? Use complete sentences.
(Complete Sentences, +1; Describe difference, +1; Tell why, +1)

3. Give two reasons why soils of New York State differ from the soils in other places. Use complete sentences.
(Each reason, +1; Complete sentences, +1)

4. Describe the formation of horizontal sorting near the mouth of a stream. Tell how it forms and what it looks like. Be sure to use complete sentences.
(Complete description, +2; Complete sentences, +1)

5. Many times in Earth's history large areas of its surface have been covered with thick sheets of ice called glaciers. Answer the following questions in complete sentences. How do glaciers form? Why do they move? What is one way valley glaciers are different from continental glaciers?

(Complete Sentences, +1; Formation, +1; Movement, +1; Difference, +1)

6. The landscape shown below represents an area shaped by a continental glacier. Note the four glaciation features labeled. Tell how any two were made. (You do not need to give their technical names.) In a single complete sentence, briefly explain the process that made each.
(Complete Sentences, +1; Origin of the first, +1; Origin of the second, +1)

7. In one or more complete sentences, explain how weathering is different from erosion. Can you have weathering without erosion? Can you have erosion without weathering?
(Complete Sentences, +1; Each correct answer, +1)

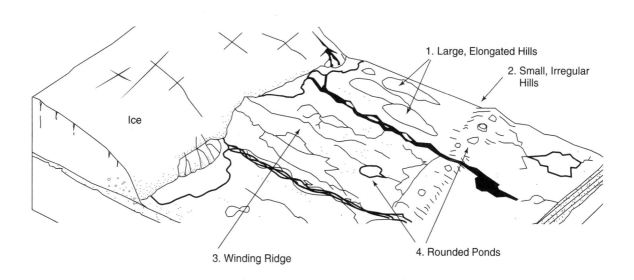

1. Large, Elongated Hills
2. Small, Irregular Hills
3. Winding Ridge
4. Rounded Ponds

Ice

Weathering, Erosion, Deposition, and Landscapes   **87**

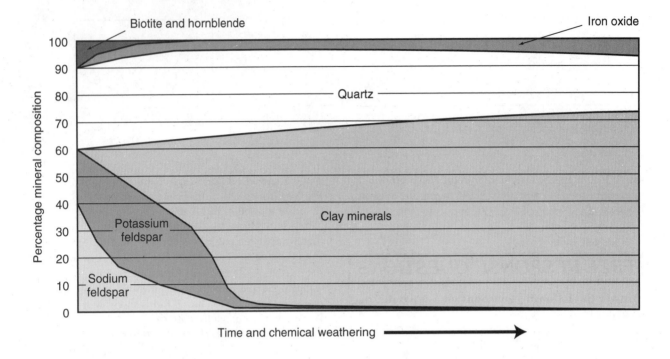

Biotite and hornblende

Iron oxide

Quartz

Clay minerals

Potassium feldspar

Sodium feldspar

Percentage mineral composition

Time and chemical weathering →

8. What features could we find in New York State to show that glaciers covered our area in the past? For each glacial feature you list, tell how it formed. Describe three features.
(Each feature, +1; Formation, +1)

Directions: The diagram above shows changes in mineral composition as rock is left to weather in a warm, humid climate over a period of several hundred years. Base your answers to questions 9 through 13 on the information in the *Earth Science Reference Tables* and the diagram and your knowledge of earth science.

9. The left edge of the graph shows the initial (starting) mineral composition of the fresh, unweather rock. If the sample started as a coarse-grained, igneous rock, what kind of rock was it?
(Correct answer, +1)

10. Name a mineral that appears to be stable both within Earth where this rock formed as well as under the weathering conditions at the surface.
(Correct answer, +1)

11. What is the approximate percentage of clay minerals in this sample at the end of the time period shown on the graph?
(Correct answer, +1)

12. Name one element that is common to all these minerals.
(Correct answer, +1)

13. Briefly state a single major conclusion based upon the information displayed in the diagram.
(Conclusion, +1; Complete sentence(s), +1)

14. The diagram below shows the profile of a typical soil. List two different kinds of changes (processes), in proper chronological order, that occur in the development of most soils.
(Processes, +1 each; Correct chronological order, +1)

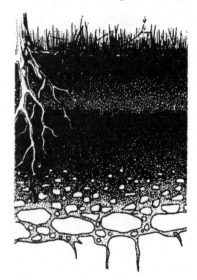

15. Throughout Europe, many of the oldest limestone and marble cathedrals and monuments are crumbling from the outer surface inward. The problem has become worse in the last century. How can this deterioration be stopped or slowed to preserve the European historical heritage without having a major negative impact on the European economy?
(Reasoning, +1; Complete sentence(s), +1)

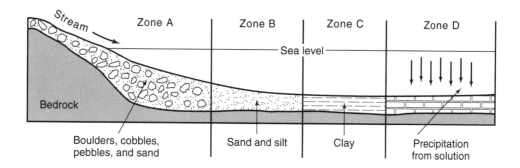

Stream Zone A Zone B Zone C Zone D

Sea level

Bedrock

Boulders, cobbles, pebbles, and sand

Sand and silt

Clay

Precipitation from solution

Directions: The diagram above shows a profile view of a stream entering the ocean. The horizontal distance is several kilometers, and the vertical scale is greatly exaggerated. Base your answers to questions 16 through 18 on the information in the diagram and your knowledge of earth science.

16. If the sediment in Zone C were compressed to form a sedimentary rock, what kind of rock would it be?
(Correct answer, +1)

17. What is the approximate metric diameter of the largest particles in Zone B?
(Number, +1; Units, +1)

18. Why is there a progressive change in the size of the sedimentary particles from Zone A through Zone D?
(Response, +1; Complete sentence(s), +1)

19. Olivine is a mineral that is stable deep within Earth, but very unstable at the surface. Suppose you collected a 2 kilogram (about $4\frac{1}{2}$ pounds) sample of fresh olivine from a deep mine shaft and placed it outside for many years. Describe two ways in which the olivine would probably change.
(Changes, +1 each)

20. Draw two (and only two) complete layers of graded bedding. The changes in grain size, both gradual and sudden, must be clearly shown.

(One layer of graded bedding, +1; Two unclear layers, +1; Two clear layers, +2)

21. What three characteristics would be common to most of the particles of sediment that settle most slowly, near the top of each of the layers shown in the drawing you made for question 20? That is, how are the last grains to settle unlike the grains found near the bottoms of each layer of graded bedding?
(Correct response, +1 up to a maximum of 2)

CHAPTER 5 Interpreting Earth's History

THE GEOLOGIST AS DETECTIVE

Planet Earth probably formed from an accumulation of rock, dust, and gases drawn together by its own gravity about 4.6 billion years ago. The rocks of Earth's crust preserve clues that help us unravel the mystery of our changing planet, its environments, and the development of terrestrial life. Like detectives hunting for the evidence that will allow them to determine how a crime occurred, geologists locate, observe, and interpret the clues recorded in Earth's rocks. A primary role of geologists is to take the evidence from rocks and reconstruct a sequence of geologic events. There are several fundamental principles that guide geologists in interpreting Earth's history.

Uniformitarianism.

Geologists think that the forces that they observe today are similar to processes that occurred throughout Earth's history. For example, if mountains are currently being built up today by volcanic action and collisions of Earth's tectonic plates, then they were built up by these processes in the past. However, these Earth-shaping processes do not necessarily occur at a steady, uniform rate. Most erosion, for example, occurs when strong storms and floods attack the land, while the quiet periods between storms involve relatively little erosion. The idea that the processes that shape Earth's surface today are the same processes that occurred in the geologic past is called **uniformitarianism**. Another way to state the principle of uniformitarianism is "The present is the key to the past."

Superposition.

The second fundamental principle is the **law of superposition**, which states that the rocks at the bottom of an undisturbed exposure are usually the oldest. After all, the lower layers must be in place before the younger layers can be deposited on top of them. For this reason, geologists generally date the relative ages of the rock layers starting from the bottom and proceeding to the top (oldest to youngest). There are occasional exceptions to the law of superposition, some of which will be explained in the sections that follow.

Original Horizontality.

The third fundamental principle is that a rock is always older than the processes that changed it. Sediments, such as those at the bottom of an ocean or lake, are usually deposited in layers. Even if the underlying surface is not flat, sediments fill in the low places first and then continue as horizontal strata. When we see sedimentary layers that are tilted, we usually assume that these layers were deposited level, and that they were tilted after they had turned into sedimentary rock.

Igneous Intrusions and Extrusions.

Igneous formations can provide clues about the sedimentary layers around them. An **extrusion** occurs when molten rock flows onto Earth's surface, where it crystallizes to form igneous rock. An extrusion is thus younger than the rock below it, but older than rock that later forms on top of it. The rock beneath an extrusion will show a zone of contact metamorphism where the hot lava baked it. The rock above an extrusion, however, will not show contact metamorphism, because the sediments that were deposited to form them are deposited after the lava had cooled and solidified. As you can see in Figure 5-1, an extrusion, commonly known as a lava flow, is an external process.

An **intrusion**, on the other hand, is an internal process. Intrusion occurs when magma squeezes into or between layers of pre-existing rock. The hot, molten rock changes the surrounding rock immediately above, below, and next to it by contact metamorphism. An intrusion can therefore be identified by the narrow zones of metamorphism that completely surround it. See Figure 5-1.

Folds and Faults.

Certain processes on our restless planet can warp rock layers, making it harder for geologists to piece together the clues in Earth's rocks. **Folds** are bends in rock layers produced by movements of Earth's crust, generally related to Earth's tectonic plates. **Faults**, as you may recall from Chapter 3, are breaks in the rock where movement has occurred, often associated with earthquakes. Offset layers, such as those shown in Figure 5-2, are indications of faulting. In accordance with the principle of original horizontality, folds and faults occur after the rock has formed.

Folding or faulting can lead to exceptions to the law of superposition. As you can see in Figure 5-2, in some places where folding or faulting have taken place, older rocks can be found on top of younger rocks.

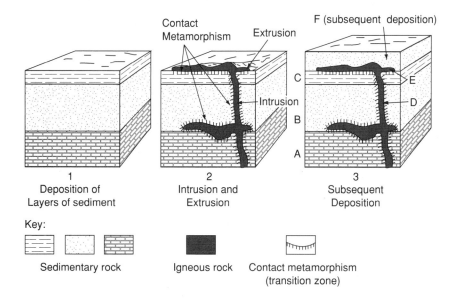

1
Deposition of
Layers of sediment

2
Intrusion and
Extrusion

3
Subsequent
Deposition

Key:

| Sedimentary rock | Igneous rock | Contact metamorphism (transition zone) |

Figure 5-1. Intrusion and extrusion. (1) The original sedimentary rocks formed horizontal layers (strata). (2) Volcanic activity forced magma through and between sedimentary layers (intrusion), and some of the molten rock flowed out at the surface as lava (extrusion). (3) A new layer of sandstone has been deposited on top of the extrusion. Notice that although layers A, B, and C show contact metamorphism, there is no transition zone at the top of extrusion E.

Fossils.

Fossils, the preserved remains or traces of living things, reveal a great deal about the life forms and environments that existed in Earth's past. Fossils can also provide geologists with clues about the past geological events or relative age of rock layers. Because the processes of metamorphism (extreme heat and/or pressure) and melting almost always destroy fossils, they are generally found only in sedimentary rock. Most of the organisms that we find as fossils became extinct millions of years ago.

There are many types of fossils. Body fossils are parts of the original organism (living thing) that have been preserved. Hard parts such as shells, teeth, and bones are common among fossils because they decay relatively slowly and therefore are more likely to be preserved than the highly perishable flesh and other soft parts. In fact, some limestone layers are composed almost entirely of fossil shells. Sometimes, the original compounds that made up the preserved body part are replaced by minerals brought in by ground water. The remains are then said to be petrified.

Occasionally, whole organisms are preserved as fossils, such as insects encased in amber (fossilized tree sap), and mammoths (ice age elephants) frozen in

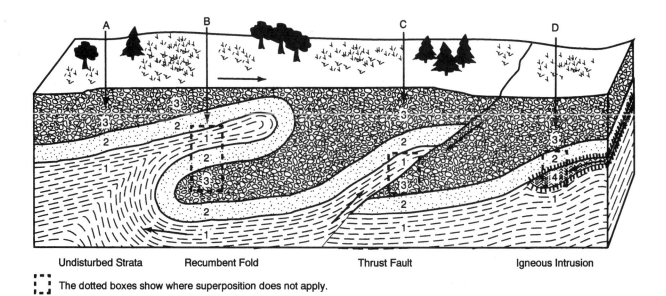

Undisturbed Strata   Recumbent Fold   Thrust Fault   Igneous Intrusion

The dotted boxes show where superposition does not apply.

Figure 5-2. In some situations, the law of superposition does not apply. Section A shows three layers in their original sequence with the oldest layer (1) on the bottom. The tight fold in section B has created a reverse order of layers within the dashed box. (The sequences both above and below the box are normal.) Section C shows a thrust fault that has pushed an older layer (1) above a younger layer (3). In the final section, D, an intrusion of magma has caused a younger igneous rock to form below layer 2, which is older.

Arctic tundra. The La Brea tar pits of Los Angeles preserved the complete skeletons of many animals unfortunate enough to wander into these death traps.

Some fossils do not contain the remains of the organisms that produced them. These trace fossils include the impressions of shells, dinosaur footprints, oddly-shaped formations resulting from sediments filling an animal's burrow, and petrified droppings (coprolites). Although trace fossils may not reveal what a prehistoric organism looked like, they can reveal much about its behavior and relationship to its living and nonliving environment.

Fossils can give important clues about environmental conditions in the geologic past. For example, New York State has fossils of coral, indicating that the area was once a warm, tropical sea. It also has more recent fossils of wooly mammoths and mastodons, revealing the cold, snowy climate of the last ice age.

QUESTIONS

Directions: Base your answers to questions 1–3 on the following diagram.

1. In the following diagram, which rock unit is most likely the youngest? (1) shale (2) basalt (3) sandstone (4) limestone

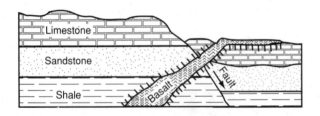

2. Which event probably happened first? (1) intrusion of basaltic magma (2) faulting (3) deposition of clay to make shale (4) precipitation of limestone

3. If the age of the basalt is 80 million years, the age of the limestone could be (1) 40 million (2) 60 million (3) 70 million (4) 90 million

4. Which sequence of events best accounts for the features shown below? (1) folding, deposition, more deposition, then erosion (2) deposition, folding, erosion, then more deposition (3) deposition, erosion, folding, then more deposition (4) erosion, deposition, folding, then more deposition

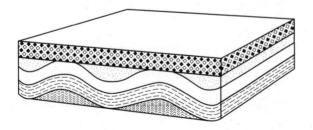

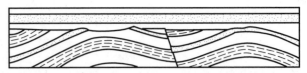

5. What sequence of events could have produced the bedrock cross section shown above? (1) folding, deposition, faulting, erosion, deposition (2) deposition, folding, faulting, erosion, deposition (3) deposition, erosion, folding, faulting, deposition (4) deposition, faulting, folding, deposition, erosion

6. Which event could cause part of a rock outcrop to be upside down, that is with younger rocks gradually changing to older rocks toward the top? (1) folding (2) deposition (3) intrusion (4) erosion

7. How does Earth's geologic past compare with the present? (1) Volcanic eruptions and earthquakes occurred more often in the geologic past. (2) There was a greater variety of life forms on Earth billions of years ago. (3) In general, the kinds of changes we see around us also occurred in the geologic past. (4) Although there were extinctions of species in the past, they no longer occur on our planet.

8. In which rock type are fossils usually found? (1) igneous (2) volcanic (3) sedimentary (4) metamorphic

9. Older layers of rock may be found on top of younger layers of rock as a result of (1) weathering processes (2) igneous extrusions (3) joints in the rock layers (4) overturning of the rock layers

10. The physical and chemical conditions which long ago produced changes on Earth's surface are still producing changes. This statement is one way of stating the principle of (1) catastrophism (2) diastrophism (3) uniformitarianism (4) isostasy

HOW CAN ROCKS BE CORRELATED?

Geologists try to match similar rock strata in different locations to see if they formed at the same time or under similar conditions. This is called **correlation**. There are several ways to correlate rock formations.

We can match the rock strata in one location with the strata in a more distant location by comparing the properties of the rocks, such as color, texture, or composition. However, the same rock types are not necessarily the same age. It is more helpful to match the sequence of rock layers from limestone to sandstone then shale. However, even if the sequence of rock layers in two locations is the same, the layers may not have formed at the same time.

Time correlation requires other methods. One way to do this is to compare **index fossils** contained in the strata. The best index fossils are of organisms that existed for a very brief time (geologically speaking, this could be as long as millions of years) but were found over a large portion of Earth. Thus, in a rock outcrop, an index fossil would not extend very far above or below vertically but would be widespread horizontally from one place to another.

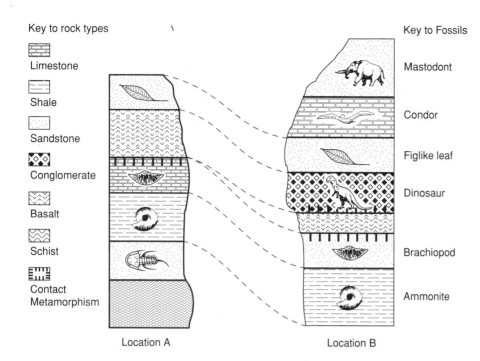

Key to rock types

- Limestone
- Shale
- Sandstone
- Conglomerate
- Basalt
- Schist
- Contact Metamorphism

Key to Fossils

- Mastodont
- Condor
- Figlike leaf
- Dinosaur
- Brachiopod
- Ammonite

Location A

Location B

Figure 5-3. Rock layers can be correlated by rock type or by geologic age. Fossil correlation is used to match rocks by age, regardless of rock types. In the diagram, although both locations have sandstone at the top, the fossils show that the top layers cannot be the same age. Although the layers that contain the brachiopods are made of different rocks, the fossils tell us they are the same age. Some possible explanations of why there is no dinosaur at location A include that dinosaurs did not live in that area, that the dinosaurs did not have any recognizable fossils, or the layer that contained the dinosaur fossils was eroded.

I. Fossils in two distant outcrops

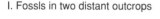

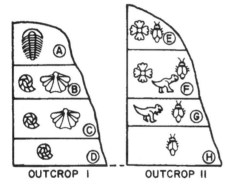

OUTCROP I   OUTCROP II

Figure 5-4. An exercise in correlation. Please note that if a fossil species is not shown you must assume that it was not alive in that environment at that time. These diagrams can be used to reach the following conclusions: (1) outcrop I is from the ocean, while II is from the land, (2) layer A must be either Cambrian or Ordovician in age, (3) outcrop I is overturned (the oldest fossil is on the top), while outcrop II is right-side-up, and (4) layer D must be the same age as layer F, even though they contain different fossils. (If you do not understand how to arrive at these conclusions, ask your teacher for help.)

II. Correlation chart

GEOLOGIC TIME PERIODS WHEN ORGANISMS LIVED (time expressed in millions of years before the present)		OCEAN ORGANISMS			LAND ORGANISMS		
		Trilobites	Ammonites	Spirifers	Insects	Dinosaurs	Flowering Plants
Tertiary	0				●		❀
	66						
Cretaceous	144		●		●	●	❀
Jurassic	190		●	●	●	●	
Triassic	245		●	●	●	●	
Permian	286	●	●	●	●		
Carboniferous	360	●	●	●	●		
Devonian	408	●	●	●			
Silurian	438	●		●			
Ordovician	505	●					
Cambrian	540	●					

It is likely that, millions of years from now, humans will be an excellent index fossil. Humans have existed for only about two million years, yet our remains and signs of our existence can be found worldwide. See Figure 5-3.

If layers lack a specific index fossil, they can sometimes be tentatively correlated by the kinds of fossils they contain. For example, a layer of rock that contains dinosaur fossils could be correlated with another layer that contains fossils of plants that existed at the same time as the dinosaurs. Figure 5-4 shows an instructive exercise in fossil correlation.

QUESTIONS

11. In what kind of rock are fossils the most common?
(1) igneous (2) metamorphic (3) volcanic (4) sedimentary

12. The three columns below show three widely separated rock outcrops and the fossils found in rocks of different geologic ages at each location.

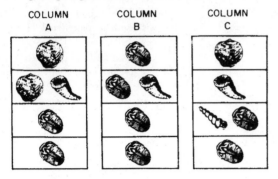

Which fossil would be the best index fossil?

13. The following diagram names the six fossil organisms shown in this geologic profile. Within this area there has been no faulting, overturning, or folding. It appears that all of these organisms lived in (1) deserts (2) oceans (3) mountains (4) outer space

14. Which kind of organism seems to have been alive most recently? (1) honeycomb coral (2) crinoid (3) sea shell 2 (4) plankton

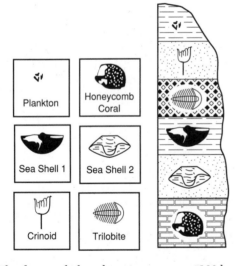

15. The diagram below shows two outcrops 100 km apart. Some of the rock types at Location 1 are identified by rock type. These patterns are consistent with the symbols used in Location 2. Which rock type at Location 2 could be Jurassic in age? (1) volcanic ash (2) limestone (3) sandstone (4) conglomerate

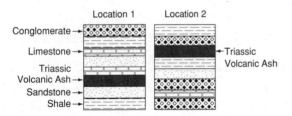

16. Four different kinds of fossils were collected from a number of widely separated bedrock exposures. Which of these, fossil A, B, C, or D, would probably be the most useful in determining the geologic ages of rocks worldwide? (1) A is found only in one layer at one location (2) B is found throughout the layers at all locations (3) C is found throughout the layers at one place (4) D is found in a single layer in all locations

17. Fossils are (1) ancient forms of life that are still alive today (2) forms of life that left no rock record (3) hard parts of modern organisms (4) any remains of prehistoric life

18. What feature of two rock outcrops 100 km apart would be the best evidence that they are the same geologic age? (1) similar rock types (2) similar fossils (3) similar elevations (4) similar climate

19. Fossils are seldom, if ever found in (1) granite (2) sandstone (3) shale (4) limestone

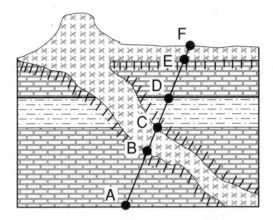

20. Which graph below best shows the relative ages of the rock units along line A-F in the diagram above?

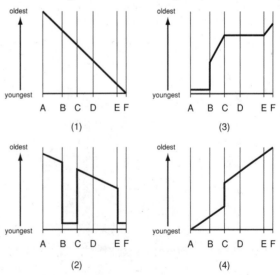

21. The best index fossils are from organisms that (1) lived in a limited area (2) had no hard parts (3) existed for a brief time (4) lived only on land

GEOLOGIC TIME SCALE

In the late 18th and early 19th centuries, geologists in Europe noticed that rock formations could often be identified by the fossils they contained. They also found that certain formations were consistently located above or below other formations. From these observations, they established a relative time scale with a sequence of fossil groups from oldest to youngest. Each of these groups was named for a location where its characteristic fossils could be observed in the rocks. For example, fossils characteristic of Devon, in the south of England, were named Devonian. See Figure 5-4 on page 93.

Over the years, further observations from around the world established a geologic time scale based on rock formations that contained these characteristic fossil groups. Refer to the *Geologic History of New York State at a Glance* in the *Earth Science Reference Tables*. The scale is divided into eras, periods, and epochs. Note, however, that they do not represent exact units of measure for time, like the hour. For example, no two eras span the same amount of time on the scale. See Figure 5-5 on page 96. You should use the geologic time scale when studying major events in New York State's geologic history, as shown in the map of *Generalized Bedrock Geology of New York State* in the reference tables.

The geological time scale is also based on changes in the kinds of organisms that inhabited Earth. (Indeed, the names Paleozoic, Mesozoic, and Cenozoic literally mean "ancient animals," "middle animals," and "recent animals.") The Precambrian can be defined as the dawn of life. For the most part, Precambrian organisms had no hard parts that were easily fossilized. At the beginning of the Paleozoic, a wide variety of animals with hard parts developed, including corals, shellfish, trilobites and fishes. The Mesozoic Era was dominated by reptiles, including land-dwelling dinosaurs and flying pterosaurs. We live at the end of the Cenozoic Era, which is sometimes called the Age of Mammals.

Note that the most recent portion of the geologic time scale has been expanded on the right side of this diagram. An orogeny is the process of mountain building. The center of the diagram shows the major orogenies in New York's geologic history. For example, the Taconic Orogeny occurred during the Ordovician Period.

EVOLUTION OF LIFE

Early geologists noticed that the oldest rocks found in Europe lacked fossils. They inferred that life began with the life forms whose fossils characterized the early Cambrian Period, about 540 million years ago.

Today, scientists are not yet sure how life began, but they know that it began before the Cambrian Period, sometime during the billions of years of the Precambrian. Fossils of simple marine organisms, such as algae that left calcite reefs, have been found in rocks over three billion years old. Geologists believe that many other forms of life may have existed in the Precambrian, but they had no hard parts and, therefore, left few fossils. Precambrian fossils are very rare, not only because

the life that existed then was probably difficult to preserve, but also because these oldest rock formations are more likely to have been altered by erosion and metamorphism, which would destroy the fossils. In the Cambrian Period, a variety of more complex life forms developed, many with skeletons and shells that left a good fossil record.

As geologists studied the fossil record, they found that more and more complex organisms developed as time went on. Some organisms disappeared from the fossil record, that is, they became extinct. Scientists sought an explanation for these changes. They found that within each species there are individual variations in size, shape, and other traits. The **theory of organic evolution**, proposed by Charles Darwin, postulates that individuals that have traits that better adapt them to their environment would survive longer and have more offspring to whom they would pass on these desirable traits. Eventually, more and more individuals of a species would possess the desirable traits, while those that lacked them would become fewer and fewer. This process, called natural selection, leads to the extinction of some species and the formation of new ones.

The fossil record shows evidence of many of these variations in traits. Paleontologists (geologists who study fossils) have found remains of a wide variety of plants and animals that lived in many different environments. Some of these organisms still exist. Most have become extinct.

Because most individual organisms decompose or are consumed by other organisms after they die, only a very small percentage leave any fossil remains. As a result, many forms of life will never be known.

Humans are probably the most complex life form to have evolved. Fossils found in Africa indicate that we evolved from apelike creatures over the past four million years. This is only about $\frac{1}{10}$ of 1% of Earth's age. Thus, humankind is a very recent form of life.

Life and the Atmosphere.
When life first developed on Earth, about 3.8 billion years ago, the atmosphere probably consisted of a mixture of carbon monoxide, carbon dioxide, hydrogen, nitrogen, ammonia, and methane. Today, the mixture of gases in the atmosphere is 78% nitrogen and 21% oxygen. Amazingly, this dramatic change was caused by microscopic organisms that developed about 2.2 billion years ago.

The very first forms of life that developed on Earth were anaerobic, which means that they didn't need oxygen to obtain energy from food. Then organisms evolved that could make their own food using an energy source, such as sunlight, and simple raw materials, such as carbon dioxide and water. The organisms that made food from carbon dioxide and water released oxygen as a waste product. Over time, the oxygen built up in the atmosphere to the point that the earliest, anaerobic organisms could not survive. (While oxygen is necessary for aerobic organisms like us to obtain energy from our food, it is also highly reactive, and thus interferes with the chemical reactions necessary for life in many anaerobic organisms.) As the oxygen in the air was increasing, aerobic organisms evolved and came to dominate the planet.

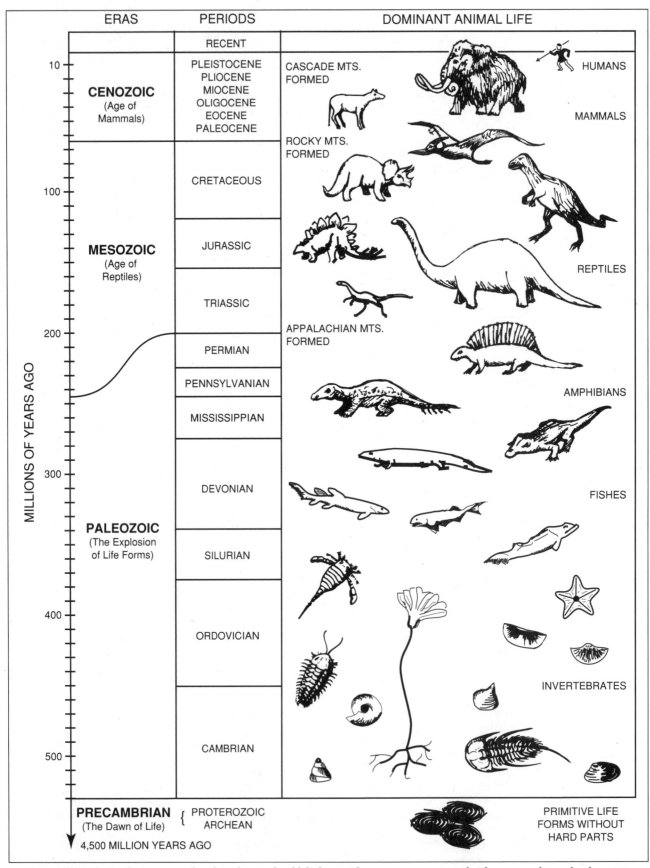

Figure 5-5. The geologic time scale is based upon fossil life forms. If we were to continue the diagram at this scale, the origins of Earth and of the solar system would be located nearly two meters off of the bottom of the page.

Now, human activities are affecting the composition of the atmosphere. Are we again changing the atmosphere with our pollutants in a way that will doom current forms of life and favor some forms of life yet to evolve? Only time will tell.

GEOLOGIC EVENTS OF THE PAST

No single location shows a complete record of the geologic past. If an area was above sea level for a while, it is likely that sediments were not deposited and that older sediments or rocks were destroyed by erosion. Thus, erosion causes gaps in the geologic record. When a new layer of rock is laid down on a surface left by erosion, it forms a buried erosion surface, or an **unconformity**.

When a rock outcrop shows an unconformity, it indicates that the area, at some time in the past, was uplifted above water level and then eroded. Later the area subsided below water level and new layers of sediment were deposited on top of the eroded surface. The gap in the geologic record is sometimes indicated by an uneven interface or gaps in the fossil record in the strata. See Figure 5-6.

Many rock outcrops show evidence of a variety of geologic events. The original rock layers were created by deposition of sediments or the solidification of molten magma or lava. Folding may bend the layers and faulting may cause them to be offset. Intrusion of magma can result in veins of igneous rock and metamorphism. In turn, metamorphism can form new minerals and distort or destroy layering and other structures. Weathering and erosion can destroy rock strata.

A geologist can study a rock outcrop to determine its geologic history, that is, the sequence of events that made the rock outcrop what it is today. If fossils are present, they will aid the geologist in dating the layers of rock and the events that occurred in them. Figure 5-7 on page 98 shows the step-by-step development of a complex geologic profile.

QUESTIONS

Directions: Base your answers to questions 22–25 on the diagram below.

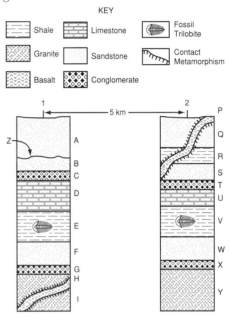

The two rock exposures shown above have not been overturned.

22. Which rock layer is probably sedimentary in origin? (1) E (2) H (3) P (4) Y

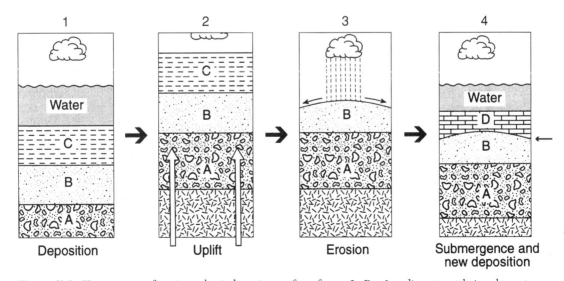

Figure 5-6. How an unconformity, or buried erosion surface, forms. In Box 1, sediments settle in calm water, first layer A, then B, then C (deposition). In Box 2, the layers are pushed above the water from below (uplift), exposing layer C to surface erosion (wind action, rain, etc.). In Box 3, the top layers (C and part of B are worn away (erosion). In Box 4, the layers sink, or subside, below water level. A new layer (D) is deposited onto the erosion surface. The arrow to the right of Box 4 marks the unconformity, or buried erosion surface.

23. Rock layer F is probably the same layer as (1) P (2) S (3) T (4) W

24. According to the *Earth Science Reference Tables*, approximately how long ago could layer E have formed? (1) 50 million years (2) 150 million years (3) 540 million years (4) 950 million years

25. The line labeled Z is a buried erosion surface (an unconformity). From this information, we might conclude that (1) no rocks ever existed between layers A and B (2) layers A and B were deposited within the same geologic time period (3) the same kinds of fossils must be found in both layers, A and B (4) layers A and B do not form a continuous geologic time record.

26. How can we best document organic evolution? (1) Use radioactive elements to find the age of any one fossil. (2) Use the law of superposition to find the relative ages of igneous intrusions. (3) Study the rock layers to identify boundaries where part of the rock record is miss-

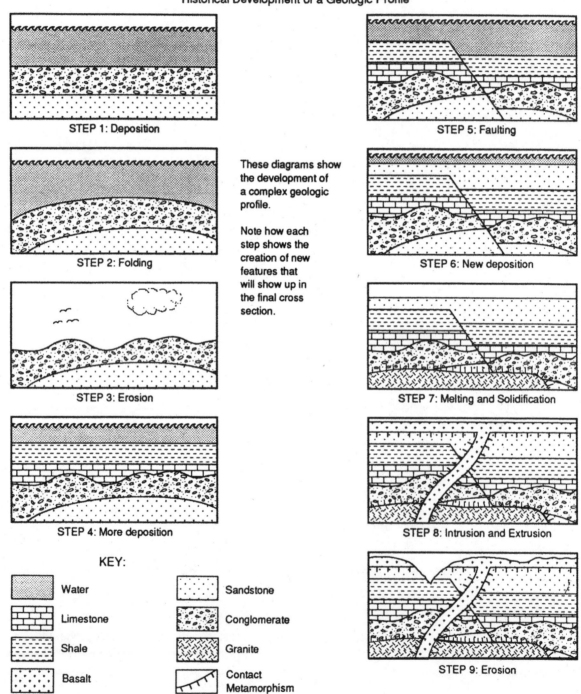

Figure 5-7. Development of a complex geological profile. Each successive box shows one change needed to produce the final profile in step 9.

ing (4) Compare similar fossils of various geologic ages from different rock layers.

27. According to the *Earth Science Reference Tables*, when did the armored fishes inhabit Earth? (1) the Precambrian (2) early to mid-Paleozoic (3) the late Paleozoic (4) the Cenozoic

28. According to the *Earth Science Reference Tables*, which episode of mountain building occurred in the Devonian time period? (1) Grenvillian (2) Taconian (3) Acadian (4) Alleghanian

29. Based on the *Earth Science Reference Tables*, during which geologic era did the dinosaurs live? (1) Precambrian (2) Paleozoic (3) Mesozoic (4) Cenozoic

30. According to the *Geologic History of New York* in the *Earth Science Reference Tables*, which of the following life forms was alive earliest in the history of Earth? (1) the dinosaur, Coelophysis (2) ocean bottom trilobites (3) mastodons (ice-age elephants) (4) stromatolites (clumps of algae)

31. According to the *Earth Science Reference Tables*, throughout a large portion of geologic history, the East coast of North America was next to (1) India (2) Africa (3) Antarctica (4) Australia

32. Which scale below best shows the relative durations of the four geologic eras?

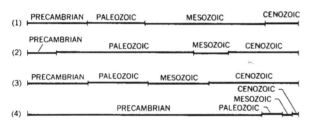

33. If you could observe a shallow, tropical sea environment during the early Paleozoic Era, how would it compare to a similar environment of today? (1) You would be unable to see any differences. (2) Although the physical environment would be similar, there would be many different plants and animals. (3) Although the plants and animals would be the same, the physical environment would look very different. (4) There were no tropical seas in the geologic past.

34. According to the *Earth Science Reference Tables*, from which segment of Earth's geologic history are fossils the most rare? (1) Precambrian (2) Paleozoic (3) Mesozoic (4) Cenozoic

35. Evolution is best characterized as a change (1) in individuals as they become older (2) that only happened in the distant past (3) from old organisms to young organisms (4) from a few simple organisms to greater variety

36. According to the *Earth Science Reference Tables*, which two towns or cities would probably have similar fossils in the local bedrock? (1) Massena and Albany (2) Old Forge and Utica (3) Watertown and Syracuse (4) Buffalo and Rochester

37. According to the *Earth Science Reference Tables*, which geologic time period is most completely represented within the bedrock of New York State? (1) Precambrian (2) Devonian (3) Triassic (4) Tertiary

38. According to the *Earth Science Reference Tables*, New York State has only a partial record of which geologic age? (1) Jurassic (2) Permian (3) Devonian (4) Cambrian

39. According to the *Earth Science Reference Tables*, in what geologic age did the earliest forms of life exist on Earth? (1) Precambrian (2) Paleozoic (3) Mesozoic (4) Cenozoic

40. How can we best define organic evolution? (1) How a monkey can change into a human being. (2) The change in an organism through its lifetime. (3) The written history of our human civilization. (4) The development of the diversity of life forms.

41. Why are Precambrian fossils rare? (1) No life existed in the Precambrian era. (2) Most Precambrian fossils have been destroyed. (3) All forms of life became extinct during the Precambrian era. (4) No new life forms evolved after the Precambrian era.

42. According to the *Earth Science Reference Tables*, which geologic time period was the longest? (1) Cenozoic (2) Mesozoic (3) Paleozoic (4) Precambrian

43. According to the *Earth Science Reference Tables*, New York State has no rocks or fossils from the (1) Precambrian (2) Devonian (3) Permian (4) Triassic

44. The time line below shows the whole history of Earth. Which position best shows the time that dinosaurs inhabited Earth? (1) a (2) b (3) c (4) d

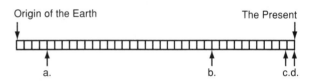

WHAT IS RADIOACTIVE DATING?

Through fossil evidence, geologists established the geologic time scale discussed earlier in this chapter. This was only a relative time scale, however, an inferred order of events. Fossils could not tell geologists how long ago, in years, the organisms lived or the rock strata formed. Measurements of natural radioactivity in the rocks have allowed the geologic time scale to become an absolute time scale, one that gives the **absolute age** (numerical age) of an object (measured in years).

Chemical elements often have several forms, called **isotopes**, that differ in the number of neutrons in their atomic nuclei. For example, carbon-12 has 6 protons and 6 neutrons in its nucleus, whereas carbon-14 has 6 protons and 8 neutrons in its nucleus. If the nucleus of an isotope has more or fewer than the normal number of neutrons, the isotope may be radioactive. A radioactive isotope will break down naturally into a lighter element called a **decay product**. In the process, it gives off radioactivity. For example, the most common form of carbon, carbon-12, is not radioactive; but carbon-14, with two extra neutrons in its nucleus, is unstable. Carbon-14 will change into its stable decay product, nitrogen-14.

Since atoms decay at random, we cannot predict when a single atom will decay. But even a small sample of a radioactive element contains millions of atoms, from which we can predict a rate of decay.

Half-Life.

The rate of decay of a radioactive element is measured by its half-life. Different radioactive elements have different half-lives. A **half-life** is the time required for half of an element's atoms in a sample to change to the decay product. At the end of one half-life, a sample contains equal amounts of the radioactive element and its decay product. In each succeeding half-life, half of the remaining atoms decay (no matter how large the sample). See Figure 5-8.

As the element decays, fewer radioactive atoms remain in the sample, and more and more decay product accumulates. Therefore, the higher the ratio of decay product to radioactive element, the older the sample.

The Decay-Product Ratio.

The ratio between the mass of a radioactive element and its decay product in a sample is the **decay-product ratio**. After we determine this ratio, we can calculate how many half-lives have gone by since the sample was formed, and, in turn, determine its age. See Figure 5-9.

For example, if a sedimentary rock contains equal amounts of carbon-14 and its decay product, nitrogen-14, the rock must have gone through one half-life; which for carbon-14 is 5.7×10^3 years. The half-lives of commonly used radioisotopes are printed in the *Earth Science Reference Tables*. If three-quarters of the sample is nitrogen-14 and one-quarter carbon-14, then the rock is two half-lives (11.4×10^3 years) old. After three

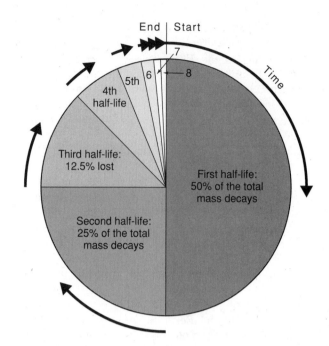

Figure 5-8. A model of radioactive decay. In the first half-life, half of the radioactive sample changes to the decay product. With each additional half-life, half the remaining atoms decay. Each arrow represents an equal amount of time. (1 half life.) In theory, the radioisotope never gets to zero mass.

half-lives, the amount of carbon-14 would be cut in half again, so that the sample would be one-eighth carbon-14 and seven-eighths nitrogen-14. See the top boxes in Figure 5-9.

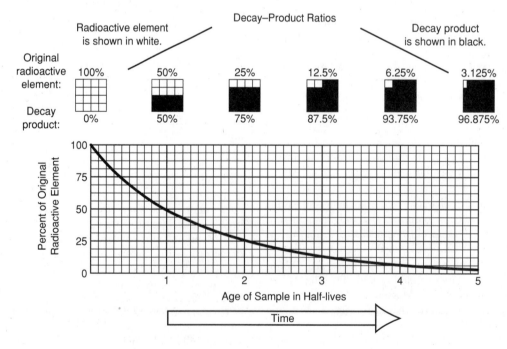

Figure 5-9. This diagram is another way to illustrate the half-life of a radioactive substance. It presents the same information as Figure 5-8, only in a different format.

Laboratory studies show that the half-life for each element is not affected by environmental conditions, such as temperature, pressure, or chemical combinations. Thus, when geologists estimate an age for a particular sample, they can be confident that conditions within Earth have not caused an error.

Selecting the Best Radioactive Element for a Sample.
Radioactive dating is a complex process. Several decisions must be made to get the best results. First, the sample to be dated must contain a measurable quantity of a radioactive element and its decay product. A sample containing the remains of living organisms is likely to contain radioactive carbon-14.

The next factor to consider is the sample's estimated age. With a half-life of only 5700 years (5.7×10^3 years), carbon-14 can date samples no older than about 50,000 years. On the geologic time scale, this is very recent, covering only the latest epochs of the Cenozoic Era. If the sample is older than 50,000 years, so many half-lives have passed that too little of the original carbon-14 remains to be measured accurately. But uranium-238, with a half-life of 4.5×10^9 years, can measure samples of the oldest rocks on our planet. For very recent samples of rocks, however, too little uranium-238 would have decayed to lead-206 to make the decay product measurable. Thus, a geologist must select the radioactive isotope whose half-life best measures the age of a sample. See Table 5-1.

Table 5-1. Radioactive Decay Data

Radioactive Isotope	Disintegration	Half-Life (years)
Carbon-14	$C^{14} \rightarrow N^{14}$	5.7×10^3
Potassium-40	$K^{40} \nearrow Ar^{40}$ $\searrow Ca^{40}$	1.3×10^9
Uranium-238	$U^{238} \rightarrow Pb^{206}$	4.5×10^9
Rubidium-87	$Rb^{87} \rightarrow Sr^{87}$	4.9×10^{10}

GEOLOGIC MAPS

Geologists use the variety of techniques explained in this unit to study the local bedrock, to relate it to other regions, and to construct geologic maps. Large scale maps, such as the New York State maps in the *Earth Science Reference Tables* give you general information about rock types, the ages of the bedrock, and the geologic history of your community. More detailed maps, as well as texts and field guides, are available from the United States Geological Survey, the State Geologic Survey, universities, and other professional organizations. These resources can help you to understand the unique geologic setting in which you live.

QUESTIONS

45. Which graph below best shows the decay of radioactive carbon-14?

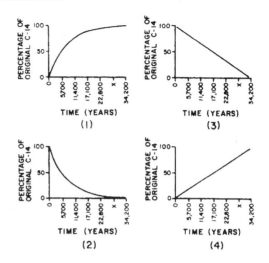

46. Radioactive carbon-14 would be the most useful in determining the age of (1) trilobite fossils (2) buried tree stumps (3) intensely metamorphosed gneiss (4) the Palisades Sill intrusion of magma

47. As the mass of a sample of carbon-14 increases, its half-life (1) decreases (2) increases (3) remains the same

48. If 100 grams of pure carbon-14 start to decay, how much nitrogen-14 will be created in 1.14×10^4 years? (1) 25 g (2) 50 g (3) 75 g (4) 100 g

49. What radioactive isotope would be most useful in finding the absolute ages of the Dead Sea Scrolls, written more than 2000 years ago? (1) carbon-14 (2) potassium-40 (3) uranium-238 (4) rubidium-87

Directions: Base your answers to questions 50–52 on the following graph and the *Earth Science Reference Tables*.

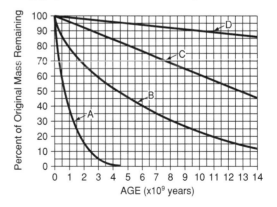

50. Which of the four radioactive elements shown in the graph has the shortest half-life? (1) A (2) B (3) C (4) D

51. Which substance shown above could be uranium-238? (1) A (2) B (3) C (4) D

52. One kilogram of which substance would create the most decay product after 4×10^9 years? (1) A (2) B (3) C (4) D

The local historical society is planning to celebrate the town's centennial next year. They have requested that you illustrate important events in your local geologic history by identifying geologic features and writing brief text about each that can be posted to help your neighbors appreciate the geologic history revealed in your community.

CHAPTER 5
REVIEW QUESTIONS

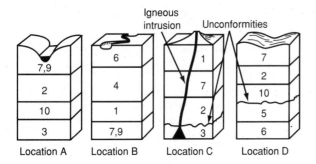

Igneous intrusion Unconformities

Location A Location B Location C Location D

Directions: Base your answers to questions 1–5 on the diagrams above that show four widely scattered bedrock outcrops. The numbers represent 10 different fossil types found in these locations. The rocks have not been overturned. An unconformity is a buried erosion surface.

1. Which location probably contains the oldest fossil? (1) A (2) B (3) C (4) D

2. Why is fossil 7 the best index fossil in this region? (1) It is found in igneous rocks. (2) It lived for a short time, but is widely found. (3) It contains uranium-238, used for relative dating. (4) It lived for a long period of geologic time.

3. According to the *Earth Science Reference Tables*, if 5 is the earliest reptile fossil, how old is the layer that contains 5? (1) 260 years (2) 300 years (3) 260 million years (4) 300 million years

4. Which feature at location C is probably the youngest? (1) the igneous intrusion (2) the layer containing fossil 1 (3) the layer containing fossil 2 (4) the layer containing fossil 3

5. The wavy lines at locations C and D show (1) eruptions of nearby volcanoes (2) movement along a geologic fault (3) folds in the rock layers above and below (4) where some of the rock record is missing

6. According to the *Earth Science Reference Tables*, what is the absolute age of the bedrock found at 43° 30' N, 76° W? (1) 100 million years (2) 200 million years (3) 460 million years (4) 570 million years

7. According to the *Earth Science Reference Tables*, when were dinosaurs alive? (1) in the Precambrian (2) in the Paleozoic (3) in the Mesozoic (4) in the Cenozoic

8. According th the *Earth Science Reference Tables*, the bedrock near Oswego, NY, is likely to include (1) shale (2) quartzite (3) basalt (4) conglomerate

9. According to the *Earth Science Reference Tables*, the bedrock of New York State contains the most complete record of the (1) Cenozoic (2) Mesozoic (3) Paleozoic (4) Precambrian

Directions: Base your answers to questions 10–13 on the *Earth Science Reference Tables* and the diagrams below.

10. The diagrams below show outcrops 5 km apart. Which is the oldest layer in all three diagrams (1) glacial till with wood (2) sandstone (3) shale with trilobites (4) gray limestone

11. What is the likely age of the shale with trilobites? (1) Cretaceous (2) Ordovician (3) Triassic (4) Tertiary

12. How can we explain the unconformity at X? (1) Faulting occurred between the limestone and the sandstone layers. (2) A continuous record of deposition is shown. (3) Intrusion has destroyed part of the limestone. (4) Deposition was interrupted in this location.

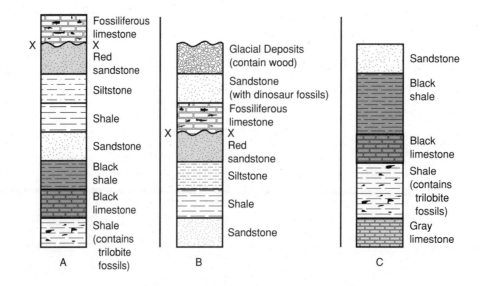

13. Carbon-14 would be the most useful in dating (1) the trilobite fossils in the shale (2) the wood fragments in the glacial till (3) calcite crystals in the black limestone (4) iron oxide within the red sandstone

14. As the quantity of a radioactive material decreases, the half-life of the remaining atoms (1) decreases (2) increases (3) remains the same

15. The diagram to the right represents the relative amounts of potassium-40 and argon-40 after one half-life. Which diagram best shows these amounts after two half-lives?

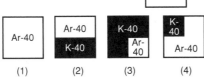

16. According to the *Earth Science Reference Tables*, at a scale of 1 cm:10 million years, what length should be used to show the Mesozoic era? (1) 0.18 cm (2) 1.8 cm (3) 18 cm (4) 180 cm

17. According to the *Earth Science Reference Tables*, how old is the bedrock found in New York at 43°30' N latitude, 75°00' W longitude? (1) Early Ordovician (2) Devonian (3) Middle Proterozoic (4) Cambrian

18. Why is carbon-14 useful only for dating events less than about 50,000 years ago? (1) Carbon-14 has a relatively short half-life. (2) The half-life of carbon-14 is very long. (3) Carbon-14 is an impurity in older sediments. (4) There was no carbon-14 before this time.

19. According to the *Earth Science Reference Tables*, which of the following geologic periods had the greatest duration? (1) Triassic (2) Silurian (3) Cretaceous (4) Tertiary

20. According to the *Earth Science Reference Tables*, dinosaurs (1) first appeared in the Paleozoic era (2) increased in numbers before extinction (3) lived at the same time as trilobites (4) lived only on land

FREE-RESPONSE QUESTIONS

(Answer the following questions on a separate sheet of paper.)

1. This diagram shows a profile view of a bedrock outcropping. None of the layers have been overturned. How can we tell that the sandstone is younger than the basalt below it? Use one or more complete sentences.
(Sentence, +1; Quality of response, +2)

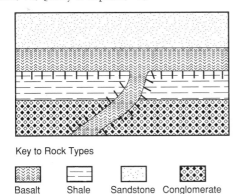

2. Use the symbols for rock types shown (bottom, left) to draw a neat geologic profile to illustrate the following sequence of events (1) Deposition (2) Faulting (3) Erosion (4) Deposition
(Neatness, +1; Correct profile, +2)

3. Explain two methods that can be used to compare the age of the bedrock in one location with the age of bedrock several kilometers away. You must tell briefly how each one works. You must use complete sentences.
(Complete sentences, +1; Each correct response, +1)

4. Draw a bedrock profile that clearly shows the four geologic events listed below, but only these events. Please choose from the rock symbols (patterns) shown on the right side of page 7 of your *Earth Science Reference Tables*, except when you show an igneous rock. (Igneous rocks can be shown by any symbols you choose.) You must also provide a key that explains what rock type is represented by each pattern. You must show at least two different kinds of rock created or changed by each event. For example, when you show deposition, you must show the deposition of one kind of rock, followed by the deposition of another. That's one event. (Deposition)

Events: (1) Deposition (2) Faulting (3) Erosion (4) More Deposition (No other events)
(Symbols, +1; Events, +1; Neatness, +1)

5. Geologists value fossils because they are used to discover things about the prehistoric past. Of course, fossils help us to understand things about the organism (size, or what it has eaten), but they also help us understand many other things. Give two examples of what fossils tell us, but you must use examples that are *not about the fossil organism itself*. State each briefly, in a complete sentence.
(Each example, +1; Complete sentences, +1)

6. List the steps needed to create the geologic profile below. Please number them in sequence, 1, 2, 3, etc. (A single step may include more than one rock type. For example, deposition may lay down several different kinds of sediment/rock.)
(Each step in correct sequence, +1)

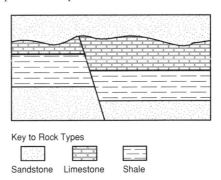

Key to Rock Types
Sandstone   Limestone   Shale

7. Briefly explain how the diagram to the right makes a good model to represent the decay of a radioactive element. You are encouraged to copy and label the diagram. You must use complete sentences.
(Sentence(s), +1; Quality of response, +1, +2, or +3)

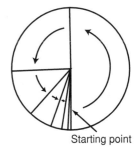

Geologic History of the Earth

Life first develops in the oceans

Early humans evolve

Plants grow that become Carboniferous coal deposits

Dinosaurs dominate Earth

Origin of Earth

Four billion years ago | Three billion years ago | Two billion years ago | One billion years ago | The present

8. Draw a time line similar to the one shown above. Indicate where each of the four pictured events belongs on your timeline.
(Correct placement, +1 each)

9. On what is the geological time scale based? What are its four major divisions?
(Correct response, +1; Parts, +2; Complete sentence(s), +1)

10. List the three things you must do, in proper order, to use radioactive decay in finding the absolute age of a particular rock sample.
(3 steps, +1; Correct sequence, +1)

11. The diagram below shows a profile view of a bedrock outcropping. None of the layers has been overturned. How can we tell that the sandstone is older than the basalt below it?
(Reason, +1; Complete sentence(s), +1)

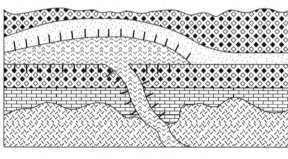

Key to Rock Types

Limestone   Shale   Sandstone   Conglomerate

Granite   Basalt   Schist   Contact metamorphism

12. Use the symbols for rock types shown in the key for question 11 to draw a geological profile that shows the following sequence of events: (1) Deposition, (2) Tilting, (3) Erosion, and (4) Deposition
(Correct profile, +2; Neatness, +1)

13. Briefly explain two methods that can be used to compare the age of the bedrock in one location with the age of bedrock several miles away.
(Method, +1 each)

14. A student used the illustration below in a report about Earth's history. Identify the most serious error in this illustration.
(Identification of error, +1; Reasoning, +1; Complete sentence(s), +1)

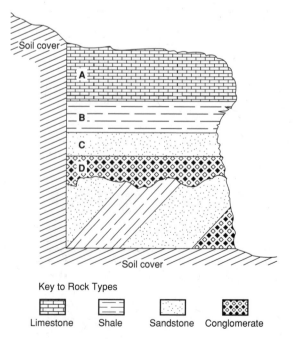

15. What is a fossil? Why are fossils important to geologists?
(Definition, +1; Importance, +1; Complete sentence(s), +1)

Directions: Use the following diagram of a rock outcrop to answer questions 16 and 17.

Soil cover

A

B

C

D

Soil cover

Key to Rock Types

Limestone   Shale   Sandstone   Conglomerate

16. List the five events that produced the profile shown in the diagram.
(Sequence mostly correct, +1; Sequence completely correct, +2)

17. Suppose none of the layers have been turned upside down, layer D is Silurian and layers A and B are Devonian. What is a possible relative age (geologic name) of layer C?
(Geologic name, +1)

18. The first pie chart below shows the phases in the life of a person who lives to the age of 80. Using the chart on the bottom as a starting point, draw a similar pie chart to show the four major geologic ages in the history of Planet Earth in proper order and correct proportions. Label each age. (Hint: Use the *Earth Science Reference Tables*.)
(Four divisions clearly shown, +1; Correct names, +1; Proper order, +1; Correct proportions, +1)

Phases in the life of a professional person

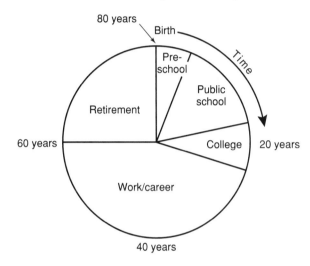

Earth's geologic ages

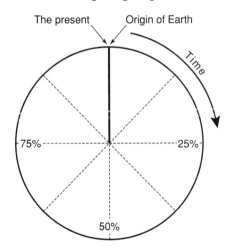

19. The three fossils shown here were found in bedrock in a location in New York State. Based upon this information, state two conclusions about this location when the animal remains that produced these fossils were deposited.
(Conclusions, +1 each; Complete sentences, +1)

20. Use information (two charts) in the *Earth Science Reference Tables* to determine where you would be likely to find bedrock containing fossils of the official New York State fossil, the eurypterid (sea scorpion). Then mark an "X" on a map of New York State to indicate a single spot where a lucky geologist might discover a fossil eurypterid. (Hint: You might begin by tracing the map shown here.)
(Correct placement of X, +1)

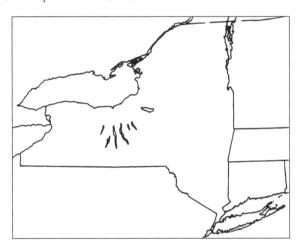

CHAPTER 6 Properties of the Atmosphere

WHAT IS WEATHER?

Weather is important to everyone. No matter what your outdoor plans, it is likely that weather will be a vital issue. If you are hiking, attending a baseball game, picnicking, or even driving somewhere, the weather can enhance the experience or ruin the best-made plans. Weather can be defined as the short-term condition of the atmosphere at a given location, where short-term generally means a few hours or days. The weather conditions that concern us most are temperature, sky conditions, precipitation, atmospheric pressure, humidity, wind speed, and wind direction. Scientists who study and predict the weather are called **meteorologists**.

It may help you to understand weather if you think of the dynamics of the atmosphere in terms of energy distribution. Planet Earth gets most of its energy in the form of radiation (heat and light) from the sun. However, the distribution of solar energy is not the same all over the world. The tropical regions, near the equator, receive the most solar energy. As you travel toward the poles, which receive the least solar energy, the strength of the sunlight decreases. Weather acts to help distribute solar energy over the whole of Earth's surface. If it were not for its atmosphere and weather, Earth would be a much less comfortable place, with extreme temperature changes from day to night, from season to season, and from place to place.

WHAT IS THE STRUCTURE OF THE ATMOSPHERE?

In Chapter 1, you learned that the atmosphere is divided into four layers: troposphere (where most weather occurs), stratosphere, mesosphere, and thermosphere. The troposphere is the lowest layer. Although it is relatively thin, the troposphere is the most important layer because it contains most of the mass of the atmosphere.

The upper boundaries of the atmospheric layers have names that end with the suffix -*pause*, such as tropopause or stratopause. Each boundary is identified by changing trends in temperature. For example, as you move higher within the troposphere, the temperature grows cooler. When you cross the tropopause and enter the stratosphere, however, the temperature of the air increases with increasing altitude. The chart *Selected*

Properties of Earth's Atmosphere in the *Earth Science Reference Tables* shows the layers of the atmosphere.

CHANGES IN AIR TEMPERATURE

At Earth's surface, changes in air temperature tend to be cyclic. Two cycles dominate our weather: the daily weather cycle and the seasons. The temperature is usually lowest in the early morning and warmest at mid-afternoon. The *Earth Science Reference Tables* contain a chart that shows the relationship among Fahrenheit, Celsius, and Kelvin temperatures. In much of the United States, winters are generally cold, while summers tend to be hot. Superimposed upon these cycles are short-term factors such as cloud cover and regional weather systems that affect temperature. Clouds reduce daytime temperature by reflecting sunlight (solar energy) back into space. At night the clouds help hold heat energy to Earth.

Figure 6-1. A weather shelter. Official measurements of temperature and humidity are taken in a weather shelter louvered to let air move through, but also to protect the instruments from direct sunlight.

106

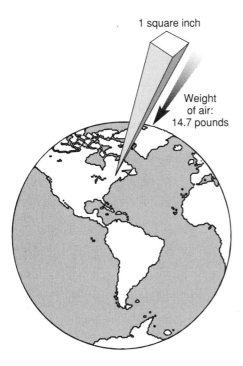

1 square inch

Weight
of air:
14.7 pounds

Figure 6-2. Air pressure is caused by the weight of the atmosphere. Above each square inch of Earth's surface at sea level is a column of air that weighs 14.7 pounds.

We measure temperature with a thermometer. The most common kind of thermometer has a bulb that contains liquid, such as colored alcohol, that expands into a narrow, calibrated neck when it is heated. When the temperature decreases, the liquid contracts and moves down the neck. You can make your own thermometer with a laboratory flask, a one-hold stopper, and a thin glass tube. When meteorologists record official air temperature reading, the thermometer is kept in a special weather shelter like the one shown in Figure 6-1.

WHAT CAUSES AIR PRESSURE?

Air pressure is caused by the weight of the atmosphere. You can prove that air has weight by using a sensitive scale to first weigh a deflated soccer ball, then inflate the ball and weigh it again. The inflated ball weighs more. Although air is relatively light, the atmosphere extends many kilometers above Earth's surface and therefore air exerts a pressure of nearly 15 pounds per square inch. See Figure 6-2. Air pressure is greatest at Earth's surface and decreases with altitude. You may notice that in this chapter not all measurements are given in metric units. Most weather maps in newspapers and on television have the more familiar measurements of Fahrenheit temperature and wind speeds in miles per hour, therefore these traditional units have been used in this portion of the text.

Because air pressure is exerted in all directions, we are seldom aware of it. However, it is air pressure that allows you to drink liquids through a straw. As you begin to drink through a straw, you lower the air pressure in the straw. The air pressure on the surface of the liquid is now higher than the pressure in the straw. The pressure on the surface of the liquid pushes the liquid up the straw and into your mouth. In fact, normal air pressure is so great that in a thin tube, such as a water pipe, it can raise water to a height of nearly 10 meters (33 feet). Above that height, even if you could create a total vacuum, the water would not move any higher.

The fact that air pressure can support a column of liquid is the principle behind the **barometer**, an instrument used to measure air pressure. However, instead of using water, which would require a very long tube, scientists more often use the dense, liquid metal, mercury. See Figure 6-3. Atmospheric pressure can support a column of mercury about 76 centimeters (30 inches) high. This is the principle behind the first barometers. Most modern barometers do not use mercury, water, or any other liquid. See Figure 6-4. They use the pressure of the air exerted on an evacuated,

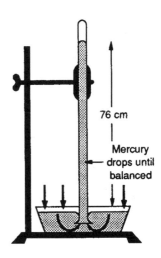

76 cm

Mercury
drops until
balanced

Figure 6-3. In a simple mercury barometer, atmospheric pressure balances a column of mercury. As pressure increases and decreases, the column of mercury rises and falls. At standard sea level pressure, the height of the column is about 76 centimeters (roughly 30 inches).

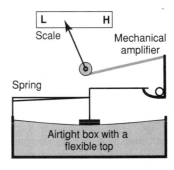

L   H
Scale   Mechanical
amplifier
Spring
Airtight box with a
flexible top

Figure 6-4. An Aneroid Barometer. The airtight box expands and contracts in response to changing air pressure. The mechanism amplifies the change and makes it easy to determine.

airtight box to rotate a pointer across a calibrated dial. All barometers measure the effect of the weight of the atmosphere. Meteorologists measure air pressure in millibars. Standard sea level pressure is 1013.2 millibars. In the *Earth Science Reference Tables*, you will find a chart that equates millibars to inches of mercury. On a weather map, **isobars** connect places that have the same air pressure.

Because air becomes less dense with increasing altitude, people who climb very high mountains may need to bring along oxygen tanks to help them breathe. Airplanes that fly most efficiently many kilometers above Earth are pressurized because the crew and passengers would certainly be uncomfortable and might even lose consciousness from a lack of oxygen at the reduced pressure of these altitudes. The reason that atmospheric pressure decreases with altitude is that as you go up there is less of the atmosphere above you pushing down.

Factors That Affect Atmospheric Pressure.

If air is cooled, it contracts, becoming denser. Because the air exerts pressure on whatever is below it, this causes atmospheric pressure to rise. If air is heated, it expands, becoming less dense, and causing atmospheric pressure to fall. In other words, there is an inverse relationship between temperature and atmospheric pressure.

The relationship between atmospheric pressure and humidity (the water vapor content of the air) is less intuitive. You may have noticed that when a towel becomes very wet, it becomes heavier, or thought that the air on a hot, humid day felt heavy. However, humid air is actually lighter than dry air. This is because equal volumes of gases at the same temperature and pressure have the same number of molecules, and molecules of water are comparatively light. As you can see in Figure 6-5, when water molecules enter the air, they displace heavier air molecules (mostly nitrogen). Replacement

of heavy molecules by lighter molecules lowers the density of the air, and lower air density results in lower atmospheric pressure. This is why atmospheric pressure usually decreases as humidity increases.

MOISTURE IN THE ATMOSPHERE

When the air is holding as much moisture as it can, the air is **saturated**. The air's ability to hold water vapor depends upon the temperature. The warmer the temperature, the more moisture the air can hold before it becomes saturated. For every 10°C rise in temperature, the air can hold approximately twice as much water vapor. At colder temperatures, the air can hold less water vapor before it becomes saturated. It follows that, if the temperature of the air is lowered enough, then the air will become saturated. At this point, we say that the temperature is at the dew point. The **dew point** is defined as the temperature to which the air must be cooled to become saturated. If the temperature falls below the dew point, condensation occurs as water vapor changes to liquid water.

Measuring Moisture in the Atmosphere.

Meteorologists use several methods to determine the moisture content of the atmosphere. They use a sling psychrometer (sigh-CRAH'-met-er) and a dew-point temperature table to determine the dew point. See Figure 6-6. The sling psychrometer has two thermometers mounted so that they can be swung through the air. One thermometer records the air temperature. The bulb of the second thermometer is covered by a cloth wick that is soaked with water before the instrument is used. Evaporation from the wick causes the wet thermometer to register a cooler temperature. The cooling effect of evaporation is the key to measuring the humidity. The drier the air, the greater the evaporational cooling and

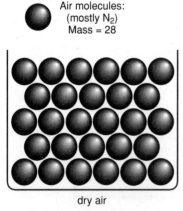

Air molecules:
(mostly N₂)
Mass = 28

dry air

Total mass of air molecules
= 30 × 28 = 840

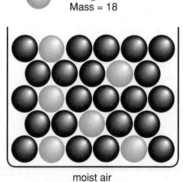

Water molecules:
H₂O
Mass = 18

moist air

Air molecules = 24 × 28 = 672

Water molecules = 6 × 18 = 108
Total mass = 780

Figure 6-5. When moisture is added to air, the air becomes less dense. Water vapor molecules are less dense than air (mostly nitrogen) molecules. When water vapor is added to air, the light water molecules replace the heavier nitrogen molecules. (The units of mass in these diagrams are atomic mass units.)

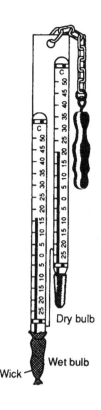

Figure 6-6. The sling psychrometer consists of two thermometers mounted side by side on a narrow frame, which can be swung through the air. One thermometer measures the air temperature. The bulb of the other thermometer is covered by a wet cloth. As the thermometers are swung through the air, evaporational cooling causes the wet-bulb thermometer to register a lower temperature. The dryer the air, the greater the evaporational cooling.

Dry bulb

Wet bulb

Wick

grees, Celsius (or Fahrenheit), we use dew point to indicate the water vapor content of the atmosphere. You should also note that although the dew point is a temperature, the only way to change the dew point is by adding or removing moisture from the air.

Sample Problem

If the dry-bulb temperature is 20°C and the wet-bulb temperature is 15°C, find the dew point.

Solution:

To find the temperature difference, subtract the wet-bulb temperature from the dry-bulb temperature. (Unless the wet-bulb and dry-bulb temperatures are equal, the wet-bulb temperature will always be lower.) The temperature difference is 5°C (20° − 15° = 5°). This step of subtracting is the one most often forgotten by students. Now, turn to the *Dew-Point Temperature* table. At the left side of the table locate 20°C, follow that row over to where it meets the column coming down from 5°C (the temperature difference). They meet at 12°C. Therefore, the dew point is 12°C, and the air would be saturated if it were cooled to that temperature.

Finding Relative Humidity.
The **relative humidity** expresses how full of moisture the air is. Relative humidity compares how much moisture the air is actually holding with how much moisture it could hold

the greater the difference between the air temperature and the wet-bulb temperature. When you subtract the wet-bulb temperature from the dry-bulb temperature, you can use dew-point temperature table to determine the dew point. See Figure 6-7. It is important to remember that although the dew point is expressed in de-

Dewpoint Temperatures

Dry-Bulb Temperature (°C)	Difference Between Wet-Bulb and Dry-Bulb Temperatures (C°)														
	1	2	3	4	5	6	7	8	9	10	11	12	13	14	15
−20	−33														
−18	−28														
−16	−24														
−14	−21	−36													
−12	−18	−28													
−10	−14	−22													
−8	−12	−18	−29												
−6	−10	−14	−22												
−4	−7	−12	−17	−29											
−2	−5	−8	−13	−20											
0	−3	−6	−9	−15	−24										
2	−1	−3	−6	−11	−17										
4	1	−1	−4	−7	−11	−19									
6	4	1	−1	−4	−7	−13	−21								
8	6	3	1	−2	−5	−9	−14								
10	8	6	4	1	−2	−5	−9	−14	−28						
12	10	8	6	4	1	−2	−5	−9	−16						
14	12	11	9	6	4	1	−2	−5	−10	−17					
16	14	13	11	9	7	4	1	−1	−6	−10	−17				
18	16	15	13	11	9	7	4	2	−2	−5	−10	−19			
20	19	17	15	14	12	10	7	4	2	−2	−5	−10	−19		
22	21	19	17	16	14	12	10	8	5	3	−1	−5	−10	−19	
24	23	21	20	18	16	14	12	10	8	6	2	−1	−5	−10	−18
26	25	23	22	20	18	17	15	13	11	9	6	3	0	−4	−9
28	27	25	24	22	21	19	17	16	14	11	9	7	4	1	−3
30	29	27	26	24	23	21	19	18	16	14	12	10	8	5	1

Figure 6-7. Dew-point temperature

Properties of the Atmosphere

if the air were saturated. Air is **saturated** if it is holding all the moisture it can hold at its present temperature. Relative humidity is expressed as a percent of saturation. For air that is saturated, the relative humidity is 100%. To determine relative humidity you need a sling psychrometer and a relative humidity table. See Figure 6-8.

Sample Problem

Find the relative humidity when the dry-bulb temperature is 14°C and the wet-bulb temperature is 9°C.

Solution:

First, find the temperature difference. It is 5°C (14° − 9° = 5°). On the relative humidity table, follow the row across from 14° and the column down from 5°. As you can see, they meet at 50. Therefore, under these conditions, the relative humidity is 50%.

When the relative humidity is 50%, that means that the air could actually hold twice as much water vapor as it is holding. If the relative humidity were 20%, then the air would be holding only one fifth the water vapor it could before it became saturated. Figure 6-9 illustrates how changes in air temperature and changes in the amount of water vapor in the air affect the relative humidity. As temperature of the air approaches the dew point, the relative humidity approaches 100%.

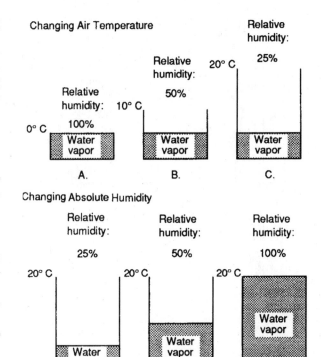

Figure 6-9. The effects of changing air temperature and of changing the moisture content of the air. In diagrams A-C, you can see that the air can hold more moisture as it gets warmer. If moisture is not added to the air, the relative humidity decreases as the temperature increases. In diagrams D-F, the temperature remains constant. As moisture is added to the air, the relative humidity increases.

Relative Humidity (%)

Dry-Bulb Tempera-ture (°C)	Difference Between Wet-Bulb and Dry-Bulb Temperatures (C°)														
	1	2	3	4	5	6	7	8	9	10	11	12	13	14	15
−20	28														
−18	40														
−16	48	0													
−14	55	11													
−12	61	23													
−10	66	33	0												
−8	71	41	13												
−6	73	48	20	0											
−4	77	54	32	11											
−2	79	58	37	20	1										
0	81	63	45	28	11										
2	83	67	51	36	20	6									
4	85	70	56	42	27	14									
6	86	72	59	46	35	22	10	0							
8	87	74	62	51	39	28	17	6							
10	88	76	65	54	43	33	24	13	4						
12	88	78	67	57	48	38	28	19	10	2					
14	89	79	69	60	50	41	33	25	16	8	1				
16	90	80	71	62	54	45	37	29	21	14	7	1			
18	91	81	72	64	56	48	40	33	26	19	12	6	0		
20	91	82	74	66	58	51	44	36	30	23	17	11	5	0	
22	92	83	75	68	60	53	46	40	33	27	21	15	10	4	0
24	92	84	76	69	62	55	49	42	36	30	25	20	14	9	4
26	92	85	77	70	64	57	51	45	39	34	28	23	18	13	9
28	93	86	78	71	65	59	53	47	42	36	31	26	21	17	12
30	93	86	79	72	66	61	55	49	44	39	34	29	25	20	16

Figure 6-8. Relative Humidity (%)

QUESTIONS

1. The boundary that separates the troposphere from the stratosphere is the (1) tropopause (2) thermopause (3) mesopause (4) stratopause

2. A barometer is used to measure (1) temperature (2) wind speed (3) pressure (4) humidity

3. As air absorbs moisture, its density (1) decreases (2) increases (3) remains the same

4. The lowest layer of the atmosphere is the (1) stratosphere (2) thermosphere (3) troposphere (4) mesosphere

5. As your height above the surface of Earth increases, the atmospheric pressure usually (1) decreases (2) increases (3) remains the same

6. According to the *Earth Science Reference Tables*, a temperature of 50°C is equal to (1) 0°F (2) 118°F (3) 122°F (4) 212°F

7. Which gas is *not* generally found within Earth's atmosphere (1) nitrogen (2) oxygen (3) hydrogen (4) carbon dioxide

8. Atmospheric pressure is often measured in (1) °C (2) °F (3) g/cm^3 (4) millibars

9. Atmospheric pressure is a result of what property of the air? (1) volume (2) temperature (3) transparency (4) weight

10. Which of the following events would change the dew-point temperature of the atmosphere? (1) evaporation and condensation (2) heating and cooling (3) precipitation and strong winds (4) snow

11. Which graph below best shows the typical cycle of air temperatures over a 24-hour period?

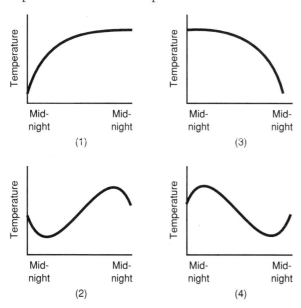

Directions: Use the information in the following diagram to answer questions 12–15.

The diagram top right shows three conditions of the atmosphere. The height of each bucket shows the air temperature and the "water level" shows the water vapor content of the air.

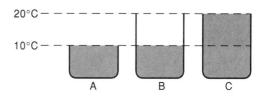

A Model of Atmospheric Humidity

12. What is the approximate relative humidity shown in Diagram B? (1) 0% (2) 10% (3) 50% (4) 100%

13. These diagrams show that the ability of the atmosphere to hold water vapor depends upon the (1) air temperature (2) air pressure (3) height above the ground (4) relative humidity

14. Which diagrams show the same relative humidity? (1) A and B (2) A and C (3) B and C (4) A, B, and C

15. What word best describes the short term condition of the atmosphere? (1) weather (2) climate (3) temperature (4) humidity

16. What generally happens to the moisture content of the atmosphere as the elevation above sea level increases? (1) it increases (2) it decreases (3) it remains constant

17. A dry-bulb and a wet-bulb thermometer are used together to determine the (1) air pressure (2) air temperature (3) dew point (4) atmospheric pressure

18. Graph I below shows temperature change in the afternoon. What change in atmospheric pressure might be expected on the same afternoon? (Select one of the four lines, A, B, C, or D, from graph II.)

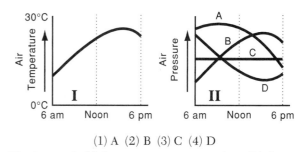

(1) A (2) B (3) C (4) D

19. Air can hold the most water vapor when (1) the atmospheric pressure is high (2) the air temperature is high (3) the wind is from the north (4) the wind speed is slow

20. If the relative humidity is 50% and the dry-bulb temperature is 14°C, what is the wet-bulb temperature? (1) 7°C (2) 9°C (3) 14°C (4) 28°C

HOW CAN WE MEASURE THE WIND?

Wind is heat flow by convection within the atmosphere. In general, winds are the result of uneven heating of Earth's surface. This uneven heating causes differences in air pressure to develop. Winds always blow from areas of high pressure to areas of low pressure. Winds blow fastest where the gradient in air pressure is greatest, where the isobars (lines of equal atmospheric pressure) are close together. See Figure 6-10 on page 112. Sea and land breezes are good examples, as shown in Figure 6-11 on page 112. On a hot

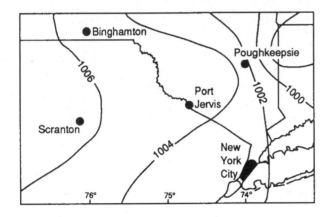

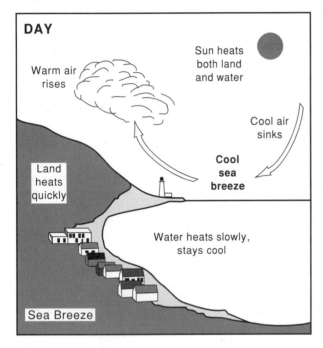

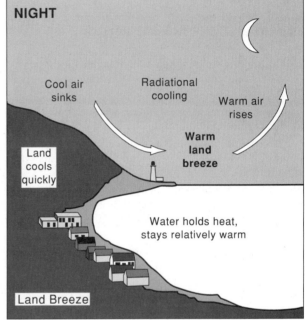

Figure 6-10. *(left)* On this map, the strongest winds will occur near Poughkeepsie. The isobars are the closest together in that area indicating the greatest pressure gradient.

Figure 6-11. *(below)* During the day, the sun warms the land, which causes the air above the land to expand, become less dense, and rise. As this warm air rises, a cool breeze from the ocean blows in to replace the rising air. At night, the situation is reversed. The land cools quickly cooling the air above, which sinks. The warmer air over the ocean rises. Then the breeze blows out to sea. These breezes make the shore a popular destination in hot summer weather.

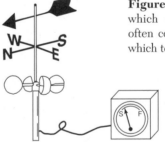

Figure 6-12. An anemometer, which measures wind speed, is often combined with a wind vane, which tells wind direction.

summer day, the land heats more quickly than the ocean. This causes low pressure over the land as the warm air rises. The result is a cool sea breeze that blows in off the water. At night, the land cools quickly, which cools the air above it. Now the air over the water is warmer than the air over the land. Therefore, low pressure develops over the water. The result is a land breeze that blows at night from the land to the sea.

To measure winds, you need to determine both the wind speed and the wind direction. Wind speed is measured with an anemometer. The cups on an **anemometer** catch the wind, causing the anemometer to spin. An indicator shows the wind speed. The wind direction is indicated by a wind vane, which is built to point into the wind. See Figure 6-12. It is important to remember that *winds are named by the direction from which they come.* A north wind usually brings cold weather because it comes from the north. There is another important factor that influences the direction of the winds. If Earth were not spinning, the pattern of wind circulation would be relatively simple. Winds would blow from the poles straight to the equator. But Earth rotates, so the paths of the winds curve. See Figure 6-13. Rather than

blowing straight from areas of high pressure, such as the North Pole, to places of low pressure, such as the equator, the winds in the Northern Hemisphere curve to the right of their original path. This curvature is called the **Coriolis effect**. But, in the Southern Hemisphere, the Coriolis effect causes winds to curve to the left of their original path.

In the Northern Hemisphere, the winds blowing out of a high pressure area turn clockwise. The winds blowing into a low pressure area turn counterclockwise. Areas of low pressure are called cyclones, and areas of high pressure are called anticyclones. See Figure 6-14.

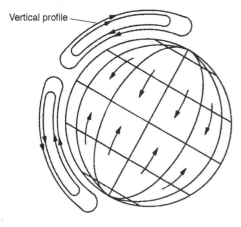

A. Stationary Planet

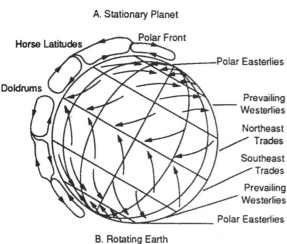

B. Rotating Earth

Figure 6-13. If Earth did not spin, wind patterns would be much simpler. However, because of Earth's rotation, winds curve to the right in the Northern Hemisphere and to the left in the Southern Hemisphere.

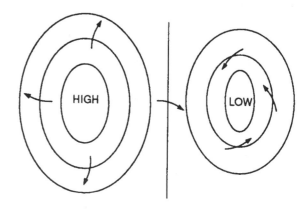

Figure 6-14. Wind direction and the Coriolis effect. Winds move in a clockwise outward spiral around high-pressure systems. Winds move in a counterclockwise inward spiral around low-pressure systems.

midity. Figure 6-16 on page 114 shows the relationship between temperature and other weather variables. Atmospheric pressure is indirectly related to temperature. When the air temperature is highest, the air expands and becomes lighter. This causes atmospheric pressure to go down. Then, at night when the air cools, air pressure increases. See Figure 6-16A. Winds are primarily the result of uneven heating of the atmosphere, most of which occurs during the day. The wind speed is highest when the temperature is highest. See Figure 6-16B. During the course of a day, the dew point and relative humidity change as water leaves the atmosphere by condensation at night and enters the air by evaporation during the day. The dew point rises until the air temperature drops to the dew point in the evening. At this point, the relative humidity is 100%, where it remains,

Prevailing Winds and Ocean Currents.

If you compare Earth's prevailing winds, shown in Figure 6-13B, with the surface ocean currents depicted in the *Earth Science Reference Tables*, you will find that they generally move in the same direction. This is not a mere coincidence. Wind is a major factor in moving the surface waters of Earth's oceans. Like the winds, ocean currents also curve in response to the Coriolis effect. Usually, currents curve to the right of their original direction in the Northern Hemisphere and to the left of their original direction in the Southern Hemisphere.

Winds blow in response to these changes. The wind always blows from places of high pressure to places of lower pressure. Figure 6-15 illustrates how surface winds are part of atmospheric convection currents that include a return flow high above Earth.

HOW ARE WEATHER VARIABLES RELATED?

The daily temperature cycle of the atmosphere affects atmosphere pressure, wind speed, and relative hu-

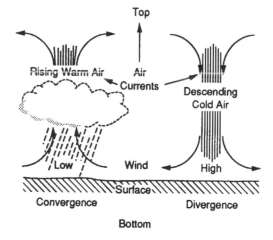

Figure 6-15. High- and low-pressure systems as zones of convergence and divergence. Rising warm, moist air at the center of the low causes winds and air masses to blow into the low-pressure system. The rising air cools, which causes cloud formation and precipitation. The descending air within an anticyclone turns a high-pressure system into a single mass of cool, dry air that spreads across the surface of Earth.

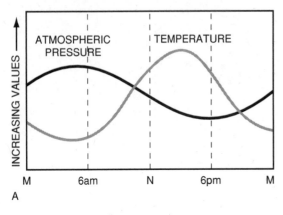

A

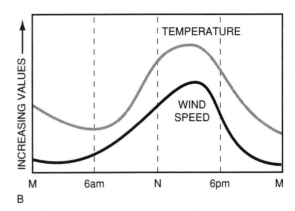

B

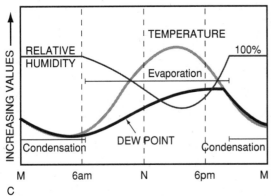

C

Figure 6-16. Daily cycles of atmospheric change. Graph A shows that atmospheric pressure varies indirectly with temperature. Graph B shows the relationship of temperature and wind speed. The winds are primarily a result of uneven heating of the atmosphere, most of which occurs during the daylight hours. Graph C shows the relationship between relative humidity and temperature. The dew point and relative humidity change as water leaves the atmosphere by condensation at night and enters the air by evaporation during the day.

and condensation occurs until the air temperature rises above the dew point in the morning. See Figure 6-16C.

HOW DO CLOUDS FORM AND CAUSE PRECIPITATION?

Clouds form when rising air is cooled below its dew point. But what causes the air to rise? Air rises for several reasons. One reason is that a portion of air is lower in density than the surrounding air due to its high temperation and/or humidity. But air can also be lifted when a moving mass of air encounters a mountain range. When an advancing cold front moves forward, the dense air at the front pushes under the warmer air mass ahead, causing that air to rise and cool.

Why Does Air Cool as it Rises?
When you pump up a tire and feel the lower end of the pump, it feels warm. You might guess that friction causes the heating. But only the very bottom of the pump, where the air is compressed the most, becomes very warm. It takes energy to compress air, and that energy changes to heat, which makes the pump warm. The opposite occurs as air rises into the atmosphere. The rising air expands due to decreasing pressure. Just as compression warms a gas, this expansion of rising air causes it to become cooler.

If the air is cooled below the dew point, and if tiny particles called condensation nuclei are present, a cloud will form. If the air is too clean, the temperature can actually fall below the dew point without condensation

occurring. A variety of processes adds these particles to the air: salt sprays, dust storms, fires, and the exhaust from burning fossil fuels.

Have you ever noticed how clear the air seems after a rainstorm? The process of precipitation brings down not only the water, but also the condensation nuclei on which the clouds formed. In this way precipitation cleans the atmosphere.

What is Precipitation?
What causes precipitation? Scientists know that the cloud droplets (or ice particles) must join together to become heavy enough to fall through the atmosphere. But they do not know what causes them to join. Since a raindrop may be a million times the size of a cloud droplet, it is clear that a great many cloud droplets must join to make each drop of rain. See Figure 6-17. Actually, most precipitation starts as snow, high in the atmosphere. In summer, when the snow falls into the air at lower elevations, the temperature rises and the snow melts, changing to rain.

Rain is measured with a rain gauge. This instrument can be as simple as a cylindrical container open at the top. The amount of rain is reported as a depth in inches or other convenient unit.

Although rain and snow are the most common forms of precipitation, there are several others. Drizzle is small raindrops that fall slowly. Sleet is a partially frozen mixture of rain and snow that occurs when the surface temperature is just above freezing. Hail is precipitation in the form of ice balls, which usually occurs in violent thunderstorms. Hailstones begin as snowflakes that start to melt and gather more moisture as they fall. Up-

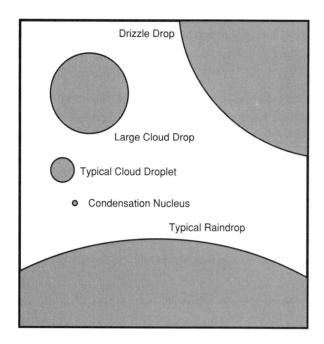

Figure 6-17. Cloud droplets and raindrops. Raindrops are much larger than cloud droplets. That is why they fall as precipitation.

drafts in the storm cloud repeatedly blow the partially melted flakes back up into cooler air high in the cloud, where the coating of water freezes. This process of falling and rising continues until the hailstones are too heavy to be carried by the updrafts. Hailstones larger than baseballs sometimes fall in the American Midwest.

QUESTIONS

21. The winds do *not* blow directly across the pressure gradient because of (1) Paleozoic force (2) Coriolis effect (3) gravitational force (4) magnetic force

22. The gaseous form of water is (1) ice (2) water vapor (3) snow (4) carbon dioxide

23. When water evaporates into the atmosphere, which property of the atmosphere is likely to increase? (1) air pressure (2) air temperature (3) density of the air (4) volume of the air

24. Winds always blow from (1) high temperature to low temperature (2) high humidity to low humidity (3) west to east (4) high pressure to low pressure

25. Winds are affected mainly by differences in (1) air pressure (2) the dew point (3) elevation (4) time of day

26. Which of the following units of measure would most likely be used to measure precipitation? (1) degrees Celsius (2) miles per hour (3) millibars (4) inches

27. If the amount of moisture in the air does not change, and the temperature is the lowest in the early morning, when is condensation the most likely? (1) midnight (2) early in the morning (3) noon (4) late in the afternoon

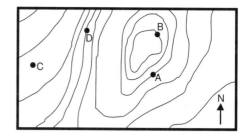

28. The isoline map above shows air pressures at Earth's surface. Where are the winds likely to be moving the slowest; that is, the most nearly calm? (1) A (2) B (3) C (4) D

29. At which boundary in the diagram to the right is the dew point likely to be the highest? (1) the thermosphere-mesosphere boundary (2) the mesosphere-stratosphere boundary (3) the stratosphere-troposphere boundary (4) the troposphere-hydrosphere boundary

30. As a mass of moist air rises into the atmosphere, the probability of condensation within the air (1) decreases (2) increases (3) remains the same

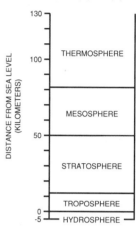

Directions: Base your answers to questions 31–35 on the diagram below, which illustrates how atmospheric variables change over a 24-hour period.

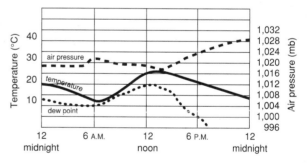

ATMOSPHERIC VARIABLES OVER A 24-HOUR PERIOD

31. What was the approximate atmospheric pressure at noon? (1) 1012 mb (2) 1013 mb (3) 1019 mb (4) 1020 mb

32. When did the air contain the greatest amount of water vapor? (1) 6 A.M. (2) 1 P.M. (3) 6 P.M. (4) 8 P.M.

33. When was the relative humidity the greatest? (1) 7 A.M. (2) noon (3) 2 P.M. (4) midnight

34. How can we best account for the air pressure drop between 6 A.M. and noon? (1) Condensation reduced the absolute humidity (2) The air was cooled by northerly winds. (3) The dew point temperature decreased. (4) The air was heated by sunlight.

35. What was the most likely time for condensation to occur? (1) 7 A.M. (2) noon (3) 6 P.M. (4) 8 P.M.

36. A cloud will form if the air is (1) cooled below the dry-bulb temperature (2) warmed above the dry-bulb temperature (3) cooled below the dew-point temperature (4) warmed above the dew-point temperature

37. When the air temperature is below 0°C, as a cloud forms, we can see the cloud because it contains (1) ice crystals (2) condensation nuclei (3) liquid water (4) dust and smoke

38. Which of the following is *not* a form of precipitation? (1) hail (2) dew (3) snow (4) sleet

---

The Scientist, Engineer, and Citizen

Choose your fate: global warming or a new ice age. Report to the mayor's office about either as an impending disaster. Tell the town government which you think is more likely to occur, and how the town should react to protect its citizens. To add to the gravity of the situation, assume that a credible government commission has predicted that this inevitability will occur in the brief time span of 50 years.

CHAPTER 6 REVIEW QUESTIONS

Directions: Base your answers to questions 1–5 on your knowledge of earth science, the *Earth Science Reference Tables*, and the following drawing. The drawing represents five positions of a balloon after being released from a ship. The drawings of the balloon are not to scale compared with the altitude distances, but are to scale with each other.

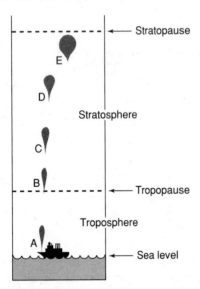

1. Which letter in the diagram above best shows a position 12 km above Earth? (1) A (2) B (3) C (4) D

2. The balloon constantly expands as it rises because of a/an (1) increase in temperature (2) decrease in temperature (3) increase in air pressure (4) decrease in air pressure

3. If the air temperature at the ship is 15°C, what is the probable temperature at position B? (1) −55°C (2) 0°C (3) 15°C (4) 30°C

4. The balloon will rise only if the gas inside is (1) less dense than the air at sea level (2) equal in density to the air at sea level (3) more dense than the air at sea level

5. Which graph below best shows the change in the water vapor content of the air as the balloon rises?

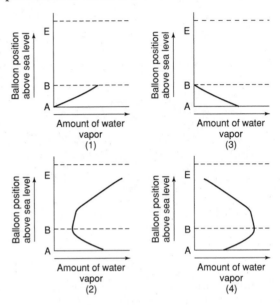

6. What is the dew point when you swing a sling psychrometer and get a dry-bulb temperature of 10°C and a wet-bulb temperature of 7°C? (1) −9°C (2) 3°C (3) 4°C (4) 7°C

7. When we record the weather, we usually do *not* measure the (1) air temperature (2) angle of the sun (3) wind direction (4) wind speed

8. The atmospheric pressure usually increases when which of the following variables also increases? (1) density of the air (2) elevation above sea level (3) relative humidity (4) temperature

9. According to the *Earth Science Reference Tables*, an atmospheric pressure of 29.65 inches of mercury is equal to how many millibars? (1) 984 (2) 989 (3) 1001 (4) 1004

10. What is the dew point of the air under the conditions shown below?

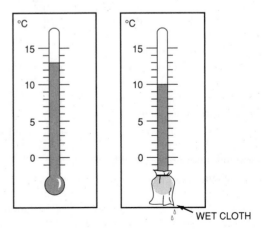

(1) −25°C (2) 7°C (3) 3°C (4) 4°C

11. Which quantity is not measured in °C or °F? (1) wet-bulb temperature (2) air temperature (3) relative humidity (4) dew point

12. What is the most abundant element in the troposphere? (1) helium (2) oxygen (3) hydrogen (4) nitrogen

13. Winds blow from regions of (1) high temperature to low temperature (2) high humidity to low humidity (3) high pressure to low pressure (4) low pressure to high pressure

14. Which of the following values is always the highest at a particular time and place? (1) the wet-bulb temperature (2) the dry-bulb temperature (3) the dew-point temperature

15. What do you see when you look at a cloud high in the sky? (1) condensation nuclei (2) water vapor (3) dust from meteors (4) ice crystals

16. Air is the most dense when it is (1) cool and dry (2) warm and dry (3) cool and moist (4) warm and moist

17. How many thermometers are there on a sling psychrometer? (1) 1 (2) 2 (3) 3 (4) 4

18. What happens to the air temperature as your elevation increases within the troposphere? (1) The temperature decreases. (2) The temperature increases. (3) The temperature remains constant.

19. What kind of instrument helps us measure the wind? (1) anemometer (2) rain gauge (3) barometer (4) sling psychrometer

20. What name is applied to a large group of tiny ice crystals suspended high in the sky? (1) storm (2) wind (3) snow (4) cloud

21. Which of the following procedures is most likely to reveal several cycles of a cyclic event? (1) Three days of hourly air temperature measurements (2) Three hours of minute by minute wind direction and speed data (3) Daily recordings of atmospheric pressure for a week (4) Six consecutive months of monthly average temperatures

FREE-RESPONSE QUESTIONS

(Answer the following questions on a separate sheet of paper.)

1. Explain what it means when we say that the relative humidity is 25%. Use one or more complete sentences.
(Quality of response, +1 or 2; Complete sentence +1)

2. What happens to the atmospheric pressure when evaporation makes the air more moist? Why does this happen? Answer in one or more complete sentences.
(Correct change, +1; Explanation, +1; Complete sentence, +1)

3. Make a list of three (3) events that need to happen, in proper sequence, for clouds to form in the sky.
(Each event, +1)

4. The diagram below shows the wind speed and direction over a period of three consecutive days. In a complete sentence, tell one way the weather changed during the period illustrated.
(Conclusion, +1; Sentence, +1)

5. Add an arrow to this diagram to show a wind of 1.5 meters/second from the Northeast.
(Correctly drawn vector, +1)

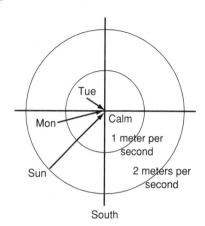

Legend: The length shows the wind speed, and the arrow shows the direction.

This is a West wind.

6. What change in the weather could cause air pressure to decrease? Be sure to answer in one or more complete sentences.
(Change +1; Complete Sentences, +1)

7. At what time was the relative humidity the highest on the day shown by the graph below?
(Correct time ±2 hours, +1)

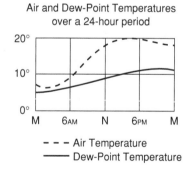

Air and Dew-Point Temperatures over a 24-hour period

- - - Air Temperature
——— Dew-Point Temperature

8. Clouds often have flat bottoms. Why? Answer in one or more complete sentences.
(Reason, +1; Complete sentence, +1)

9. In what direction must the air be moving for a cloud to form?
(Correct answer, +1)

10. When a cold glass of soda is left outside on a summer day, a layer of moisture forms on the outside of the glass. Explain why this occurs.
(Name and description of process, +1; Complete sentence(s), +1)

CHAPTER 7 Weather Systems

HOW DOES ENERGY GET INTO THE ATMOSPHERE?

It takes a great deal of energy to drive Earth's weather. Where does this energy come from? The sun is the major source of energy for Earth. Stars, including our sun, give off electromagnetic energy over the wide range of wavelengths that make up the electromagnetic spectrum. Figure 7-1 shows the range of the **electromagnetic spectrum** from short wave radiation, such as X rays and ultraviolet, to long wave radiation, that includes infrared and radio waves. Earth's atmosphere filters out most of the short-wave radiation (some ultraviolet radiation does get through). Most of the output from the sun that reaches the surface of Earth is in the narrow band that we perceive as visible light. Earth also radiates electromagnetic energy, mostly in the infrared (heat) part of the electromagnetic spectrum, a part of the spectrum we cannot see.

Earth intercepts only a very small fraction of the energy radiated by the sun. Of the solar radiation that reaches Earth, approximately three quarters of this energy evaporates water from the oceans. See Figure 7-2. Evaporation is the change of state from liquid to gas, or vapor. Evaporation adds energy and matter to the atmosphere. Several factors affect the rate of evaporation of water. Evaporation decreases when water is covered or cooled. The rate of evaporation increases when water is uncovered, heated, and when wind blows over it. See Figure 7-3.

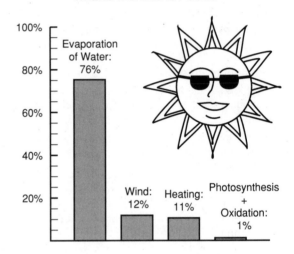

WHERE THE ENERGY GOES

Figure 7-2. The effects of solar heating. About three-quarters of the energy that reaches Earth's surface evaporates water into the atmosphere. This is a major source of atmospheric energy.

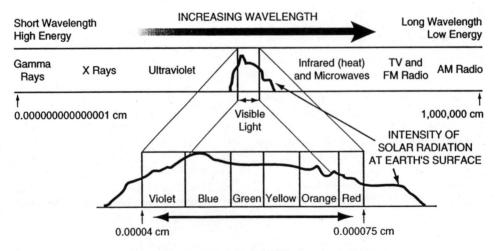

Figure 7-1. The sun produces energy across the electromagnetic spectrum. Earth's atmosphere absorbs most of the high-energy, short-wavelength radiation. Our eyes detect visible light.

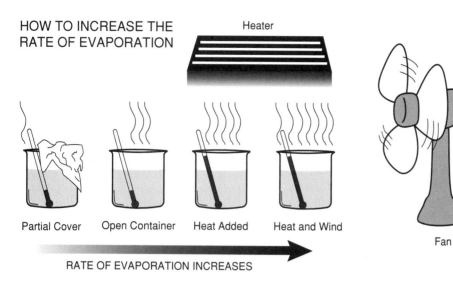

HOW TO INCREASE THE
RATE OF EVAPORATION

Heater

Partial Cover   Open Container   Heat Added   Heat and Wind

RATE OF EVAPORATION INCREASES

Fan

Figure 7-3. Factors that affect the rate of evaporation. Water will evaporate more quickly when more surface area is exposed, if heat energy is added, and when wind blows in a constant supply of dry air.

Three States of Water.

You are probably familiar with the three states of water: ice, liquid water, and water vapor. Figure 7-4 shows how the temperature of a 1-gram sample of ice changes as it is heated. The sloping parts of the graph show changes in temperature. The level parts of the graph, where the temperature does not change, show that energy is used for a change in state. Energy that is absorbed or released during a change in state is called latent (hidden) heat, a form of potential energy. It is latent energy because it does not cause a change in temperature. People often confuse heat and temperature. Heat is a form of energy that is the result of the vibrational motion (kinetic energy) of atoms and molecules. Heat is measured in calories. Temperature is a measure of the average kinetic energy of the atoms and molecules of a substance. Temperature is measured in degrees (Kelvin, Celsius, or Fahrenheit) by means of a thermometer.

According to the graph, before the ice was heated its temperature was −25°C. Heating caused the temperature of the ice to increase to 0°C, at which point it began to melt. As the ice changed to liquid water, it absorbed 80 calories per gram (latent heat). The energy needed to melt one gram of a substance at its melting point is called the **heat of fusion**. The heat of fusion of ice is 80 calories per gram (80 cal/g). The temperature of the ice does not change until all the ice has melted. Heating continued and the temperature of the liquid water increased until it reached 100°C, the boiling point of water. At the boiling point, liquid water changed to water vapor. The energy necessary to change one gram of a substance from the liquid to the vapor state is called the **heat of vaporization**. The heat of vaporization of water is 540 cal/g. The gram of water absorbed 540 calories of latent heat as it changed to vapor. After all the liquid water became vapor, the temperature began to rise again. The specific heat of water vapor is 0.5 cal/g•°C.

If the water vapor is cooled to 100°C, it will condense and release the 540 calories of latent heat it absorbed. As

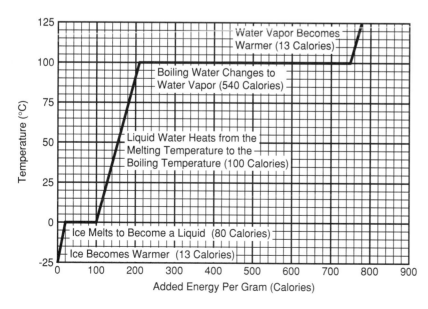

Figure 7-4. Energy used for change in state is known as latent heat. This graph shows how the temperature of a 1-gram sample changes as it absorbs energy at a constant rate. The horizontal parts of this graph show that water does not change temperature as it changes from solid (ice) to a liquid (water) or from a liquid to a gas (water vapor). These changes of state involve much more energy than changes in temperature. Latent heat is a form of potential energy.

cooling continues, the water will release the heat it absorbed while it was heated. It also releases the 80 calories per gram that was needed to melt the original ice.

Water also evaporates at temperatures lower than its boiling point. You can observe this by leaving a glass of water indoors undisturbed for a few days. You will notice that the amount of water in the glass decreases. Every time a gram of water evaporates into the atmosphere it carries with it 540 calories of latent heat. It may help you to understand how much energy that is if you realize that the potential energy alone is over five times as much energy as it takes to heat the water from the freezing temperature (0°C) to boiling point (100°C). When one gram of water changes from vapor to liquid, it releases 540 calories of latent heat.

Energy in the Atmosphere.

Condensation and freezing release energy while melting and evaporation absorb energy. Within the atmosphere, water vapor, which holds an enormous amount of energy, is the principal reservoir of energy. That energy is released when clouds form by condensation or deposition. (Deposition occurs when water vapor changes directly into ice. The opposite process, sublimation, occurs when ice or snow evaporates without first melting.) In Chapter 6 you learned about severe weather, such as hurricanes, tornadoes, and thunderstorms. These storms are supported by latent heat energy released when condensation and deposition occur in the atmosphere. See Figure 7-5.

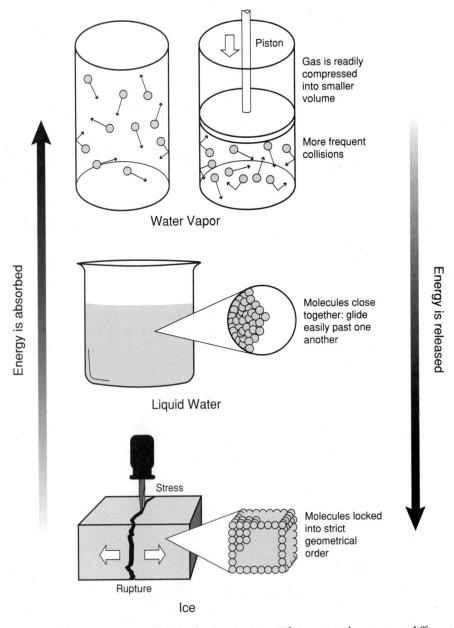

Figure 7-5. Energy associated with changes in state. When water changes to a different state, potential energy (latent heat) is absorbed or given off. Condensation and freezing release energy. Melting and vaporization require the addition of energy.

1. What is the main reservoir of energy within the Earth's atmosphere? (1) water vapor (2) carbon dioxide (3) oxygen (4) nitrogen

2. Which of the following processes adds both matter and energy to the atmosphere? (1) condensation (2) precipitation (3) evaporation (4) deposition

3. What instrument is generally used to measure the average kinetic energy of the molecules in a substance? (1) thermometer (2) barometer (3) wind vane (4) psychrometer

4. Which change would cause more water to evaporate from a lake? (1) a decrease in wind velocity (2) a decrease in the strength of sunlight (3) an increase in the air temperature (4) an increase in the relative humidity

5. A cup of water left outside evaporates more slowly if (1) the air temperature is high (2) the cup has a large exposed surface area (3) there is little or no wind (4) the air has little water vapor

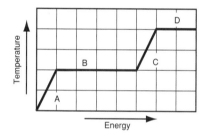

6. This graph shows a substance being heated and changing in state. Which parts of the graph show the change in state? (1) A&D (2) B&D (3) C&D (4) A&C

7. Clouds form directly by the process of (1) evaporation (2) radiation (3) condensation (4) melting

8. Which process releases the latent heat of water vapor to make the air warmer? (1) precipitation (2) evaporation (3) cloud formation (4) expansion

Directions: Use the diagram below and your knowledge of earth science to answer questions 9–11. The diagram illustrates that water can exist in all three states of matter: solid (ice), liquid (water), and gas (water vapor).

9. Which of the arrows in the diagram best shows the one process that can create a cloud? (1) A (2) B (3) C (4) D

10. Which process requires water to gain latent energy? (1) E (2) B (3) C (4) F

11. Which statement below is true and also identifies an error in the diagram? (1) A cloud can never form near the ground. (2) A container of ice cannot cause condensation. (3) Clouds do not contain water vapor. (4) Water vapor is not visible.

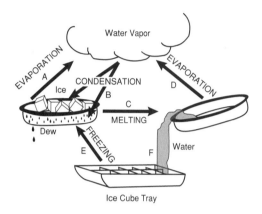

WHAT IS A SYNOPTIC WEATHER MAP?

Weather maps that show a variety of atmospheric field quantities are known as **synoptic weather maps**. See Figure 7-6. Synoptic maps may show information about temperature, air pressure, precipitation, and other weather conditions at a particular time and over a large geographic area. The temperature field is shown by isotherms, lines that connect places that have the

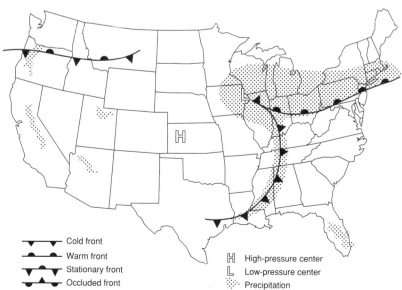

Figure 7-6. A weather map. Weather maps generally show the centers of cyclones (lows) and anticyclones (highs) as well as the frontal boundaries along which weather changes and precipitation generally occur.

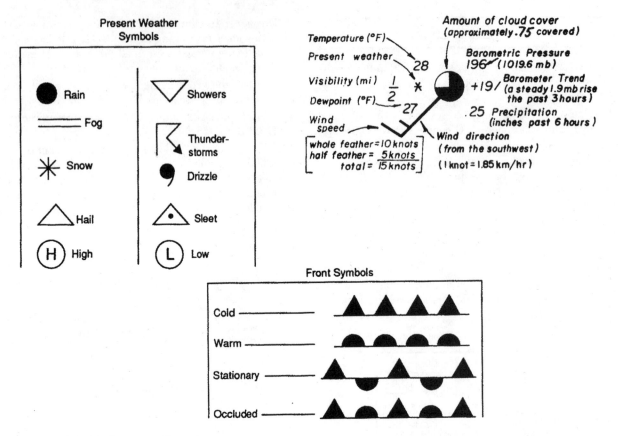

Figure 7-7. Weather map information

same temperature. Because most weather systems move across the United States from west to east, synoptic weather maps provide information that can be used to make weather predictions. Some symbols used to describe weather conditions are shown in Figure 7-7.

Interpreting Information Shown at a Weather Station.

Because so much information must be recorded at each station on a weather map, the information is shown in an abbreviated form (synoptic). Each type of measurement is shown at a prescribed position next to the circle that shows geographic location of the reporting station. See Figure 7-7.

How to interpret the information recorded at weather stations on a synoptic weather map:

1. The circle in Figure 7-7 shows the geographic location of the weather station. The cloud cover is shown by the amount of the circle that is dark. This example shows a 75% cloud cover.

2. The line connected to the circle shows the direction from which the wind is blowing. This example shows a wind from the southwest. (Winds are always shown and named by the direction from which the wind comes and not by the direction toward which the wind is going.) The feathers show the wind speed. Each whole feather is 10 knots (10 nautical miles per hour, a nautical mile is 1.15 miles), and each half feather 5 knots. In this example 1½ feathers mean a wind of approximately 15 knots.

3. The air temperature in degrees Fahrenheit is shown at the top left; here it is 28°F.

4. The dew point is shown at the bottom left. In this example, the dew point is 27°F.

5. The symbol at the left side of the circle shows the present weather. The symbol in the example above shows snow.

6. The number next to the symbol for present weather shows the atmospheric visibility in miles; here it is ½ mile.

7. At the top right is a three-digit code showing the atmospheric pressure. To decode, you must add "9" or a "10" in front of the code numbers, and a decimal point must be placed before the final digit. When the first digit is less than 5, add a 10. However, if the first digit is 5 or greater, add a 9. For example, "196" would mean 1019.6 millibars. And "979" is 997.9 millibars. The final recording should result in a number that is close to the normal reading for atmospheric pressure which is about 1000 millibars.

8. The number to the right of the circle shows the change in atmospheric pressure over the past three hours. (Again, a decimal point must be added.) The line to the right of the number shows how the atmospheric pressure has changed. This one shows a steady increase of 1.9 millibars. Decreasing atmospheric pressure often foretells the coming of clouds and rain. Rising atmospheric pressure means improving weather.

9. The number below the change in atmospheric pressure shows the amount of precipitation in inches over the past six hours. In this example, 25 hundredths of an inch of precipitation has fallen in 6 hours.

Some weather stations may display more or less information, but it will always be displayed in the format shown here.

Air Masses.

Weather maps are especially useful to identify bodies of air with uniform temperature, pressure, and humidity called air masses. It is the movement of air masses that brings changes in the weather. The leading edges of air masses are called **fronts**. When a front passes, precipitation often accompanies the changes in temperature, humidity, and atmospheric pressure that mark the arrival of a new air mass. Then, within the new air mass, conditions generally stabilize.

The character of an air mass depends on its geographic origin. For example, an air mass from central Canada that moves southward into the United States tends to be cold and dry. This air mass causes an increase in atmospheric pressure. But an air mass from the Gulf of Mexico will usually be warm and moist, and produces relatively low atmospheric pressure.

Meteorologists have specified two-letter codes to identify the temperature and humidity characteristics of air masses. Each one has a small letter followed by a capital letter. These codes are listed in the *Earth Science Reference Tables*. You should be familiar with the five air mass descriptions and with their abbreviations.

cA   continental arctic: an unusually cold and dry air mass from arctic Canada

cP   continental polar: a cold, dry air mass, that may have originated over central Canada

cT   continental tropical: a warm, dry air mass, that may have originated over Mexico or the American Southwest desert region

mT   maritime tropical: a warm, moist air mass, that may have originated over the Gulf of Mexico.

mP   maritime polar: a cold, moist air mass that may have originated over the North Atlantic or North Pacific Ocean

In particular, you should know that continental air is dry and maritime air, from off the oceans, is moist. A tropical air mass is warm and a polar air mass is cold. An arctic air mass is even colder. The geographic origins of air masses coming into the United States are shown in Figure 7-8.

HOW CAN WE PREDICT THE WEATHER?

Weather systems usually move across the United States from west to east. If you know today's weather in Chicago, you have a rough indication of the weather in New York a day or two later. Look back at Figure 7-6.

Highs and Lows.

If you look at the weather map in a newspaper or on television, you will notice a number of common features on these maps. A large "H" is used to represent the center of a high pressure system, formally known as an anticyclone. Highs are zones of divergence where sinking air at the center causes the winds to blow outward. In general, high

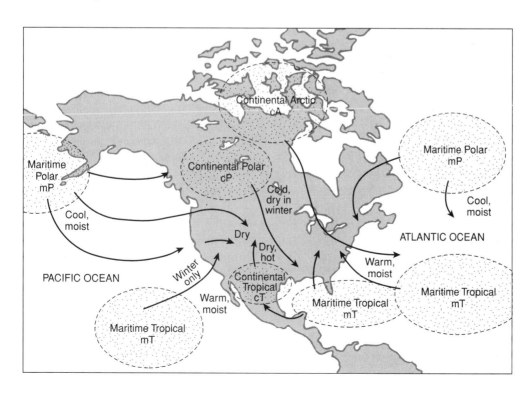

Figure 7-8. The arrows show the usual paths taken by air masses that affect weather in the United States.

pressure systems bring cool and dry air with clear skies and stable conditions.

On the other hand a large "L" is used to represent the center of a low pressure system, also known as a mid-latitude cyclone, or a zone of convergence. Lows are generally areas of warm, moist weather. Rising air at the center of the low draws in contrasting air masses with their associated weather fronts. This generally produces unsettled weather conditions. Low pressure systems are generally associated with changeable weather, cloudy skies, and precipitation.

Fronts. Fronts are shown by lines that separate two air masses. Fronts are often found in low pressure systems because of the different air masses that converge to form a cyclone. Symbols along these fronts indicate the direction in which the fronts are moving and what kind of fronts they are: cold, warm, stationary, or occluded. Warm and cold fronts are named for the temperature changes they bring. Stationary fronts are boundaries between air masses that are not moving. Occluded fronts result from warm air being pushed above the surface of Earth by cooler air closing in from both sides. The four types of fronts are illustrated in Figure 7-9. Four stages in the development of a mid-latitude cyclones are illustrated in Figure 7-10.

Predicting Weather.

Meteorologists make extensive use of technology to observe and predict the weather. In addition to such familiar instruments as thermometers, rain gauges, wind gauges and barome-

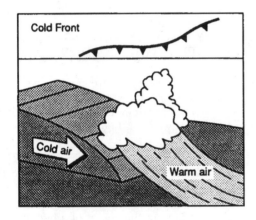

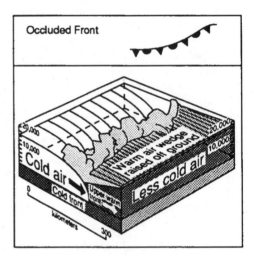

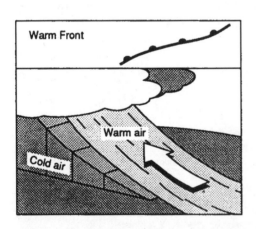

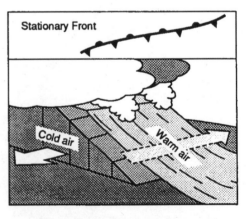

Figure 7-9. Four types of weather fronts. *Cold fronts* pass quickly. An advancing mass of cold air pushes warmer, more moist air aloft, often causing cooling, rapid cloud formation, and intense precipitation. Summer cold fronts sometimes bring thunderstorms, followed by cool, dry weather and high atmospheric pressure. A cold front may pass in a matter of an hour or two. A *warm front* is produced when warm air flows in to replace a retreating cold air mass. As the warmer, more moist air rises over the cooler air, cooling causes the formation of high, wispy clouds followed by thickening clouds and steady precipitation. The passage of a warm front may take several days and bring in warm, hazy weather conditions with relatively low atmospheric pressure. An *occluded front* is produced when an advancing cold air mass pushes a lighter warm air mass completely above the ground. Occluded fronts are commonly associated with large areas of rainy, unsettled weather. A *stationary front* occurs where the winds blow in opposite directions along a boundary between warm and cold air masses. The front is called stationary because the boundary is not moving.

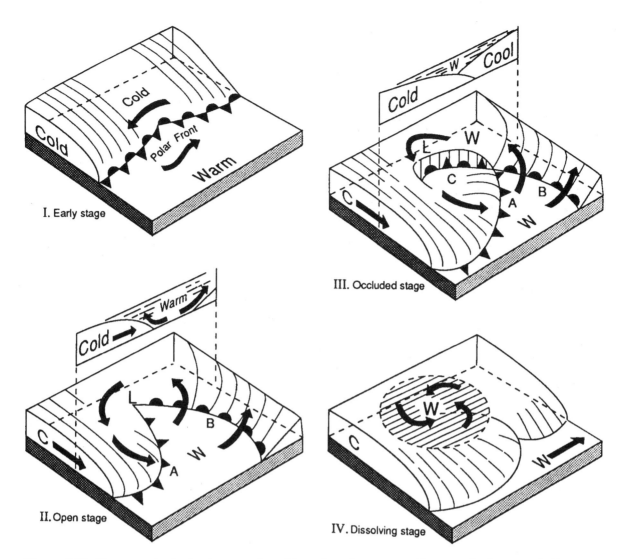

Figure 7-10. Four stages in the development of a mid-latitude cyclone. *I*. A swirl begins to develop as winds blow in opposite directions along a stationary front. *II*. The cold, dry, and more dense air begins to close in on the warmer and more moist air mass. Note the appearance of the cold front (A) and warm front (B). Cloud formation and precipitation will tend to take place in front of the warm front (B) and in a narrow band along the cold front (A) when warm, moist air is cooled as it is pushed aloft. (Note the cross-sectional profile above the three-dimensional diagram.) *III*. The cold front (A) had overtaken the warm front (B) to produce an occluded front (C) where the whole warm air mass has been pushed up. Cloudy weather and precipitation can be found along all three fronts. *IV*. A portion of the warmer air is isolated as the swirl closes in. This isolated portion of the warmer air mass will lose its identity as it is absorbed by the cold air mass. At the dissolving stage of cyclonic development, the life of the cyclone usually ends. However, the first stage may redevelop, in which case the life cycle of the cyclone will take place again.

ters, they use weather balloons, radar, and satellite photographs to observe weather conditions over the whole planet.

When electronic computers were developed in the 1950s, meteorologists were quick to use them to analyze more data in order to increase the reliability of weather forecasts. Computers help meteorologists determine the kind of weather that resulted in the past from similar weather patterns. Based upon these calculations, meteorologists make predictions that include a probability of occurrence. For example, if a low pressure system with specific measurements of temperature and dew point is advancing from the west, computers may indicate that these conditions produced rain approximately 80% of the time in the past. This means that in four out of five similar events, local rainfall followed these conditions.

The more information meteorologists have about present weather conditions, the more reliable their forecasts become. At present, day-to-day forecasts are correct about 90% of the time. Meteorologists also want to make accurate long-range forecasts weeks or months in advance. They found that as their ability to collect and analyze data increased, the reliability of short-term forecasts has improved. But long-range forecasts continue to be unreliable.

Chaos theory, a modern branch of science and mathematics, has shown meteorologists that predictions for more than a week or two in the future are unlikely ever to be reliable. The complex development of global circulation and its extreme sensitivity to even minor fluctuations in conditions, probably make accurate long-term weather predictions impossible.

QUESTIONS

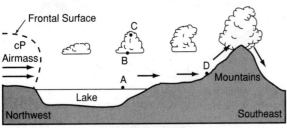

(NOT DRAWN TO SCALE)

12. The diagram above shows a weather system approaching a location in New York State. Which surface weather map below best represents the atmospheric conditions in the diagram above?

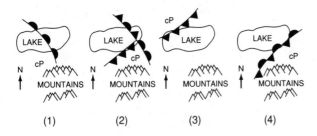

(1) (2) (3) (4)

13. What is the likely source of the air mass labeled cP? (1) the Gulf of Mexico (2) the North Atlantic (3) Texas and Arizona (4) central Canada

14. Which diagram below best shows fronts and air circulation around a Northern Hemisphere cyclone?

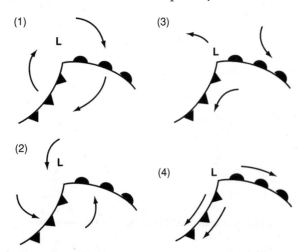

15. What weather conditions is most likely when the air is rising? (1) clearing skies (2) decreasing relative humidity (3) cloud formation (4) increasing temperatures

16. Which diagram below best shows the profile view of a warm front moving from left to right?

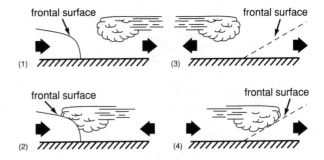

17. Why are accurate weather forecasts of more than a week or two never likely to be possible? (1) Over long time periods, very small factors can have a great influence on weather. (2) Pollution caused by humans will stop influencing the weather in a few years. (3) Future computers are unlikely to be more powerful than computers of today. (4) Government funding of weather-related scientific research has been stopped.

18. Which symbol is used to show a weather front in which the winds blow in opposite directions along the two sides of the front, but warmer places stay warm, and cooler places stay cool?

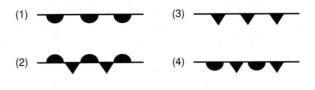

Directions: Use the three diagrams below to answer questions 19–23. The air pressure on Wednesday has been left out intentionally.

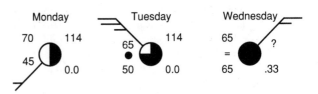

Three Days of Weather at Noon

19. On which day were the winds the fastest? (1) Monday (2) Tuesday (3) Wednesday (4) all the same

20. What was the approximate air temperature at noon on Tuesday *in degrees Celsius*? (1) 18°C (2) 20°C (3) 22°C (4) 24°C

21. What was the wind direction at noon on Monday? (1) Northeast (2) Northwest (3) Southeast (4) Southwest

22. On which day did a maritime polar air mass dominate? (1) Monday (2) Tuesday (3) Wednesday (4) none came in

23. What was the most likely air pressure at this station at noon on Wednesday? (1) 114 mb (2) 1011.4 mb (3) 1020 mb (4) 1005 mb

CAN WE LEARN TO LIVE WITH NATURAL HAZARDS?

Each year, violent storms cause property damage and loss of life. The destructive power of these storms is a consequence of their energy. That energy becomes available through the process of condensation, which occurs when clouds form within these storms.

Thunderstorms.

Most thunderstorms occur in the summer when the air is warm and moist. An advancing cold front may push the warm air upward, causing the formation of giant cumulus clouds and heavy precipitation. Lightning, damaging hail, and even tornadoes can occur in especially strong thunderstorms. However, such storms usually pass in less than an hour.

Because you are familiar with thunderstorms, you may underestimate their danger. Nevertheless, lightning strikes, flash floods, and tornadoes spawned by thunderstorms, each cause roughly 100 fatalities per year in the United States. To avoid these hazards, you should seek shelter inside a vehicle or modern building well above any potential flood areas.

Tornadoes.

Tornadoes are most common in the spring and early summer over the central United States, when maritime tropical air masses from the Gulf of Mexico collide, with cooler and drier air from the north. However, tornadoes can occur in any part of the United States.

Although the winds in a hurricane may blow at speeds up to 150 miles per hour (240 kilometers per hour), tornadoes have even stronger winds. Tornado winds are difficult to measure because most tornadoes are very small and short-lived. They are usually less than 0.3 miles (0.5 kilometers) in diameter, and although some have lasted for hours, most tornadoes last 10 minutes or less. As you might imagine, measurements of wind speeds in tornadoes are very difficult to take. Instruments in the paths of tornadoes have been destroyed along with the buildings they were attached to. Winds in some tornadoes have been clocked at 280 miles per hour (450 kilometers per hour) before the recorder broke. But winds in excess of 300 miles per hour (500 kilometers per hour) have been identified based upon radar measurements and observations of damage caused by powerful tornadoes.

Hurricanes.

Tropical depressions, areas of low pressure, usually develop in the late summer and early autumn in the Atlantic Ocean between South America and Africa. This region has an abundance of solar energy and warm tropical water. These storms gather strength as they drift across the Atlantic Ocean. When sustained winds in the storm exceed 74 miles per hour (120 kilometers per hour), the storms' designation is changed from a tropical storm to a hurricane. See Figure 7-11.

Hurricanes grow into huge rotating systems, which average 400 miles (600 kilometers) across. At the center of a hurricane, the air pressure is very low; therefore, a large pressure gradient develops, which generates the strong winds associated with these storms. Winds whirl around the center of a hurricane, which is called the eye. However, in the eye itself, winds are relatively calm. If a hurricane comes ashore, such as along the southern and eastern coasts of the United States, the combined effects of fierce winds, intense precipitation, and unusually high tides wreak havoc on coastal properties. Because of the large size of hurricanes, it may take many hours for a storm to pass. During this time, flying debris and flooding can cause great destruction.

When the storm moves inland, it is deprived of its source of energy: warm, tropical ocean water. It soon expends its most violent winds and in a matter of days becomes a mid-latitude cyclone with a fraction of the power it had as a hurricane.

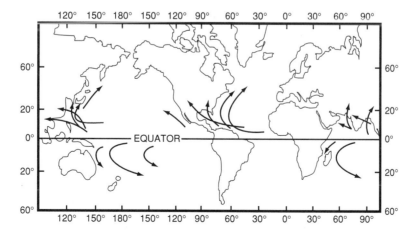

Figure 7-11. Common paths of tropical storms. Although we call them hurricanes, in other parts of the world these storms are also known as typhoons and cyclones. Notice that they begin over tropical waters near the equator and expend their energy when they move into mid-latitudes.

24. Why are hurricanes and tropical depressions more common in the tropics and in the mid-latitudes during the warmer months? (1) Strong winds cannot exist when there is snow on the ground. (2) Cold air cannot hold any water vapor. (3) These storms develop only where there is an abundance of solar energy and warm tropical water. (4) The equatorial regions are closer to Earth's center.

25. Why does a hurricane cause more damage and fatalities than a tornado? (1) The winds in hurricanes are faster. (2) Tornadoes do not occur on land. (3) There are more hurricanes than tornadoes. (4) Hurricanes are much larger than tornadoes.

26. Which states are especially susceptible to hurricane damage? (1) Florida, North Carolina, and Texas (2) Tennessee, Alaska, and South Dakota (3) Vermont, Illinois, and Montana (4) Washington, New Mexico, and Idaho

27. As an Atlantic hurricane is born, intensifies, and later fades, what is its most likely path as it moves toward the mainland of the United States. (1) It moves east, south, and then west. (2) It moves south, east, and then north. (3) It moves west, north, and then east. (4) It moves steadily to the south.

28. What change is most likely to cause a hurricane to diminish in power? (1) It stalls over warm ocean currents. (2) It moves over a continent. (3) Cloud formation intensifies. (4) The eye of the hurricane becomes very distinct.

29. What feature on a weather map is most likely to be associated with tornadoes? (1) a warm front (2) an anticyclone (3) a cold front (4) a high pressure system

30. What causes the most injury in hurricanes? (1) the direct force of the wind (2) flooding and flying debris (3) vertical wind gusts (4) violent shaking of the ground

31. Where would hurricanes (also known as typhoons or cyclones in other parts of the world) be most likely to form? (1) over central Asia (2) over the Arctic Ocean (3) over South America (4) over the Indian Ocean

32. Which kind of weather event is likely to last the longest? (1) a hurricane (2) a tornado (3) a thunderstorm (4) a bolt of lightning

33. Which arrow on the map below best shows a typical path of an Atlantic hurricane? (1) A (2) B (3) C (4) D

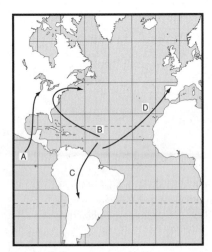

34. What factor helps to determine the paths of most hurricanes? (1) the phase of the moon (2) the distance to the sun (3) the length of daylight hours (4) Earth's rotation

35. In which location are hurricanes most likely to form? (1) 15°N, 30°E (2) 60°N, 20°W (3) 15°N, 30°W (4) 20°S, 60°W

36. Which role of our government is the most important for saving lives in violent storms? (1) reducing highway speed limits (2) enforcing building codes and zoning laws (3) increasing federal income and property taxes (4) making strict laws to prevent environmental pollution

37. Which of the following weather features is likely to be smallest? (1) a tornado (2) a hurricane (3) a thunderstorm (4) a mid-latitude cyclone

38. What is the primary energy source for violent weather? (1) clouds (2) terrestrial radiation (3) carbon dioxide (4) condensation

---

The Scientist, Engineer, and Citizen

Imagine you are located in a community that experiences devastating storms: hurricanes, flash floods, blizzards, or tornadoes. Generate a community-wide action plan to deal with the most probable local weather hazard. Make use of any existing guidelines you can find.

CHAPTER 7 REVIEW QUESTIONS

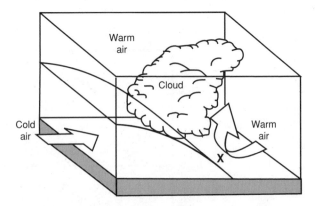

Directions: The diagram above shows a weather front in a three-dimensional view. The bottom of the diagram is a map as seen from above. Use this diagram to complete questions 1–4.

1. At location X, (near the bottom, right) how will the temperature most likely change within the next few hours? (1) It will decrease. (2) It will increase. (3) It will not change.

2. How is the atmospheric pressure at location X likely to change in the next few hours? (1) It will decrease. (2) It will increase. (3) It will not change.

3. What change is causing the cloud to grow larger? (1) decreasing winds and sinking air (2) ice changing to water vapor by sublimation (3) air becoming warmer as it rises (4) condensation as warm air rises and cools.

4. What kind of air mass is probably moving in? (1) maritime tropical (2) warm and dry (3) continental polar (4) warm and moist

Directions: Base your answers to questions 5 and 6 on the weather map shown below.

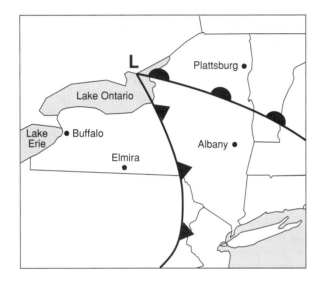

5. Which city is located in the warmest air mass? (1) Buffalo (2) Elmira (3) Albany (4) Plattsburg

6. Which city has most recently experienced a change in wind direction, brief heavy precipitation, and a rapid drop in air temperature? (1) Buffalo (2) Plattsburg (3) Albany (4) Elmira

7. A weather station records a barometric pressure of 1013.2 millibars. Which diagram below would best represent this weather station on a weather map? [Refer to the *Earth Science Reference Tables*.]

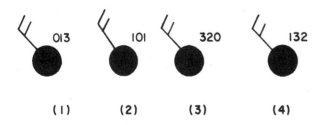

Directions: Base your answers to questions 8 through 11 on your knowledge of earth science, the *Earth Science Reference Tables*, and the map (top, right), which represents a weather system located over the central United States. Letters *A*, *B*, *C*, *D*, and *E* locate weather stations on the map.

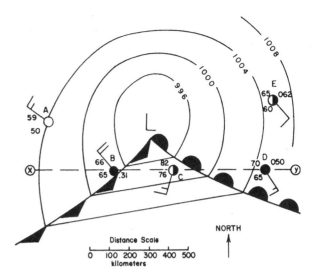

8. What is the air pressure at weather station A? (1) 1069 mb (2) 1064 mb (3) 1004 mb (4) 1000 mb

9. Which weather station is experiencing clouds, heavy precipitation, and rapidly decreasing air temperature? (1) *A* (2) *B* (3) *E* (4) *D*

10. In which diagram do the arrows best represent the wind direction in the weather system?

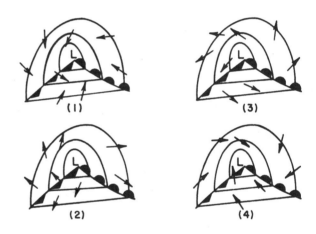

11. Which diagram best represents a cross section of the earth's atmosphere showing the fronts between air masses as they would appear along line x–y?

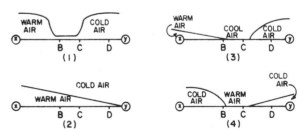

12. Why do clouds usually form at the leading edge of a cold air mass? (1) Cold air contains more water vapor than warm air does. (2) Cold air contains more dust particles than warm air does. (3) Cold air flows over warm air, causing the warm air to descend and cool. (4) Cold air flows under warm air, causing the warm air to rise and cool.

13. Condensation of water vapor in the atmosphere is most likely to occur when a condensation surface is available and (1) a strong wind is blowing (2) the temperature of the air is below 0°C (3) the air is saturated with water vapor (4) the air pressure is rising

14. Where is precipitation most likely to occur? (1) near the frontal surface between two air masses (2) in descending air currents (3) on the leeward slopes of mountains (4) near the center of a high-pressure area

15. New York State weather usually comes from which direction? (1) east (2) northeast (3) west (4) north

16. The weather characteristics of an air mass are caused primarily by its (1) rate of movement (2) size and shape (3) direction of movement (4) geographic origin

17. Which diagram best represents the air circulation as seen from above in a high-pressure center (anticyclone) in the Northern Hemisphere?

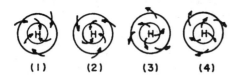

18. The characteristics of an air mass which formed over the Gulf of Mexico would probably be (1) cool and dry (2) warm and dry (3) cool and humid (4) warm and humid

19. How does air circulate within a cyclone (low-pressure area) in the Northern Hemisphere? (1) counterclockwise and toward the center of the cyclone (2) counterclockwise and away from the center of the cyclone (3) clockwise and toward the center of the cyclone (4) clockwise and away from the center of the cyclone

20. An mT air mass would most likely originate over which type of Earth surface? (1) cold and moist (2) warm and moist (3) cold and dry (4) warm and dry

21. At which location will a low-pressure storm center most likely form? (1) along a frontal surface between different air masses (2) near the middle of a cold air mass (3) on the leeward side of mountains (4) over a very dry, large, flat land area

22. The diagram below represents a cross-sectional view of air masses associated with a low-pressure system. The cold frontal interface is moving faster than the warm frontal interface. What usually happens to the warm air that is between the two frontal surfaces?

(1) The warm air is forced over both frontal interfaces.
(2) The warm air is forced under both frontal interfaces.
(3) The warm air is forced over the cold frontal interface but under the warm frontal interface. (4) The warm air is forced under the cold frontal interface but over the warm frontal interface.

FREE-RESPONSE QUESTIONS

(Answer the following questions on a separate sheet of paper.)

1. Use the following map to predict how the weather in St. Louis is likely to change over the next day or two. Answer in one or more complete sentences.
(Each change, +1; Sentence(s), +1)

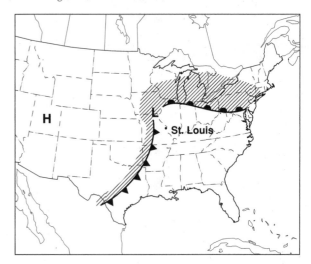

2. Copy or trace the map at the top of page 131 of the contiguous United States. Then use the data shown on the map to draw isotherms at intervals of 10°C. The numbers on the map indicate where the readings were taken.
(Each line drawn correctly and neatly, +1)

3. The graph below shows temperature changes in water as it converts from water vapor to ice as it cools. Copy the graph on a separate sheet of paper. Then circle the entire part of the graph where liquid water is changing to ice.
(Position, +1; Interval, +1)

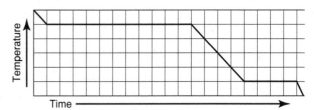

Directions: Use the data in the weather map at the bottom of page 131 and your knowledge of earth science to answer questions 4–8.

4. How is the temperature in Knoxville, Tennessee likely to change over the next 24 hours?
(Correct response, +1)

5. How is the atmospheric pressure in Knoxville likely to change over the next 24 hours?
(Correct response, +1)

6. How are the sky conditions in Knoxville likely to change over the next 24 hours?
(Correct responses, +1 each)

7. In what direction is the wind blowing at Detroit, Michigan?
(Correct response, +1)

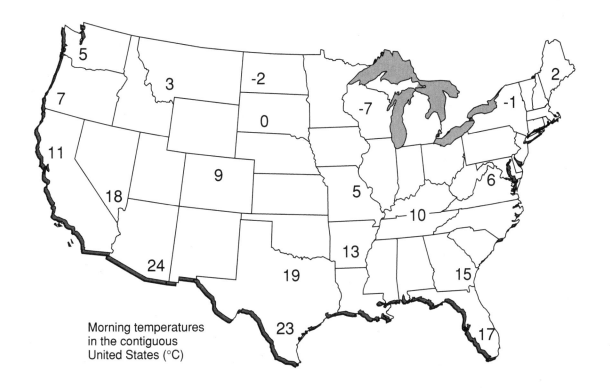

Morning temperatures
in the contiguous
United States (°C)

8. What is causing an occluded front to form southwest of Detroit?
(Explanation, +1; Complete sentence(s), +1)

9. Why is latent heat sometimes called "hidden energy"?
(Explanation, +1; Complete sentence(s), +1)

10. Why is cloud formation an important process in sustaining violent storms?
(Explanation, +1; Complete sentence(s), +1)

11. What does it mean if we say that the chance of rain tomorrow is 60%?
(Explanation, +1; Complete sentence(s), +1)

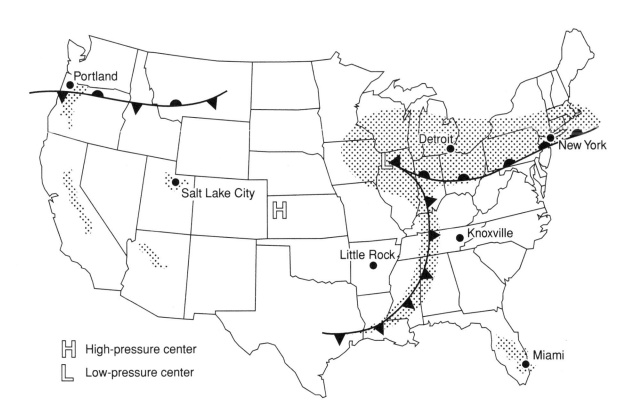

⊢ High-pressure center

∟ Low-pressure center

12. The map below shows the weather conditions in the eastern part of the United States. Note the location marked X in central Pennsylvania. How will the temperature and sky conditions at location X probably change over the next few hours?

(+1 for each of two changes)

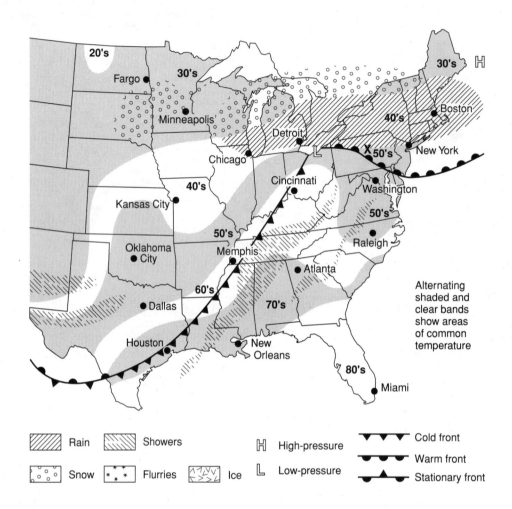

Alternating shaded and clear bands show areas of common temperature

⟋⟋⟋	Rain	⟍⟍⟍	Showers			▼▼▼▼▼	Cold front
∘∘∘	Snow	✱✱✱	Flurries	⟨⟩	Ice	●●●●	Warm front
						●▲●▲	Stationary front

Ⱨ High-pressure

Ḻ Low-pressure

CHAPTER 8 The Water Cycle and Climates

THE WATER CYCLE

Earth has a limited supply of water. See Figure 8-1. That supply is constantly being recycled between the oceans, atmosphere, and land in a process called the **water cycle**, (hydrologic cycle). During this recycling process, water enters the atmosphere by evaporation and transpiration. **Transpiration** is the process by which living plants release water vapor to the atmosphere. These two processes (sometimes called evapotranspiration) are fueled by energy from the sun. Because approximately 71% of Earth's surface is covered by the oceans, most of the water vapor in the atmosphere is the result of evaporation from the oceans. To complete the cycle, water vapor in the atmosphere condenses and returns to Earth's surface as precipitation, as shown in Figure 8-2.

Of the precipitation that falls on Earth's surface, approximately 50% returns to the atmosphere by evaporation, 18% **infiltrates** (sinks into) the ground, and 32%

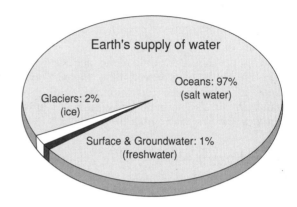

Figure 8-1. Our planet's limited supply of water. At any particular time, most of Earth's water is in the form of salt water.

is surface runoff that enters lakes and rivers. Water that infiltrates the ground is called **groundwater**.

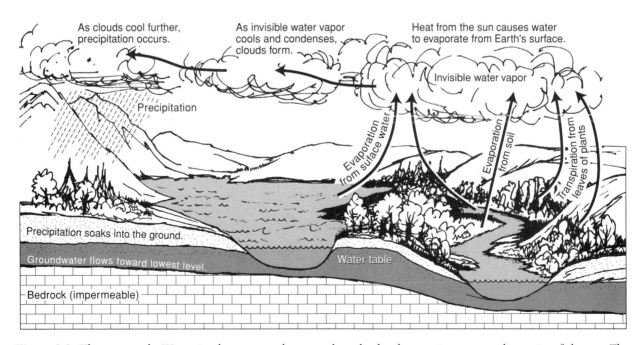

Figure 8-2. The water cycle. Water circulates among the atmosphere, land and oceans in a never-ending series of changes. The water cycle's processes include precipitation, infiltration, runoff, evaporation, transpiration, and convection (movement via the wind).

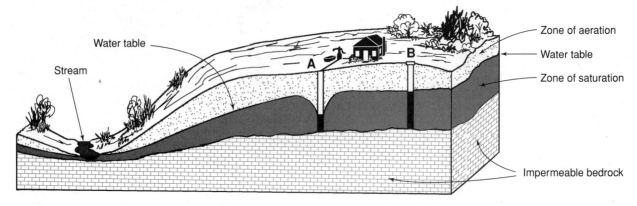

Figure 8-3. Water table depression. Pumping from well A has depressed the water table near the well. Well B is capped, so there is no pumping and no water table depression around well B.

Only about 0.6% of Earth's water exists within the ground as groundwater. Unlike the oceans, groundwater is mostly fresh water; and unlike the glaciers, it is in the liquid state. Plants need groundwater for growth. Groundwater is also an important source of water for our homes, industry, and agriculture.

Groundwater Zones.

After infiltrating soil, groundwater occupies distinct zones. Gravity pulls much of the groundwater down into the **zone of saturation**. In the saturated zone, all spaces, cracks, and other openings in soil and rock grains become completely filled with water. Water will stop sinking into the soil once it has reached a layer of solid rock underneath the saturated zone that it cannot pass through. This layer is called impermeable bedrock.

After the water sinks into the zone of saturation, a boundary can be seen at the top of the saturated zone. This boundary between the zone of aeration and the zone of saturation is the **water table**, the uppermost surface of the saturated zone. As water passes through the ground, soil and rock act as a natural filter. This makes groundwater a good source of drinking water. The location of the water table is important to us because water wells must reach below the water table in order to yield a good supply of groundwater. Pumping water from a well faster than it can be replenished can depress the water table, as shown in Figure 8-3, resulting in the well "running dry." This problem can be solved in two ways. First, we can drill a deeper well, as long as it is not extended into an impermeable layer, such as dense clay or bedrock. Alternatively, we can use less water, allowing groundwater to seep back into the well.

Factors That Affect the Storage and Movement of Groundwater.

The amount of water in the ground and the movement of water through the ground are controlled by the characteristics of the soil and rock found near the surface. Water is able to infiltrate the ground when there are many openings, or pores, between ground particles for the water to pass through. Almost all materials on Earth's surface are

Figure 8-4. Among round-shaped particles, pore spaces, capable of holding water, can account for more than one-third of the total volume of a sample.

porous. The number of pores in a material compared with its volume is called **porosity**. It is porosity, or the percentage of empty space, that determines how much air or water a sample of rock can hold. See Figure 8-4.

The porosity of a loose material, such as soil, largely depends upon shape, packing, and the mixture of sizes of the soil particles. The most porous soils are those that contain round particles that are all of the same size (**well sorted**) and that are not closely packed. The more closely packed particles of soil are, the less porous the soil; the less closely packed the particles of soil are the more porous the soil. See Figure 8-5.

Flattened and angular soil grains, such as clay particles, can pack closely together; therefore, most clay soils have little pore space and a low porosity. A soil that is composed of a mixture of particle sizes also has a low

Figure 8-5. Because of the differences in the packing arrangement, soil sample B has less pore space than does sample A. Therefore, A is more porous than B.

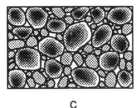

C

Figure 8-6. The porosity of soil sample C is greatly reduced because it contains particles of mixed sizes. In this sample, the smaller particles can fill the spaces between the larger ones.

porosity because its smaller particles can fit into spaces between its larger particles. See Figure 8-6.

It is important to note that particle size alone does not affect the porosity of a soil. For example, when two well-sorted samples of different soils are taken—one with large particles and one with small particles—both may have about the same porosity, especially if their soil particles are similarly shaped and packed. Figure 8-7 shows that particle size does not affect porosity.

Some rocks have low porosities because of a cementing material that reduces pore space between particles. See Figure 8-8. Nonporous rocks, such as limestone, can become permeable (able to transmit water) because of the formation of cracks through which water can pass. See Figure 8-9.

Permeability is the ability of a soil to transmit water. The rate of permeability, or how fast water can pass through a soil, depends on the size of the pores and how the pores are connected. For example, soils with high

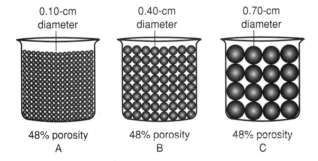

0.10-cm diameter   0.40-cm diameter   0.70-cm diameter

48% porosity
A   48% porosity
B   48% porosity
C

Figure 8-7. Changing the size of the particles does not change the porosity of a sample as long as there is no change in the shape and packing of the particles. Each of these samples has the same porosity, approximately 48%.

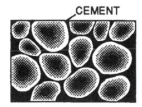

CEMENT

Figure 8-8. The presence of a natural cement between particles reduces the natural porosity of this rock material.

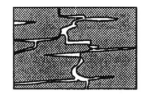

Figure 8-9. A rock with low porosity can be permeable because of cracks and fissures that develop during its formation.

permeabilities, such as sand, have large pores that are well connected. Water flows through the pores with little resistance. Soils with low permeabilities, such as clay, have small pores or pores that are not well connected. Water in very small pores moves slowly and clings to the surfaces of soil particles.

Surface **runoff** occurs when rainfall exceeds the permeability rate of a soil, when a soil is saturated, or when the slope (gradient) of a soil's surface is too great to allow infiltration to occur. Infiltration is also affected by temperature. At temperatures below 0°C, water within a soil will freeze, thus preventing further infiltration.

Capillarity is the ability of a soil to draw water upward into tiny spaces between soil grains. Soils composed of very small particles show the most capillary uptake. Capillary water moves upward against the force of gravity because of the attraction between water molecules and the surfaces of the soil particles. Capillarity, therefore, occurs most effectively in soils with small particles because these soils have more surface area per unit volume for water to cling to than do soils with large particles. Capillary water is water available for plants to draw through their roots.

WATER FOR STREAM FLOW

During and immediately after precipitation, streams receive water from overland flow. Even during dry periods when there is no ground runoff, however, many streams continue to flow. In these dry periods, stream water may come from the ground. For example, in regions where groundwater and precipitation are plentiful, water will seep into the streams where the water table comes to the surface at the streambed.

In dry climates, groundwater may be recharged by water flowing from the streams into the ground. See Figure 8-10 on page 136.

Rainfall and Stream Flow.
Streams and rivers do not respond immediately to rainfall. Most precipitation falls on the ground and then must flow over the land as runoff to reach a stream. Therefore, a time lag occurs between maximum precipitation and maximum stream discharge. See Figure 8-11 on page 136. Several other factors determine how quickly and how strongly streams respond to precipitation. If precipitation falls as snow, if the gradient of the land is low (little slope), or if a great deal of vegetation blocks overland flow, streams will respond more slowly. Large rivers respond slowly because most runoff must flow a

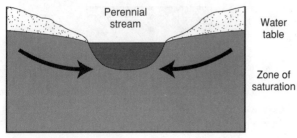

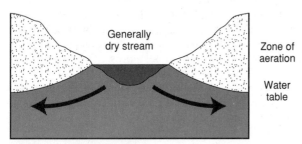

Arid climate: Stream replenishes the groundwater.

Figure 8-10. Groundwater can flow into or out of streams. In moist climates, streams are generally below the surrounding water table, therefore, groundwater flows into the streams to sustain flow between rainstorms. In dry climates, streams generally rest on top of the water table, so the stream drains into the ground.

great distance to reach the rivers. Small streams and streams in mountain areas where the land is steep and rocky respond quickly to rainfall. Less of a time lag exists between maximum precipitation and maximum discharge. Also, runoff is very rapid and very brief in regions with buildings, paved streets, and parking lots.

Watersheds.

A **watershed**, or drainage basin, is the geographic area that drains into a particular stream or other body of water. A watershed is bounded by a drainage divide, usually a line of high land, across which streams do not flow. If groundwater is polluted, perhaps by leaking chemical tanks or a fuel spill that seeps into the ground, the pollution will probably remain within the watershed and drain toward the stream

or other body of water that exits the watershed. Because all the streams in a watershed flow to the same body of water, they will not carry the pollution into other watersheds. You can trace the perimeter of a stream's watershed by carefully drawing a line around the stream that crosses the stream only where the main stream exits the drainage area. That line will follow the drainage divides that separate the watershed being outlined from those that surround it. Figure 8-12 shows several major watersheds in New York State.

QUESTIONS

1. What force causes water below the water table to flow through the ground? (1) capillarity (2) gravity (3) convection (4) surface tension

2. Why is groundwater a popular source of drinking water? (1) it is available everywhere on Earth (2) it is naturally filtered (3) it is always cool and clean (4) it contains natural ice cubes

3. How deep must a well be in order to yield a good supply of groundwater? (1) at least 5 meters (2) at least 50 meters (3) down to solid bedrock (4) below the water table

4. Where does groundwater come from? (1) water rises from Earth's center (2) groundwater flows up from the oceans (3) water circulates through the water cycle (4) clouds from outer space

5. As the size of the particles in a soil increases, there is an increase in the soil's (1) porosity (2) permeability (3) water retention (4) capillarity

6. Why is soil capillarity important? (1) It allows water to rise into the plant root zone. (2) It allows water to flow down to the water table. (3) It allows the soil to hold lots of groundwater. (4) It prevents springs from flowing under buildings.

7. Which of the following would be the most helpful in keeping a plentiful supply of water for well water and freely flowing springs? (1) an increase in precipitation (2) an increase in evaporation (3) an increase in soil capillarity (4) an increase in water-table gradient

8. The soil will be able to absorb more water if (1) the soil is composed of smaller particles. (2) the ground is covered

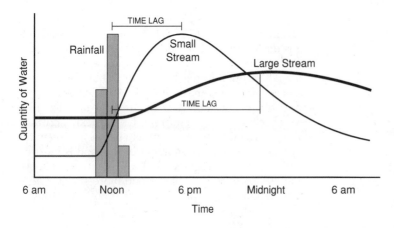

Figure 8-11. How streams respond to rainfall. The greatest stream flow occurs later than the time of maximum precipitation. This delay is called the time lag. In general, small streams respond quickly, with only a brief time lag, and they also return quickly to base flow. On the other hand, large streams respond slowly, with a longer time lag.

Figure 8-12. Watersheds of New York State. Any geographic region can be divided into drainage basins. Large watersheds can usually be divided into smaller watersheds. For example, the Oatka Creek watershed is a part of the Genesee River drainage basin, which is in turn a part of the Lake Ontario–St. Lawrence River watershed.

by roads and buildings. (3) the air temperature stays well below 0°C. (4) water stays on the ground longer.

Directions: Base your answers to questions 9 and 10 on the two diagrams below, which show a place where water-soluble, toxic wastes have been buried in the ground. Each water well (A, B, C, and D) is the same distance from the waste dump (T), and the soil is uniformly sandy.

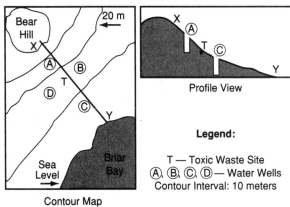

9. Which well is most likely to become unfit for drinking water first because of toxic contamination? (1) well A (2) well B (3) well C (4) well D

10. How quickly that well becomes contaminated with chemicals from the toxic waste dump depends upon the soil's (1) porosity (2) permeability (3) water retention (4) capillarity

11. Which part of Earth has the most water? (1) rivers and lakes (2) clouds (3) glaciers (4) the oceans

12. Which of the following changes will cause the porosity of a soil to increase? (1) make all the particles only half as large (2) make all the particles twice as large (3) make all the particles more spherical (round) (4) mix in much larger and smaller particles

Directions: Questions 13–16 refer to groundwater problems that might occur on Long Island, NY.

13. Which of the following changes would probably cause the water table to rise? (1) Use more well water instead of importing water. (2) Construct storm sewers leading into the ocean. (3) Pipe in drinking water from another region. (4) Pass a law making it illegal to use bottled water.

The Water Cycle and Climates

14. Suppose the land on Long Island becomes so densely populated that the residents cannot obtain enough fresh groundwater to satisfy their domestic and commercial needs. How can they restore the groundwater? (1) Require all homeowners to install sprinkler systems in their lawns. (2) Build more highways and parking lots. (3) Reduce the cost of city water for homes and businesses. (4) Clean waste water and pump it back into the ground.

15. When will salt water flow into the ground under Long Island? (1) when everybody stops all use of well water (2) when the water table is below sea level (3) when the winds blow from the northwest (4) when there is a rainy season

16. Which property of the soil under Long Island determines how much water the soil can hold? (1) porosity (2) permeability (3) capillarity (4) retention

17. The two diagrams below show magnified views of two sandy soils. Both are magnified the same amount. Which one has more porosity? (1) A (2) B (3) neither

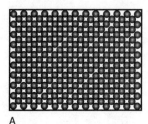 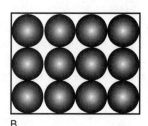

A   B

18. According to the *Earth Science Reference Tables*, water pollution that originates near Rochester, NY, is most likely to be a problem for people who live near (1) Buffalo, NY (2) Elmira, NY (3) Massena, NY (4) New York City

19. Capillary water rises the highest into a soil that is (1) very porous (2) made of very fine grains (3) very permeable (4) made of very large grains

20. Wells were dug in four types of sediment. If all four intercepted water at the same depth, and the wells were all of equal depth, which would probably be able to produce the fastest outflow of groundwater? (1) well I in gravel (particle diameter: 1 cm) (2) well II in sand (particle diameter: 0.1 cm) (3) well III in silt (particle diameter: 0.001 cm) (4) well IV in clay (particle diameter: 0.0001 cm)

21. Surface runoff will probably increase if the rain (1) falls onto a hillside with a steep slope (2) comes slowly in a long, steady rainfall (3) infiltrates the soil very quickly (4) falls as snow that does not melt

22. Which two New York cities occupy the same watershed? (1) Buffalo and Binghamton (2) Albany and Kingston (3) Oswego and Utica (4) Massena and New York City

23. What kind of bedrock would have the greatest permeability? (1) a rock with a few large and connected cracks (2) a rock with large pores that are not connected (3) a rock composed of very fine particles (4) a rock that is solid, with no open space at all

24. What name is usually applied to water that is pumped out of the ground? (1) rain (2) snow (3) dirt (4) groundwater

25. If a dangerous chemical were spilled into Lake Erie at Buffalo, NY, in which direction would it probably spread fastest? (1) North (2) South (3) East (4) West

HOW DOES HEAT ENERGY TRAVEL?

Heat is a form of energy because it can do work. When heat expand the gases in an internal combustion engine, we use it to move our motor vehicles. Heat energy is used to generate electricity. It also drives our weather. Heat energy can travel in three ways. See Figure 8-13.

Convection is heat flow by density currents within a fluid. The uneven heating of Earth's surface by the sun causes winds. Wind is a familiar example of heat flow by convection. The energetic (warm) air molecules carry their vibrational energy as they move from the tropics toward the polar areas. Ocean currents are also caused by differences in density. Like air, water is a fluid and it can carry energy by convection. When we discussed plate tectonics in Chapter 3, you learned how rock, though still a solid, can slowly flow and carry Earth's continents thousands of miles over a very long time span.

If you touch a hot object, you can feel the heat. You may even get burned. **Conduction** is a form of heat flow that occurs when a hot substance comes into contact with a cooler substance. The vibrational energy of the warmer atoms and molecules is transferred to the cooler atoms and molecules, making them vibrate more. It's one way that heat escapes from Earth's interior to its surface. A metal spoon left in hot coffee

Figure 8-13. Convection, conduction and radiation. Solar energy reaches the Earth by radiation. The boy's feet feel hot because of conduction. The wind is a form of convection.

quickly becomes hot because metals are excellent conductors of heat energy.

Earth's primary source of energy is the sun. However, that energy has to travel through millions of miles of empty space to reach planet Earth. Both convection and conduction require a substance through which to travel, but radiation requires no medium. **Radiation** is the flow of energy as electromagnetic waves, such as visible light. Radiation is also the fastest form of heat transfer. Through a vacuum, like outer space, all electromagnetic radiation travels at the speed of light; 300,000,000 meters per second.

INSOLATION

Earth receives nearly all of its energy from the sun. The sun's electromagnetic energy that reaches the earth is called **insolation** (INcoming SOLar radiATION). The intensity (strength) of insolation depends upon several factors, such as the angle of insolation, the duration of insolation, and the type of surface the insolation strikes.

Angle of Insolation.
The **angle of insolation** is a measure of how high the sun is in the sky. As the sun rises and sets, the angle of insolation changes. This angle is measured from the horizon up to the position of the sun. The noon sun has the greatest angle of insolation, and therefore, noon has the greatest intensity of insolation per unit area. In the morning and in the afternoon, when the sun is lower in the sky, the sunlight is less direct and less intense. See Figure 8-14.

The angle of insolation at a given place also changes seasonally. In the Northern Hemisphere, the lowest angle of insolation is reached at the winter solstice (about Dec. 21), and the highest angle at the summer solstice (about June 21).

Because Earth is spherical, each latitude has a different angle of insolation, as shown in Figure 8-15. Throughout the year, only one latitude within the tropics ($23\frac{1}{2}°$N to $23\frac{1}{2}°$S) will receive the vertical ray at noon each day. The vertical ray strikes Earth's surface at an angle of 90°. At all other latitudes, slanting rays of sunlight strike Earth's surface at acute angles and are weaker in intensity, distributing their energy over a larger area than the vertical ray. See Figure 8-15. For all locations north of the Tropic of Cancer ($23\frac{1}{2}°$N), the most direct and most intense insolation occurs at noon on our summer solstice (about June 21).

The vertical ray always strikes Earth somewhere in the tropic ($23\frac{1}{2}°$N to $23\frac{1}{2}°$S). This accounts for high average temperatures in the tropical zone.

The low angle (tangential) rays that strike Earth in the Arctic zone ($66\frac{1}{2}°$N to 90°N) and in the Antarctic zone ($66\frac{1}{2}°$S to 90°S) account for the low average temperatures in these zones.

Radiation can travel only through space or through transparent materials like air or glass. Heat rays, which you may be able to feel even though you can't see them with your eyes, also carry energy by radiation. In fact,

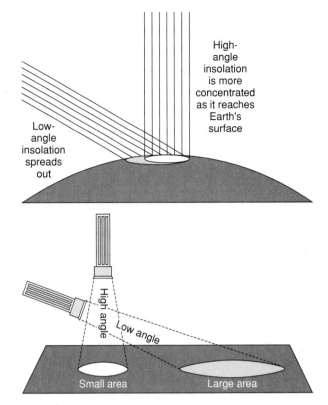

Figure 8-14. Angle of insolation. When the sun is directly overhead, the sun's rays are concentrated in a small area. When the sun is low in the sky, the same energy covers more area so the sunlight is not as strong.

some forms of radiant energy that you can't feel at all can still cause terrible damage. The sun's ultraviolet rays and radioactivity from natural or artificial sources, can cause serious illness or even death. The more we understand about these forms of radiation, the better we

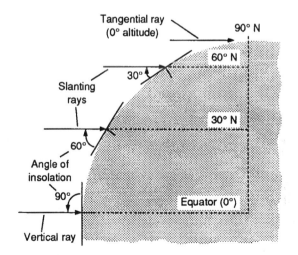

Figure 8-15. Angles of insolation at different latitudes on the equinox. As the degree of latitude increases, the angle of insolation and the intensity of insolation decrease. (If the vertical ray is at the equator, it is either the vernal or autumnal equinox.)

can deal with them. The electromagnetic spectrum chart in the *Earth Science Reference Tables* shows the broad range of electromagnetic energy, both visible and invisible.

QUESTIONS

26. Energy from Earth's core does **not** reach the surface by (1) convection (2) conduction (3) radiation (4) evaporation

27. What method of energy transfer requires no medium for transfer? (1) conduction (2) convection (3) advection (4) radiation

28. During which process of energy exchange does cold air displace warmer air? (1) absorption (2) convection (3) conduction (4) radiation

29. Which statement is the best example of heat energy transfer by conduction? (1) Heat energy is transferred from the bottom to the top of a lake. (2) Heat energy is transferred from the surface soil to the rocks below. (3) Heat energy is transferred from Earth's surface to the upper atmosphere. (4) Heat energy is transferred from the sun to Earth.

30. Which diagram best represents the transfer of heat by convection in a liquid?

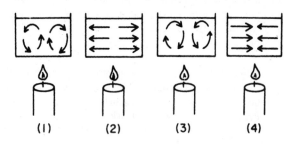

31. Which example of heat transfer is due mainly to convection? (1) heat energy transferred by air moving from Earth's surface to the upper atmosphere (2) heat energy transferred by being reflected from a lake surface to the air above (3) heat energy transferred through a solid metal door (4) heat energy transferred from the sun to Earth

Duration of Insolation.

The **duration of insolation** is the length of time (from sunrise to sunset), or daylight period, that the sun appears in the sky. A section of Earth's surface receives the most heat energy when the sun is highest in the sky and when the duration of insolation is the greatest. Generally, as the angle of insolation and the duration of insolation increase, temperatures at Earth's surface increase.

The duration of insolation varies greatly with latitude. In the Northern Hemisphere, the greatest duration of insolation occurs at our summer solstice. The further north you go, the longer the daylight period is at this time. For example, at the end of June, the sun is in the sky for the whole day (24 hours) at locations north of the Arctic Circle. At locations south of the Arctic Circle, the duration of sunlight is less at this time. At the equa-

tor, the duration of insolation is 12 hours every day. At any location on Earth, the total time the sun is above the horizon is six months of the year. At the North Pole, this means six months of sunlight followed by six months of darkness. At the equator, it means 12 hours of sunlight and 12 hours of darkness each day.

Absorption of Insolation.

When you place a damp sponge on a liquid spill, the sponge **absorbs** the water. Earth also absorbs most of the sunlight that falls on it. Of the energy that penetrates to the surface, most of it is in the form of visible light. High-energy radiation, such as X rays and gamma rays, are absorbed by ozone and other gases in the upper atmosphere. Long-wave radiations, such as *infrared rays*, are absorbed by water vapor and carbon dioxide. Visible light wavelengths, however, readily penetrate the atmosphere. See Figure 8-16. Upon reaching Earth's surface, visible light waves are absorbed, scattered, or reflected. Light-colored objects reflect most of the light that falls on them, but dark-colored objects absorb most of the light that falls on them. Some of the absorbed energy is changed into infrared heat waves that reradiated back into the atmosphere at night. See Figure 8-17.

At the same latitude, the average temperatures of land and water can differ for several reasons. First, water has a higher **specific heat** than soil or rock. This means that water must absorb more energy for a given temperature change; it heats up and cools down more slowly than does land. Second, water also reflects low-angle insolation better than land. Third, because water is transparent, insolation penetrates water more deeply and more quickly than it can be absorbed by land. Fourth, convection currents in the water carry heat energy deep into the hydrosphere. In the ground, heat energy can travel only by conduction. Thus, the same amount of insolation travels through a greater volume of water than land. The result is that land heats up faster and cools down faster than water.

Some of the insolation that is absorbed by Earth heats the ground to a higher temperature, but most of it is converted into latent potential energy. During the melting of ice and snow or evaporation of seawater, a

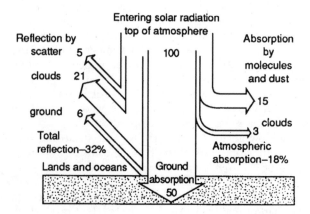

Figure 8-16. Only about half of the solar energy that reaches Earth is absorbed by the ground. The rest of the energy is absorbed or reflected by the atmosphere.

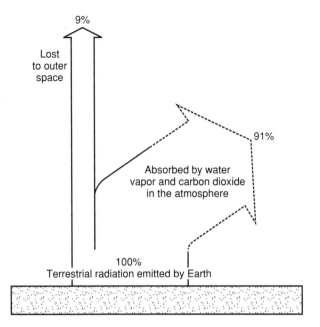

Figure 8-17. Terrestrial radiation. We are unable to see the infrared (heat) radiation given off by Earth. Most of this energy is trapped by the atmosphere.

great deal of energy is used for a change of state. Each gram of water that evaporates absorbs 540 calories of energy. The newly formed water vapor carries potential energy into the atmosphere. It is the most important reservoir of energy in the atmosphere.

You are probably aware that dark surfaces absorb more sunlight than light surfaces. That's why in hot, sunny weather it's best to wear light-colored clothing. You may not realize, however, that dark objects are better at radiating heat energy. If two nearly identical cups of hot water were left outside at night, the darker one would cool faster. Don't make the mistake of thinking that light objects are always cooler. That depends upon whether the objects are primarily absorbing or radiating energy.

Reflection of Insolation.
When you look at yourself in a mirror you can see yourself because of reflection. When light is **reflected** it bounces off a surface. Clouds reflect roughly half of the light falling on them. In addition to reflection and absorption from clouds, some incoming solar radiation is reflected from Earth's surface. The lower the angle of insolation, the greater the reflection of solar rays. More reflection also occurs when the land is light in color or covered by snow or ice.

While the North and South Poles receive the same total duration of insolation as the equator, the temperatures are much lower at the poles. There are three reasons for this. First, the snow at the poles reflects much of the insolation back into space. Second, the sun is always low in the sky, so the sunlight is more spread out and less concentrated than it is at the equator. Finally, when the sun is low in the sky, the sunlight must travel a greater distance through Earth's atmosphere. Within

the atmosphere, much of the insolation is reflected, refracted, or absorbed. Therefore, radiation of reduced strength reaches the ground at the poles.

In the atmosphere, there are tiny particles of airborne solids, such as dust, pollen, pollutants, and water droplets. These particles scatter insolation and reduce its intensity.

TERRESTRIAL RADIATION

Energy waves emitted from Earth's surface are longer in wavelength than energy waves in the range of visible light emitted from the sun. The longer infrared heat waves radiated by Earth are absorbed by gases such as carbon dioxide and water vapor and remain trapped in the atmosphere. See Figure 8-18. This process is called the **greenhouse effect** because the glass of a greenhouse traps heat in a similar way.

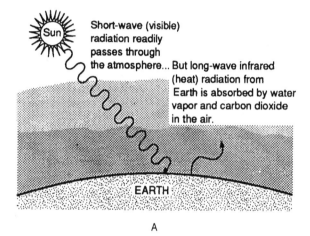

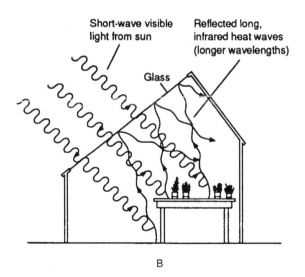

Figure 8-18. The greenhouse effect. Like a greenhouse, Earth's atmosphere traps insolation. Sunlight penetrates the atmosphere as it does the glass of a greenhouse. Because infrared radiation from the ground cannot penetrate either a greenhouse's glass or Earth's atmosphere, the energy is trapped. Thus the temperature on Earth, and in a greenhouse, is higher than it would be without the greenhouse effect.

In a greenhouse, the short wavelengths of energy from the sun (visible light) pass through the glass and into the greenhouse. When the light strikes objects inside the greenhouse, it is absorbed; the energy is then given off as long-wave infrared rays, or heat. As the objects reradiate heat outward, the glass reflects the longer infrared heat waves back into the greenhouse where they heat the air. Thus, the temperature inside a greenhouse is usually warmer than the temperature of the air outside.

Without the greenhouse effect, the temperature of our planet would be too cold for most familiar forms of life. On the planet Venus, however, the greenhouse effect apparently makes it too hot for life. Venus's thick atmosphere is composed mostly of carbon dioxide, a strong greenhouse gas. As a result, the surface of Venus is even hotter than that of Mercury, which is closer to the sun. Many scientists fear that we could be changing the climate of Earth, making it more like that of Venus. As we burn fossil fuels, we add carbon dioxide to the atmosphere. To make matters worse, we are also cutting down forests all over the world, thereby destroying a way of removing carbon dioxide from the atmosphere. (Trees and other plants take in carbon dioxide and release oxygen, which is not a greenhouse gas.) The quantity of methane (another greenhouse gas) being released into the atmosphere is also increasing. Methane is released as a waste product of petroleum extraction, and is also vented by the increasing popula-

tions of humans and domesticated animals. It is not yet clear how severe the effects of this increase in greenhouse gases might be, or how difficult it will be to reverse global warming.

The Insolation-Temperature Lag.

A time lag exists between the time of greatest intensity of insolation and the time of highest air temperature. Why? Because insolation energy is first absorbed by Earth's surface and then reradiated as heat energy that warms the air. Consider a 24-hour period. At sunrise, the ground is cool, but it becomes warmer as it absorbs solar radiation throughout the morning hours. At noon, the incoming radiation reaches a maximum. For the next two or three hours, the ground continues to absorb more energy than it radiates. Thus, the air temperature continues to rise. By mid-afternoon, Earth reaches an equilibrium between the incoming energy and the outgoing radiation. At this point, the highest air temperature is reached. After this, Earth radiates more energy than it receives from the sun and the net loss of energy causes Earth to cool off. This cooling period continues until slightly after sunrise the next morning. See Figure 8-19 (top). The time delay between maximum or minimum insolation and maximum or minimum air temperature is known as the **insolation-temperature lag**.

Seasonal variations in air temperatures also occur. As with the daily cycle, average monthly temperatures de-

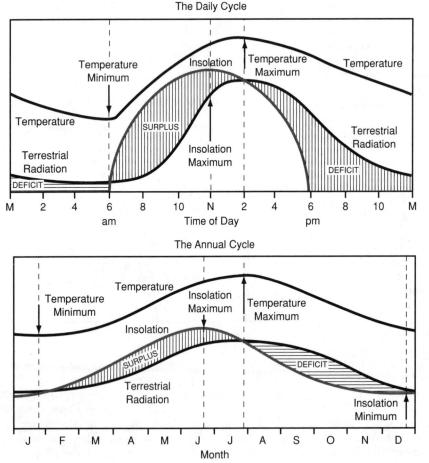

Figure 8-19. The temperature lag. Although Earth receives the most solar energy on a daily basis at noon and on a yearly basis in June, in both cases, the highest temperatures do not occur until some time later. The reason for this delay is that the temperature depends upon the balance between incoming energy and energy lost. Even after the time of maximum insolation, Earth continues to receive more energy than the ground loses, so the temperature continues to rise during this "temperature lag." After the energy received and energy lost reach equilibrium, energy lost becomes greater, so the temperature starts to drop.

pend upon the balance between insolation and terrestrial radiation. Maximum and minimum monthly temperatures occur when there is a **radiative balance** between insolation and terrestrial radiation. See Figure 8-19 (bottom).

QUESTIONS

32. Angle A shows the angle of the noon sun above the horizon. As this angle increases, the local average temperature will probably (1) decrease (2) increase (3) remain the same

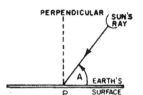

33. Infrared, ultraviolet and visible light are all a part of the electromagnetic spectrum. How do they differ? (1) wavelength (2) intensity (3) speed (4) direction of vibration

34. Which motion of Earth causes the seasonal changes in temperatures? (1) changes in speed (2) spin (3) revolution (4) rotation

35. The diagrams below show four locations on Earth where the land is flat. They all show the angle of the sun on March 21. Which location is the farthest from the equator?

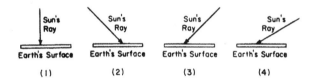

36. How does the radiation given off by Earth compare with radiation from the sun? (1) Solar radiation has a longer wavelength. (2) Earth's radiation cannot travel through space. (3) Earth gives off more energy per second. (4) Earth's radiation is not visible to our eyes.

37. In the Northern Hemisphere, why does the weather become cooler in the autumn? (1) The intensity of insolation decreases. (2) The intensity of insolation increases. (3) The duration of insolation increases. (4) The noon sun gets higher in the sky.

38. The longest period of insolation in New York State occurs about (1) January 21 (2) March 21 (3) June 21 (4) August 21

39. Most of the electromagnetic radiation that reaches Earth is known as (1) specific heat (2) heat rays (3) terrestrial radiation (4) insolation

40. As the ability of an object to absorb electromagnetic energy increases, its ability to radiate energy (1) decreases (2) increases (3) remains the same

41. Which of the following surfaces would absorb the least amount of insolation? (1) a plowed field (2) a forest (3) an asphalt parking lot (4) a glacier

Directions: Base your answers to questions 42 and 43 on the graph below which shows the intensity of incoming short-wave radiation at the top of the atmosphere and the long-wave radiation from Earth to outer space.

42. According to this graph, most of the electromagnetic energy absorbed by Earth is in what part of the spectrum? (1) ultraviolet (2) visible light (3) infrared (4) long wave

43. According to the graph below, when radiation is absorbed by Earth and then radiated back into space, the wavelength of the energy (1) decreases (2) increases (3) remains the same

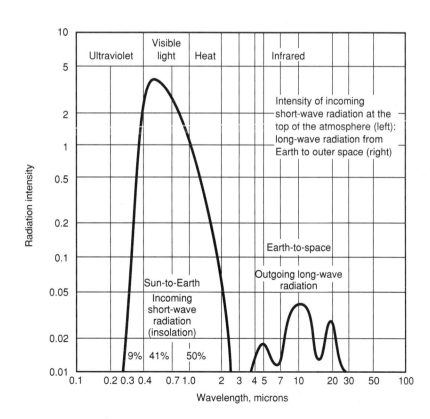

44. Why does a greenhouse stay relatively warm on sunny, winter days? (1) Earth is farthest from the sun in winter. (2) Glass is an excellent absorber of sunlight. (3) Plants growing in the greenhouse make heat. (4) The greenhouse traps long-wave radiation.

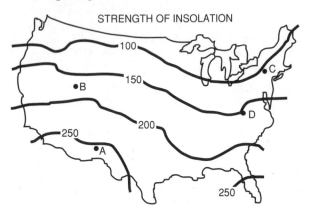

STRENGTH OF INSOLATION

45. The map above shows the average daily insolation at Earth's surface in calories/square centimeter/minute. At which location on this map above would a solar collector receive the least radiant energy? (1) A (2) B (3) C (4) D

46. As the amount of dust in the atmosphere increases, the amount of insolation reaching Earth's surface (1) decreases (2) increases (3) remains the same

47. What causes Earth's temperature to drop after the sun has set? (1) increased radiation from the sun (2) radiation from Earth into space (3) strong winds from the south (4) friction between Earth and the air

48. When does the minimum duration of insolation occur in New York State? (1) February (2) July (3) September (4) December

49. Which of the following would most likely result from an increase in the carbon dioxide content of Earth's atmosphere? (1) an increase in the number of earthquakes (2) a rise in the average temperature (3) an increase in the number of forest fires (4) more thunderstorms and hurricanes

CLIMATE

Unlike weather, the **climate** for a large geographical region is based upon atmospheric conditions measured over a long time period. The average conditions of temperature and precipitation and the annual distribution of these conditions characterize a region's climate.

Within the United States, the climate generally becomes cooler the farther north you go. The humidity factor, however, is not as simple. We classify a climate as humid or arid (dry) based upon the balance between precipitation and the potential for evaporation and transpiration. Most of the southwestern part of the United States has an arid climate because there isn't enough precipitation to satisfy the amount of water that could evaporate under its hot and dry climatic conditions. See Figure 8-20.

Factors That Affect Climate.

Major influences on the climate of a region include latitude, altitude, mountain ranges, oceans and large bodies of water, ocean currents, planetary wind belts, and typical storm tracks.

Latitude. The latitude of a location is an important factor that determines the average local temperatures. As the distance of a location from the equator increases, the average annual temperature of the location generally decreases. Hence, the coldest climates, polar climates, are found near Earth's poles. Locations near the equator have tropical climates and are generally warm throughout the year. Between the tropical and polar climate zones, locations have temperate, or middle-latitude, climates. Locations in middle-latitude climates experience large seasonal changes in temperature.

Altitude. High-altitude locations have cool climates because of the adiabatic cooling of air as it moves to higher elevations. As the air rises, reduced air pressure causes the air to expand and become cooler. Because of this, high plateaus and mountain peaks have lower tem-

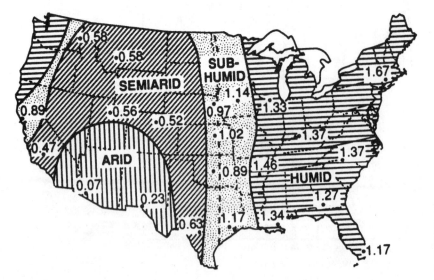

P/E$_p$ Ratio Range	Type of Climate
Over 1.2	Humid
0.8 to 1.2	Subhumid
0.4 to 0.8	Semiarid
Less than 0.4	Arid

Figure 8-20. Climate can be classified as humid or arid based upon the ratio between the total annual precipitation and the total annual potential for evaporation and transpiration.

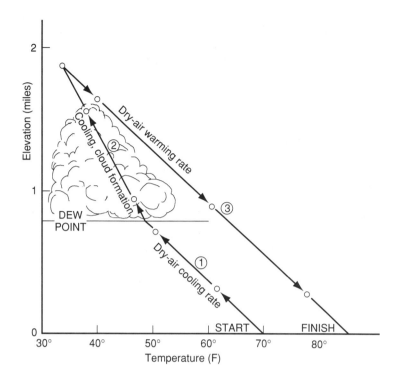

Figure 8-21. Dry and moist adiabatic lapse rates. (1) As air rises, it expands and cools quickly. (2) When a cloud begins to form (condensation), the rate of cooling is slower due to the release of potential energy. (3) When the air sinks back to the ground, there is no change in state to slow the rapid warming.

peratures than do places at the same latitude at sea level. Thus, snow is often found at the top of a mountain.

Mountain Ranges. Mountain ranges can modify precipitation and temperature patterns. For example, warm, moist air from over the Pacific Ocean is often forced to rise along the slope of a mountain barrier, such as the Cascade Mountain range in the Pacific Northwest. The rising air will undergo adiabatic cooling. If the air is cooled below the dew point, cloud formation and precipitation will make locations on the *windward* side of the mountains more moist than surrounding lowlands.

Once the air rises over the mountain range, it will then descend on the lee (downwind) side of the mountains and the air will be warmed by compression as it moves to lower elevations. This causes the climate on the lee side of the mountains to be warmer and drier than the climate on the windward side. In fact, because the moisture in the air has been depleted, the air warms very quickly as it descends. Temperatures on the *lee-*

ward side will be warmer than temperatures at the same elevation on the windward side. See Figures 8-21 and 8-22.

Oceans and Large Bodies of Water. Because of its specific heat, water heats up and cools down more slowly than land areas. Soil and rock heat up and cool down much more readily than water. See Figure 8-23 on page 146. For this reason, the climates of locations near the ocean or other large bodies of water are more moderate than inland (*continental*) climates. Seasonal temperature changes are greater at locations far from large lakes and oceans, whereas seasonal temperature changes are smaller for locations along a coastline. Coastal and *marine* climates are cooler in the summer and warmer in the winter than are inland climates. The moderating effects of large bodies of water are particularly influential wherever winds blow from the water onto land. New York's Long Island and the coastal cities of California, for example, enjoy smaller seasonal changes in temperature than nearby areas that are not so close to the oceans.

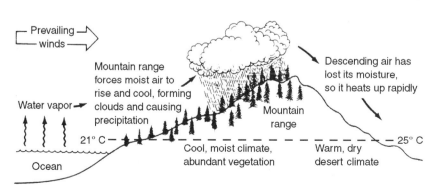

Figure 8-22. Climate differences on opposite sides of a mountain range. As air rises up the windward side of a mountain, condensation slows the adiabatic cooling of the air. But, on the leeward side, the dry air warms very quickly, making a hot desert climate.

The Water Cycle and Climates

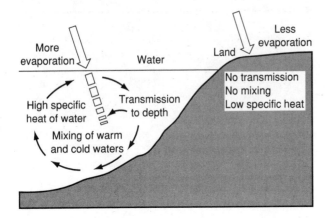

Figure 8-23. Water changes temperature more slowly than land. Large bodies of water heat and cool slowly for several reasons. (1) Water is a better conductor than land; the ground acts as an insulator. (2) Water is a fluid; surface water mixes with deeper water. (3) Much of the energy from the sun causes evaporation, rather than warming. (4) Water has a high specific heat. That is, water requires a great deal of energy input to cause a small change in temperature.

Ocean Currents.   Another factor that influences the climate of a region is its nearness to an ocean current. An ocean current is a stream of water that circulates through the ocean basin. Air above an ocean current is affected by the surface temperature of the water. Cool water will cool the air, and warm water will warm the air.

For example, palm trees can grow in some parts of southern Great Britain in spite of the fact that these places are much farther from the equator than the colder locations of New England. Warm tropical waters of the Straits of Florida move northward in the form of the Gulf Stream current. Under the influence of a warm ocean current and the prevailing westerly winds, Great Britain has a remarkably warm and equitable climate for such a high-latitude location. Because of the California current, the coast of Northern California has a cooler climate than might be expected. Winds blowing off the cold ocean water cool the temperatures of the Pacific Northwest. See the *Earth Science Reference Tables—Surface Ocean Currents*.

Planetary Wind Belts.   In Chapter 6, the influence of the Coriolis effect on the direction of Earth's prevailing winds was discussed. Prevailing winds, in turn, influence local climates. Prevailing winds are important in determining the effect of ocean currents on nearby climates. For example, the eastern coast of North America is seldom influenced by the warm waters of the Gulf Stream because of prevailing winds that come from the west, off the land. Winds from the center of a continent generally bring cold weather in the winter and hot weather in the summer.

Within the different planetary wind belts, there are various regions of rising air currents (low-pressure systems) and sinking air currents (high-pressure systems). When rising air is cooled by adiabatic expansion, moisture in the air may be released by condensation (cloud formation) and precipitation. Along the equator and in the mid-latitudes, zones of low pressure are common. Cyclonic storms often develop, and precipitation is plentiful. The local climates in these regions are humid. Near the poles and in the desert locations, about 20° to 30° on either side of the equator, zones of high pressure mark latitudes at which air sinking within the atmosphere is warmed by adiabatic compression. Most local climates in these regions are arid. See Figure 8-24.

Monsoons.   Large continents influence their own weather. For example, winter conditions over Asia cause a mass of very cold and dry air to build up. This high-pressure region results in winds that blow down and off the continent during the winter. The winds become warmer as they descend toward sea level, but they

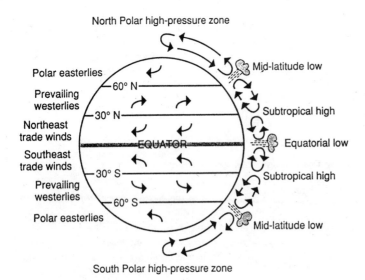

Figure 8-24. Earth's convection cells and prevailing winds. Convection cells within the atmosphere influence the local climate. Rising air in the equatorial and mid-latitude low-pressure regions causes these locations to have abundant rainfall and moist climates. The subtropical and polar high-pressure zones have very little precipitation.

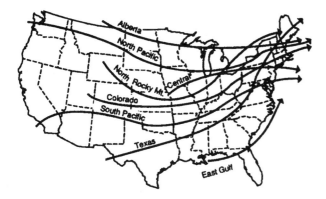

Figure 8-25. Storm tracks in the United States are named according to their regions of origin.

remain relatively dry. Southern Asia is usually dry in the winter months because of these winter winds. However, as the continent warms up in the summer, an inland low-pressure region causes the winds to reverse direction. The summer monsoons bring rainy weather to southern Asia in the summer.

Arizona and the surrounding desert regions also experience monsoon weather. A large portion of the precipitation in this region comes as summer thunderstorms fed by the moist summer inland flow of air.

Typical Storm Tracks. Weather systems usually move across the United States from west to east. As you can see in Figure 8-25, the weather in Chicago is often the weather that will influence New York about a day later. Another characteristic path of weather systems is the movement of storms from the Gulf states northward along the eastern seaboard. Hurricanes, born in the South Atlantic or in the Caribbean Sea, generally move northward and westward toward the Gulf of Mexico and into the United States. The prevailing easterly track of weather systems over North America then carries most hurricanes over the eastern states and back toward the Atlantic Ocean.

QUESTIONS

Directions: Base your answers to questions 50–52 on the graphs below, which show the average values of temperature (solid lines) and rainfall (vertical bars) for three different locations.

50. Which location is an area of high precipitation and high temperature, such as a tropical rainforest? (1) A (2) B (3) C (4) D

51. Which graph would best represent a warm, desert location? (1) A (2) B (3) C (4) D

52. Which location best represents a place near the center of the United States? (1) A (2) B (3) C (4) D

53. On a sunny summer afternoon, the temperature of the ocean water around Long Island, New York, is usually (1) cooler than the land temperature (2) warmer than the land temperature (3) the same as the land temperature

54. The average annual air temperature at point P is probably lower than the average temperature at point (1) A (2) B (3) C (4) D

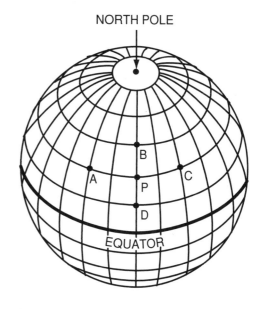

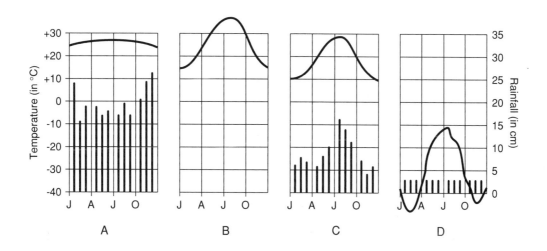

55. Which location in New York has the smallest range of temperatures measured over a period of many years? (1) Long Island (2) the Catskill Mountains (3) Albany (4) the Adirondack Mountains

56. Which location is likely to have a very dry climate? (1) the leeward (downwind) side of a mountain range (2) the windward (upwind) side of a mountain range (3) a place that is just a little above sea level (4) a place very high above sea level

57. What is the general relationship between average temperature at Earth's surface and the latitude angle from the equator? (1) direct (2) indirect (3) there is no relationship

58. Why do most inland locations have more extremes in temperature than coastal locations at the same latitude? (1) Inland forest slow down the winds and cause rainfall. (2) Salt water freezes at a higher temperature. (3) Bodies of water moderate temperature changes. (4) Strong winds always blow toward the ocean.

59. Which of the following factors does *not* affect the climate? (1) longitude (2) nearby mountains (3) altitude (4) nearby bodies of water

60. As the winds move down the lee side of the mountain shown below, the air will (1) become warmer due to compression (2) become warmer due to expansion (3) become cooler due to compression (4) become cooler due to expansion

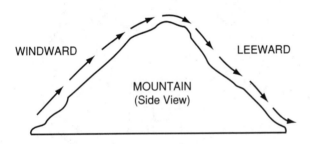

WINDWARD   LEEWARD

MOUNTAIN
(Side View)

61. Which single factor below has the greatest effect on the climate of a region? (1) the human population within 100 kilometers (2) the distance from the equator (3) the degrees of longitude (4) the phase of the moon

62. Compared with coastal locations, inland locations usually have (1) cooler summers and warmer winters (2) warmer summers and cooler winters (3) cooler summers and cooler winters (4) warmer summers and warmer winters

---

The Scientist, Engineer, and Citizen

Make a map of the water drainage around your school. Locate potential problems associated with storm water drainage and suggest ways to eliminate or reduce these problems. Include estimates of the cost of the measures you suggest.

CHAPTER 8 REVIEW QUESTIONS

1. Which property of a soil is most likely to increase as the size of the soil particles gets smaller? (1) capillarity (2) permeability (3) infiltration (4) porosity

2. As the temperature of a soil decreases from 10°C to −5°C, the rate at which water flows into the soil will probably (1) decrease (2) increase (3) remain the same

3. The monthly discharge of a small stream is recorded over a period of 5 years. The data will probably show that over this period there was (1) a decreasing discharge each month (2) an increasing discharge each year (3) a cyclic change of water discharge (4) a constant discharge from month to month

4. How deep must a well penetrate to provide a reliable supply of water? (1) into the zone of aeration (2) below the water table (3) 2 meters below the surface (4) 20 meters below the surface

5. During a dry summer period, the discharge of a stream is primarily controlled by (1) the shape of the stream channel (2) the amount of nearby plant cover (3) the potential evapotranspiration (4) the availability of groundwater

6. Which graph below best shows the relationship between porosity and particle size for soils of uniform particle size, shape, and packing?

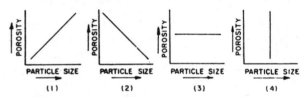

Directions: Base your answers to questions 7–10 on the diagram below, which shows three containers, each holding different size particles.

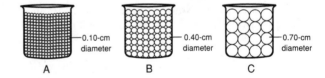

A   B   C

7. Which sample has the greatest capillarity? (1) A (2) B (3) C

8. The permeability is the greatest in (1) A (2) B (3) C

9. The spheres from A were mixed with the spheres from C in a larger beaker. Compared with C, the porosity of the spheres in the new beaker would be (1) less than sample C (2) the same as sample C (3) greater than sample C

10. Which graph below best shows the porosities of these three beakers?

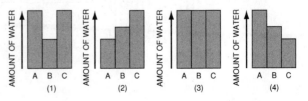

Directions: Base your answers to questions 11–13 on the graph below which shows the discharge of a stream in New York State.

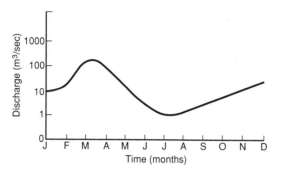

11. When does the most surface runoff occur? (1) January (2) March (3) July (4) December

12. The stream flow in June probably happened in a time period of (1) minimum evapotranspiration (2) maximum groundwater surplus (3) groundwater recharge (4) groundwater depletion

13. Which month probably had much higher potential evapotranspiration than actual evapotranspiration? (1) January (2) March (3) July (4) December

14. Flooding is most likely if (1) the soil surface is very permeable (2) the soil surface is covered with vegetation (3) the pores in the soil are filled with water (4) infiltration happens very rapidly

15. When in New York State is the duration of insolation at a minimum? (1) December (2) March (3) June (4) September

16. As the angle of the sun in the sky increases, the intensity of insolation (1) decreases (2) increases (3) remains the same

17. Which diagram below best shows how a greenhouse stays warm?

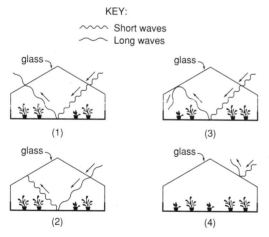

18. What happens to radiant energy that strikes Earth's surface? (1) It is completely absorbed. (2) It is completely reflected. (3) It is partly absorbed and partly reflected. (4) It is re-radiated as a shorter wavelength.

19. What gas added to our atmosphere by industrial processes is most likely to cause the climate of Earth to become warmer? (1) oxides of nitrogen (2) water vapor (3) nitrogen (4) carbon dioxide

20. Which graph below best shows the land and water temperatures on a typical sunny day?

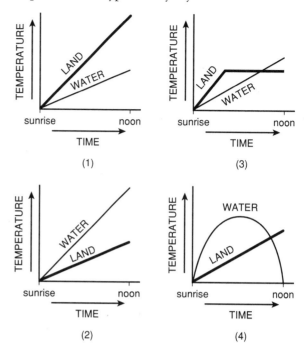

21. Where on Earth is the noon sun the highest in the sky on December 21? (1) 90° North (2) 41° North (3) the Equator (4) $23\frac{1}{2}°$ South

22. In what part of the electromagnetic spectrum does Earth receive most of its energy? (1) high energy gamma rays (2) infrared (3) visible light (4) microwaves

Directions: Base your answers to questions 23 and 24 on the diagram below.

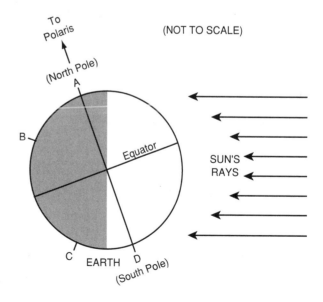

23. What month is shown in the diagram above? (1) March (2) June (3) September (4) December

24. At which position would someone not be able to see the sun over the next 24 hours? (1) A (2) B (3) C (4) D

Directions: Base your answers to questions 25–30 on the graph below, which illustrates the relationships among temperature, insolation, and terrestrial radiation.

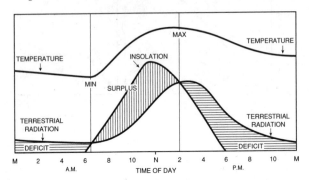

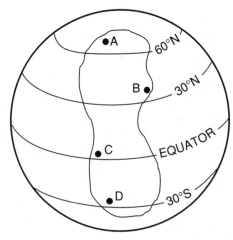

25. What is the duration of the cycle shown on the graph? (1) 12 hrs (2) 1 day (3) 1 week (4) 10 months

26. According to this graph, when does the ground give off the maximum infrared radiation? (1) 6 A.M. (2) 7 A.M. (3) noon (4) 2 P.M.

27. What can we say about both insolation and terrestrial radiation when the temperature reaches its lowest value? (1) They are in equilibrium. (2) Both reach a maximum value. (3) Both reach a minimum value. (4) Insolation is low but heat radiation is high.

28. In what hours does Earth absorb more energy than it gives off? (1) Midnight to 6 A.M. (2) 6 A.M. to 7 A.M. (3) 7 A.M. to 2 P.M. (4) 7 A.M. to 6 P.M.

29. According to this graph, what property of the ground changes and determines the amount of terrestrial radiation that is given off? (1) its moisture content (2) its density (3) its temperature (4) its color

30. When is the energy deficit the greatest? (1) midnight (2) 6 A.M. (3) noon (4) 6 P.M.

31. What property of a rock best determines how much water it can hold in storage? (1) porosity (2) permeability (3) hardness (4) density

32. Why is it cooler in the mountains than it is at nearby places at lower elevations? (1) air is compressed when it rises into the mountains (2) the absolute humidity is higher in the mountains (3) air expands when it rises into the mountains (4) mountains are farther from the noon sun

33. What part of New York State is likely to have the smallest annual range in temperature? (1) Old Forge (2) the Mohawk River Valley (3) Elmira (4) the south shore of Long Island

34. How does the latitude affect the average annual temperature at most locations on Earth? (1) as latitude increases, the average annual temperature increases (2) as latitude increases, the average annual temperature decreases (3) the latitude has no effect on the average annual temperature on Earth

Directions: Base your answers to questions 35–37 on the diagrams to the right. The three graphs of average monthly temperatures match three of the four locations on the map. Match each graph to the proper letter on this map of Earth.

35.

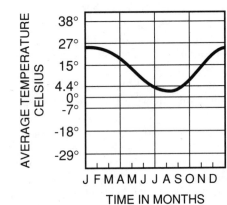

(1) A (2) B (3) C (4) D

36.

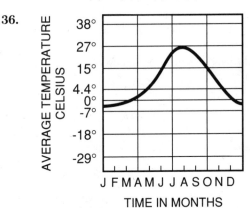

(1) A (2) B (3) C (4) D

37.

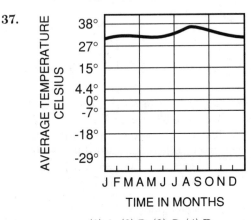

(1) A (2) B (3) C (4) D

FREE-RESPONSE QUESTIONS

(Answer the following questions on a separate sheet of paper.)

1. Explain one difficulty that can arise when soil has either poor porosity, permeability, or capillarity. Choose one property and explain your answer.
(Quality of response, +2; complete sentence(s), +1)

2. Draw a clear, neatly labeled diagram that illustrates the major processes of the water cycle. Your diagram must have water's changes of state labeled.
(For each process correctly labeled and in the appropriate location, +1)

3. In one or more complete sentences, explain why the porosity of a soil sample composed of well-sorted (uniform size) sediment is independent of the size of the particles. Assume that the particles in the sample have the same shape and packing.
(Quality of response, +1 or +2; Complete sentence(s), +1)

4. In New York State, why does the warmest weather usually occur near the end of July, although the area receives the most intense solar radiation in late June?
(Quality of response, +1 or +2; Complete sentence(s), +1)

5. Many factors affect climate; choose two and explain how they affect the climate of New York State.
(Explanation of each factor, +1; Complete sentence(s), +1)

6. The map below shows an imaginary continent on Earth. Based on this information, indicate where on the continent the following climates would be found: polar, tropical-moist, and seasonal-dry.
(Each climate, +1)

7. In one or more complete sentences, explain why the weather is usually warmer on the leeward side of a mountain range than it is at the same elevation on the windward side.
(Reasoning, +1 or +2; Complete sentence(s), +1)

8. Since Earth is constantly receiving energy from the sun, why do we not find that Earth has become constantly warmer?
(Reasoning, +1 or +2; Complete sentence(s), +1)

9. Explain *how* energy moves by conduction through the handle of this iron pan toward the person's hand.
(Mechanism, +1; Complete sentence(s), +1)

Iron pan

10. The diagram below shows a procedure to determine the porosity of a sample of sand. The diagram on the left shows the objects before water is added to the sand. The second shows the objects after water is added until it just reaches the surface of the sand. Using the information in the diagrams, calculate the porosity of the sand. Be sure to show your work.
(Formula, +1; Substituted values, +1; Numerical answer, +1; Units, +1)

11. Use the diagram at the top of page 152 to support two statements about Earth's exchange of electromagnetic energy. Statement 1 must be about insolation. Statement 2 must be about terrestrial radiation. Use complete sentences.
(Statement, +1; Statement 2, +2; Complete sentences, +1)

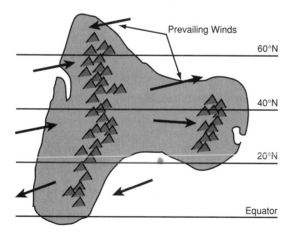

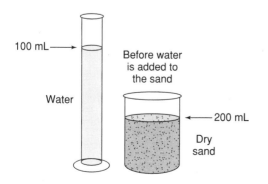

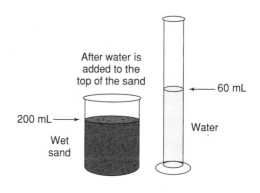

Earth's Radiative Balance

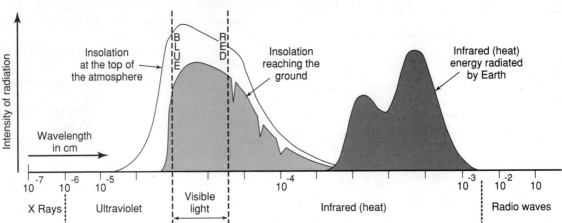

Directions: The graph below shows the response of a stream to a rainstorm. Use this graph and your knowledge of earth science to answer questions 12 and 13.

12. Draw a graph based on the one below to show how stream discharge in this location would be changed if many homes and businesses were built throughout the watershed.
(Reasonable stream discharge line, +1; Labeled axes, +1)

13. If the rate of infiltration were to increase, what effect would this have on the stream discharge graph?
(Correct response, +1; Complete sentence, +1)

14. What is the water table?
(Definition, +1; Complete sentence(s), +1)

15. In what compass direction does the Genesee River of western New York State flow?
(Direction, +1)

16. In one or more complete sentences, explain why a large portion of the rainfall in Arizona falls during the hottest months of the year. (Hint: It's the same reason India get most of its rain in the summer.) What is this event called?
(Explanation, +1; Complete sentence(s) +1; Term, +1)

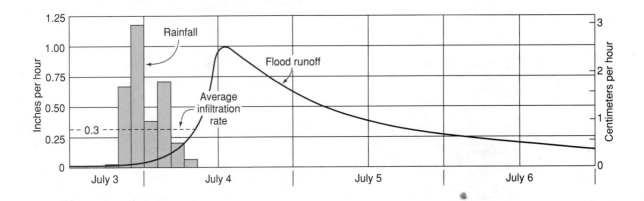

CHAPTER 9 The Earth in Space

MOTIONS OF CELESTIAL OBJECTS

To most observers, the night sky looks like a huge dome, or hemisphere, that extends down to the horizon in every direction. If an observer were to extend the dome of the sky so that it circles all of Earth, she or he would produce an imaginary sphere, the **celestial sphere**, on which all objects in the sky appear. A **celestial object**, such as the sun, the moon, a planet, a star, or any distant object visible in the sky, generally appears to rise in the east and set in the west. (The word **terrestrial** is used to refer to objects that are a part of Earth, such as rocks, oceans, and clouds.)

Most of the celestial objects appear to move along circular or curved paths. The apparent east-west, counterclockwise, motion of an object occurs at an angular rate of 15° per hour (360°, or one rotation in 24 hours). In the course of a 24-hour day, a star that is positioned near Polaris in the Northern Hemisphere will appear to move in a complete circular path about a point in the sky directly above the North Pole (the celestial North Pole). Other stars appear to move 15° per hour from east to west along arcs until they disappear below the horizon. See Figure 9-1.

Motion of the Stars and Planets.

The stars located over Earth's equator follow nearly the same path as the sun—rising in the east and setting in the west. Stars in the southern portion of the sky briefly arc across or appear over the horizon on their westward journey. Like the sun, the stars in the eastern, southern, and western parts of the sky always move to the right as they rise. They move across the southern sky, and then set in the west. Stars over the North Pole move in circles around Polaris. The motions of stars are all characterized by a circular motion of 15° per hour around the celestial North Pole.

The planets do not remain in fixed positions among the stars. In addition to their daily 15° per hour circular motion, they change their positions from night to night. Each planet has its own characteristic motion. Sometimes a planet drifts westward with respect to the stars, and sometimes a planet reverses its direction and moves eastward among the stars. The wandering motions of planets led ancient observers of the sky to recognize that these celestial objects were different from the "other" stars. In fact, the word planet means "wanderer."

WHAT ARE CONSTELLATIONS?

To our ancestors, the clear night sky was a well-known landscape. Although the stars are randomly distributed throughout the sky, ancient peoples imagined they saw patterns among them. These patterns were often associated with traditions and legends that were part of the culture of early civilizations. For example, some patterns were said to resemble people, such as Orion, the hunter. Others were thought to resemble animals, such as Taurus, the bull. Still others were thought to be objects, such as Lyra, the harp. Although some of

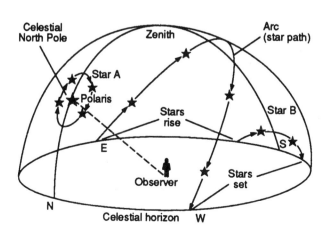

Figure 9-1. Paths of stars. The stars appear to rotate counterclockwise around Polaris. All star paths can be thought of as circles around the North and South Celestial Poles.

Figure 9-2. The Big Dipper, which is part of the constellation the Great Bear (Ursa Major), is always visible in the northern sky in New York State.

the star patterns do resemble the objects for which they are named, most do not. It takes a great deal of imagination to see the shape of a bear when you look at Ursa Major (Latin for "great bear"). See Figure 9-2. **Constellations** are figures that people have observed to mark the positions of the stars. With fire as their only source of light, the ancient peoples became familiar with the patterns of the stars and used changes in the night sky to mark the seasons. See Figure 9-3.

Figure 9-4 shows the brightest constellations of late spring and early summer, You may want to take this "map" of the stars (or an enlarged copy) outside on a clear night to locate some of the constellations visible at this time of year. Hold the star chart upside down above your head so that the directions on the map line up with their actual directions. (You may wish to consult a compass to help you determine exactly where north, south, east, and west are located relative to where you are standing.) Start by finding the Big Dipper (a part of Ursa Major), which will be nearly directly overhead.

Once you have located this "landmark," you should be able to find your way to other bright constellations and stars.

To the modern astronomer, the constellations have taken on a new meaning. Scientists have divided the night sky into 88 regions, each region associated with a constellation. When astronomers speak of a feature in Cygnus, the swan, they mean that to observe this feature you must look near the stars that form the constellation Cygnus.

MODELS OF THE NIGHT SKY

Early civilizations were aware of how celestial objects, such as the sun and moon, moved through the sky from east to west. Because these people could not feel Earth moving, they considered Earth to be a stationary object located at the center of the universe around which all celestial objects revolved. Their model of the universe was **geocentric**, or Earth-centered.

Observations by Copernicus, Brahe, Kepler, Galileo, and other scientists in the 16th and 17th centuries eventually made the geocentric model difficult to accept. When the paths of the planets were carefully measured and plotted in an Earth-centered model, some of the planetary motions were too complex and hard to explain. Therefore, astronomers prefer to support a more simple model, the **heliocentric model**, which includes all nine known planets (the solar system) revolving around the sun.

The heliocentric model includes two motions of planet Earth. Each day Earth spins on its **axis**—from west to east at the rate of 15° per hour (360° in 24 hours). This daily motion is known as **rotation**. Earth also **orbits** the sun once per **year**. This annual motion is known as **revolution**. If Earth takes $365\frac{1}{4}$ days to revolve around the sun, it revolves approximately 1° per day.

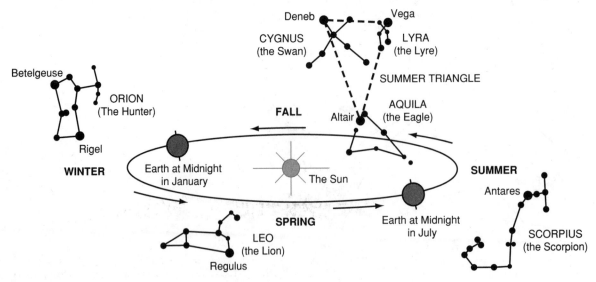

Figure 9-3. Constellations of the early evening. As Earth revolves around the sun, the night side faces toward different constellations. Only those constellations that face Earth's night side are visible.

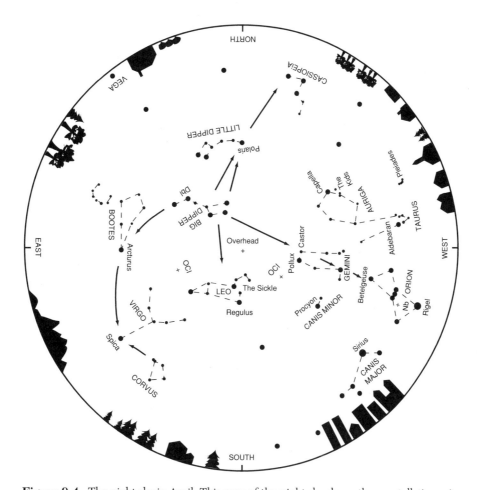

Figure 9-4. The night sky in April. This map of the night sky shows the constellations visible at about 40° North latitude after 10 P.M. in March and about 8 to 9 P.M. in April. To use this map, hold it above your head so that the directions (north, south, east, and west) are aligned properly. If you can find the Big Dipper (a part of Ursa Major) high overhead, you can use it to locate the other major constellations as shown by the arrows on this chart. Orion, one of the most impressive constellations, can be recognized by three bright stars in a row. Compare the colors of the stars Betelgeuse and Rigel. Nearby Sirius is the brightest star in the night sky. The objects labeled OCl (open clusters), Dbl (double stars), and Nb (nebulae) may look impressive if you use binoculars or a small telescope. Because planets "wander" among the stars and change their positions, they are not shown on this chart. You may be able to locate planets that are currently visible by using information found near the weather map in many daily newspapers.

Proof for the Heliocentric Model.

Experimental proof of the motion of Earth was not found until 1851, when the French scientist Jean Foucault suspended a long pendulum and set it swinging along a north-south line. The **Foucault pendulum**, mounted on a high support, is able to move in any direction. Foucault observed how the pendulum appeared to change direction as it swung freely, away from the north-south line in a clockwise direction. He interpreted this motion as the rotation of Earth under the pendulum. See Figure 9-5 on page 156. Although a Foucault pendulum mounted at the North or South Pole would appear to rotate in a complete circle in 24 hours, the period of rotation increases when the pendulum is located at lower latitudes. At the equator, the Foucault pendulum would

not appear to rotate at all. Many science museums have Foucault pendulums. They are sometimes set up to knock down small pegs as they slowly appear to rotate to a new swing direction.

The second proof of the Earth's rotation is the Coriolis effect. It was named after another French scientist Gaspard Coriolis. You may recall from Chapter 6 that winds blowing out of a high-pressure system always curve to the right in the Northern Hemisphere. Also, because of the Coriolis effect, the system of prevailing winds on Earth forms a series of symmetrical bands located north and south of the equator. From considerations of geometry, it can be shown that the Coriolis effect is the result of inertia acting on a rotating planet. See Figure 9-6 on page 156.

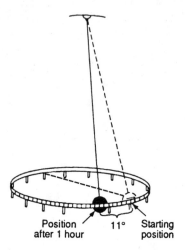

Position after 1 hour   11°   Starting position

Figure 9-5. A Foucault pendulum. At the latitude of Paris, France, the plane of a swinging pendulum appears, in one hour, to move 11° from the starting position. One full rotation takes 36 hours. At the North Pole, the pendulum would appear to rotate 15° per hour. One full rotation there takes 24 hours. This apparent rotation is caused by the rotation of Earth.

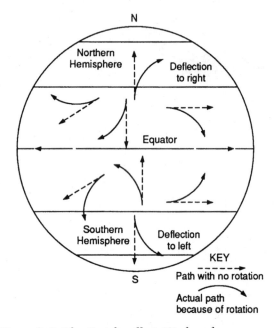

Figure 9-6. The Coriolis effect. Winds and ocean currents appear to curve because they are moving along a rotating planet. The winds and currents appear to curve to the right in the Northern Hemisphere and to the left in the Southern Hemisphere.

QUESTIONS

1. Ancient people believed that the center of our solar system was (1) Earth (2) the sun (3) Mars (4) Venus

2. Astronomers now know that the center of our solar system is (1) Earth (2) the sun (3) Mars (4) Venus

3. The Foucault pendulum provides evidence that Earth (1) rotates on its axis (2) revolves around the sun (3) has an elliptical orbit (4) has an orbiting moon

4. Which of the following cannot be explained by the geocentric model of the solar system? (1) the daily path of the stars around Polaris (2) the daily path of the sun through the sky (3) changes in the angular diameters of the planets (4) the circular motion of a freely swinging pendulum

5. Which of the diagrams below best shows a three-hour time exposure photograph of the night sky if Earth did *not* rotate?

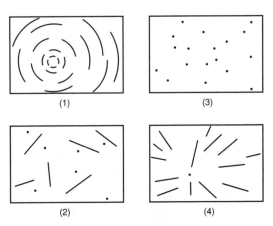

6. The Coriolis effect would be changed the most by a change in Earth's (1) rate of rotation (2) rate of revolution (3) angle of tilt (4) surface temperature

7. Which theory best explains the large-scale movement of ocean currents and wind? (1) only the heliocentric theory, in which Earth rotates (2) only the geocentric theory, in which Earth does not move (3) both the heliocentric and geocentric theories (4) neither the heliocentric nor the geocentric theory

8. In what direction do we observe stars rising? (Hint: The sun is a star.) (1) north (2) south (3) east (4) west

9. Through what angle do the stars and planets seem to move in two hours? (1) 2° (2) 15° (3) 20° (4) 30°

10. In what direction would a flagpole in New York cast a shadow at noon? (1) north (2) south (3) east (4) west

11. In most of the sky (east, south and west) the stars consistently move (1) upward (2) downward (3) to the right (4) to the left

12. According to the *Earth Science Reference Tables*, what is the approximate *diameter* of the sun? (1) 700 km (2) 1400 km (3) 700,000 km (4) 1,400,00 km

13. Where is the sun at noon? (1) high in the northern sky (2) very low in the northern sky (3) high in the southern sky (4) very low in the southern sky

Directions: Use the diagram below to answer questions 14 and 15.

A Time Exposure Photograph of the Night Sky

14. The diagram on page 156 represents a photograph of the night sky taken in New York State. In what direction was the camera pointed? (1) north (2) south (3) east (4) west

15. Lines drawn from the top of each star path to Polaris, and back to the bottom of each star path make an angle of 10°. How long was the film exposed? (1) 40 minutes (2) 1 hour and 20 minutes (3) 2 hours (4) 2 hours and 20 minutes

16. Most stars appear to move through the sky from (1) north to south (2) south to north (3) west to east (4) east to west

17. Which star appears to move the *least* through the sky over a period of 24 hours? (1) the sun (2) Polaris (3) Betelgeuse (4) Venus

18. As observed in New York State, in which part of the sky do the stars seem to move in small circles? (1) north (2) east (3) south (4) west

APPARENT MOTIONS OF THE SUN

Before there were mechanical clocks, the movement of the sun through the sky was used to track the passage of time. Sundials, such as the one shown in Figure 9-7, are among the first timekeeping devices used by humans. A sundial reveals the passage of the daylight hours as the shadow of a stick (gnomon) shifts across a marked dial or scale.

You can see how a sundial works by performing a simple demonstration with a meterstick. First, find a sunny spot outdoors where the ground is level. Then, holding the meterstick loosely at the very top, lower it until it touches the ground. (Holding it loosely will allow gravity to help you place the stick perpendicular to the ground.) Observe the shadow of the meterstick.

Repeat this procedure at different times of the day. You will discover that the shadow is very long at sunrise, decreases in length as the morning progresses, is shortest at noon, and increases in length throughout the afternoon. You will also see that the shadow points directly away from the sun. For example, if the sun is to the south at noon, the shadow points to the north.

Our system of time is based upon the **apparent motions** of the sun. The motion of a celestial object, such as the sun, the moon, or a planet, through the sky is called *apparent motion* because the object is not really moving as it appears to be. The apparent rising and setting of the sun is actually caused by Earth's rotation. The **apparent solar day** is the interval of time during which the sun passes from its highest point on one day to its highest point on the next.

Seasons.

Because Earth moves in its orbit, the sun's pathway from east to west in the sky also changes on a yearly cycle. See Figure 9-8. In New York, the noon sun is high in the sky at the beginning of the summer. Through the next six months, summer and autumn, the noon position of the sun gets a little lower in the sky each day. While this happens, the sunrise position starts north of due east and moves slowly southward as each daylight period becomes a little shorter than the day before. At the *autumnal equinox* (about Sept. 23), the sun rises due east and sets due west. Daylight lasts for 12 hours, and it is the beginning of fall, or autumn, in the Northern Hemisphere.

At the beginning of winter, the *winter solstice* (about Dec. 21), the sun rises south of due east; this is the shortest daylight period of the year, measured from sunrise to sunset. Throughout the months of winter and spring, the positions of sunrise and sunset both move northward as the daylight periods become longer.

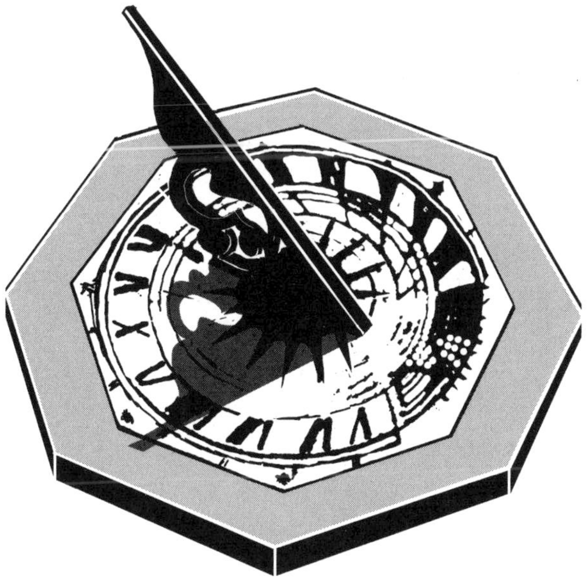

Figure 9-7. A sundial. As the sun moves across the sky, the shadow of the pointer, or gnomon, moves across the face of the dial, thereby showing the passage of the daylight hours.

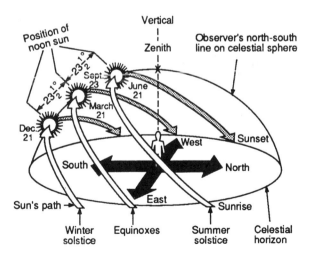

Figure 9-8. Path of the sun's apparent motion at latitude 40°N on the solstices and equinoxes. The strongest rays from the sun are those that are most direct, when the sun is the highest in the sky. To the observer, the sun's path appears to change both daily and seasonally. It is noon for the observer when the sun crosses a north-south line through the sky (the observer's meridian).

The Earth in Space

At the *vernal equinox* (about March 21), the sun rises exactly in the east and sets due west; the daylight period is 12 hours long, and it is the beginning of spring in the Northern Hemisphere. When the *summer solstice* (about June 21) arrives, the sun rises north of due east, is high in the sky at noon, and sets north of due west. The summer solstice is the longest daylight period of the year, measured from sunrise to sunset; it is the beginning of summer.

Please keep in mind that the length of daylight changes because the part of the sun's apparent circle of motion that is above the horizon changes. The changing length of daylight hours is not due to changes in the rate of motion of the sun. The sun always seems to move 15°/hour. In spring and summer, when the sun is higher in the sky, more than half of the sun's motion (more than 180°) is above the horizon. In fall and winter, the days are short because the sun is lower in the sky and most of the time the sun is below the horizon.

LATITUDE AND THE ANGLE OF THE SUN

The path of the sun through the sky depends upon where you are when you observe it. People who live near the equator know that the noon sun is always high in the sky. But the noon sun only can be directly overhead for an observer within the tropics. Specifically, the Tropics of Cancer, $23\frac{1}{2}°$ North, and Capricorn, $23\frac{1}{2}°$ South, mark the latitudes within which the noon sun can be directly observed overhead.

Observed anywhere within the continental United States, the sun is higher in the sky in the summer than it is in the winter. But the noon sun is *never* directly overhead. Therefore the position of the noon sun in New York varies from about half way up into the sky in the winter, to a summer position that is much higher, but not directly overhead. See Figure 9-8.

As you travel northward from any mid-latitude location, the noon sun will move lower and lower in the sky. At the Arctic Circle, the sun can be as high as 47° on the first day of summer, but on the first day of winter the noon sun only gets as high as the horizon. (On that day, it wouldn't start to get light until about 10 or 11 A.M. At noon, the sun would be just visible on a flat horizon, and by 1 or 2 in the afternoon it would be dark.) For observers within the Arctic and Antarctic circles, the summer sun moves around the sky without actually setting. But the sun doesn't come up at all on the first day of winter.

Observers at the poles see the summer sun move in a circle $23\frac{1}{2}°$ above the horizon. As the autumnal equinox approaches, the sun spirals downward toward the horizon. After the sun sets in the autumn, it does not appear until the first day of spring, when it begins to spiral up to its summer position. Thus, observers at the poles see six months of daylight, followed by six months of darkness in a yearly cycle.

Figure 9-9 shows that our annual cycle of the seasons is caused by a combination of the $23\frac{1}{2}°$ tilt of Earth's axis and our revolution around the sun. Although Earth's spin axis always points toward the same direction in space, our journey around the sun causes the North Pole to tilt alternately toward and away from the sun.

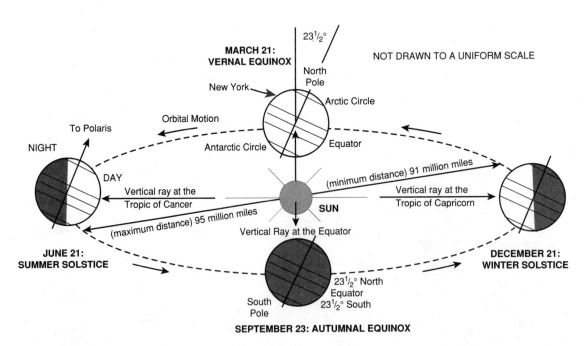

Figure 9-9. Earth's orbit and the seasons. The $23\frac{1}{2}°$ tilt of Earth's axis and our orbit around the sun cause the seasons. Our summer occurs when the Northern Hemisphere is tilted toward the sun. In the winter, we are tilted away from the sun. If Earth's axis were not tilted, we would have no seasons. In the Southern Hemisphere, the seasons are six months out of phase. Please note that our closest approach to the sun occurs in our winter, although the change in distance is relatively small. However, because of the angle of the view in this diagram, Earth may look closer to the sun at the spring and autumn positions. A view from directly above would show the distances correctly. Also note that throughout Earth's revolution around the sun, Earth's axis always points in the same direction.

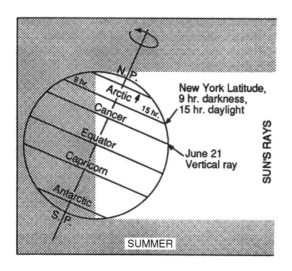

SUMMER

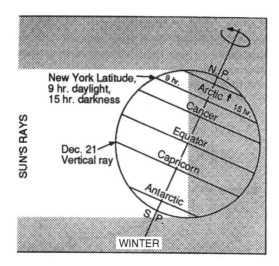

WINTER

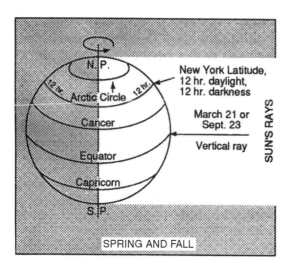

SPRING AND FALL

Figure 9-10. These diagrams show how the vertical ray of sunlight strikes Earth's surface during the course of a year and how day and night are distributed on Earth on the Northern Hemisphere's longest day (June 21) and its shortest day (December 21). These days are the solstices. Day and night are equal in length everywhere on Earth only on the two equinoxes (about September 23 and March 21).

Daylight Hours.

At equinox, the sun rises due east and sets due west. For all locations except the poles, daylight lasts 12 hours. At the equator throughout the year, there are 12 hours of daylight and 12 hours of night. As you approach the poles, the amount of seasonal variation in the length of daylight increases until a maximum six months of daylight and six months of darkness is reached at the North Pole or the South Pole.

Of course, the changes in the sun's daily path across the sky are not caused by motions of the sun. They are the result of Earth's spin on its axis. Earth's axis is tilted $23\frac{1}{2}°$ from a line perpendicular to the plane of the orbit of Earth around the sun. Earth also exhibits parallelism—this means that Earth's axis always points in the same direction. It never changes. See Figure 9-10.

QUESTIONS

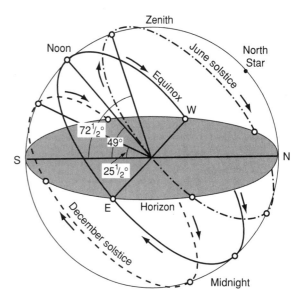

Directions: Use the diagram above to answer questions 19–26. The diagram shows the path of the sun at various times in the year for an observer in New York City. The flat surface in the middle represents the ground.

19. When does the noon sun appear highest in the sky? (1) March (2) June (3) September (4) December

20. As we move northward from New York City, the angular altitude of the sun in the sky at noon would (1) increase (2) decrease (3) remain the same

21. In what direction does the sun set in June, as observed in New York City? (1) northwest (2) southwest (3) northeast (4) southeast

22. In the month of December, how long is the sun visible in the sky? (1) less than 12 hours (2) just 12 hours (3) more than 12 hours (4) 24 hours

23. For an observer in New York State, where is the sun at about 10 o'clock in the morning? (1) in the northeast part of the sky (2) in the northwest part of the sky (3) in the southeast part of the sky (4) in the southwest part of the sky

24. The number of hours from sunrise to sunset is the longest when the sun rises in the (1) northeast (2) northwest (3) southeast (4) southwest

25. When is the sun directly overhead in New York State? (1) only on June 21 (2) only on December 22 (3) in both March and September (4) never

26. Throughout the month of September, the number of hours of daylight is (1) decreasing (2) increasing (3) remaining constant

27. In what general direction does the sun rise? (1) north (2) south (3) east (4) west

28. When is the sun highest in the sky? (1) 6 A.M. (2) 12 noon (3) about 2 P.M. (4) midnight

29. Why are our days longer in the summer than they are in the winter? (1) The sun moves faster through the sky in summer. (2) The sun moves slower through the sky in summer. (3) The path of the sun through the sky is longer in the summer. (4) The path of the sun through the sky is longer in the winter.

30. What location on Earth has no seasons as we know them, because both the length of daylight hours and the altitude of the sun at noon do not change very much through the course of a year? (1) South Pole (2) about 45° south (3) equator (4) North Pole

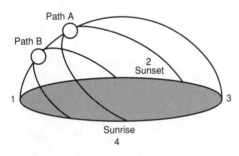

Directions: Use the diagram above to answer questions 31–34. The diagram shows the paths of the sun in New York on the summer and winter solstices.

31. Which number on the diagram above best represents the direction west? (1) 1 (2) 2 (3) 3 (4) 4

32. Path A represents a day in (1) March (2) June (3) September (4) December

33. When the sun follows Path B, it rises (1) due (exactly) east (2) in the northeast (3) in the southeast (4) due south

34. When does the sun move the fastest through the sky measured in degrees per hour? (1) when it follows path A (2) when it follows path B (3) the angular velocity does not change (4) the velocity is constantly increasing

35. During the afternoon, the length of a shadow of a vertical meterstick (1) decreases (2) increases (3) decreases, then increases (4) increases, then decreases

Directions: Base your answers to questions 36–40 on the diagram below.

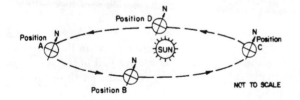

36. Which position on the diagram below, left best shows Earth at the winter solstice in the Northern Hemisphere? (1) A (2) B (3) C (4) D

37. At which position is Earth the closest to the sun? (1) A (2) B (3) C (4) D

38. If Earth were at position A, where would the sun appear to rise in New York State? (1) due west (2) due east (3) northwest (4) northeast

39. At which position would the sun be the highest at noon in New York? (1) A (2) B (3) C (4) D

40. Which position best represents March 21? (1) A (2) B (3) C (4) D

The Scientist, Engineer, and Citizen

Construct a device of your own design to measure time by the apparent motions of the sun. First, prepare a list of materials you will need. Then prepare illustrated, step-by-step instructions for constructing your device. If possible, build and test your sun clock.

CHAPTER 9 REVIEW QUESTIONS

1. When does the sun move the fastest through the sky? (1) in the morning (2) in the afternoon (3) at night (4) its speed is constant

2. In what part of the sky do the stars seem to move in small circles? (1) north (2) south (3) east (4) west

3. Our units of time were devised based upon (1) Earth's real motions in space (2) the real motions of the sun through space (3) the longitude of the observer (4) the latitude of the observer

4. For observers in New York State, where is the sun at noon during late spring and early summer? (1) straight overhead, at the zenith (2) low in the southern sky (3) high in the southern sky (4) high in the northern sky

5. Which diagram below best shows a two-hour time-lapse photograph of the night sky with the camera pointed due east?

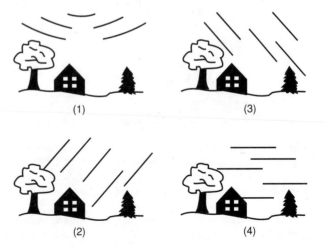

6. In the Northern Hemisphere, the days from sunrise to sunset grow longer throughout the month of (1) March (2) June (3) September (4) December

Directions: Base your answers to questions 7–10 on the following diagram.

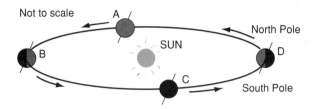

7. Which position of Earth in the diagram best shows the motion of December? (1) A (2) B (3) C (4) D

8. What feature of this diagram is responsible for the seasons: Winter, Spring, Summer, and Autumn? (1) the changing distance from Earth to the sun (2) the tilt of Earth's spin axis (3) the moisture content of Earth's atmosphere (4) the portion of Earth in sunlight

9. How long does it take Earth to move from position A, through B, C and D, and back to A? (1) one day (2) one week (3) one month (4) one year

10. In which position is sunlight the strongest at the North Pole? (1) A (2) B (3) C (4) D

11. When is the sun directly overhead at the Tropic of Cancer, $23\frac{1}{2}°$ north of the equator? (1) late March (2) late June (3) late September (4) late December

12. Which location has the *least* change in the length of daylight hours over a period of one year? (1) the equator (2) the Tropic of Cancer (3) New York State (4) the North Pole

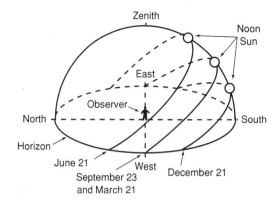

Directions: Base your answers to questions 13 and 14 on the diagram above, which represents the apparent daily path of the Sun across the sky in the Northern Hemisphere on the dates indicated.

13. At noon on which date would the observer cast the longest shadow? (1) June 21 (2) March 21 (3) September 23 (4) December 21

14. Which observation about the Sun's apparent path at this location on June 21 is best supported by the diagram? (1) Sunrise occurs north of east. (2) Sunset occurs south of west. (3) The sun appears to move across the sky at a rate of 1° per hour. (4) The sun's total daytime path is shortest on this date.

15. Approximately how far does Earth revolve each day in its orbit? (1) 1° (2) 15° (3) 45° (4) 360°

16. In New York State, the noon sun is (1) always in the north (2) always in the east (3) always in the south (4) always at the zenith

Directions: Base your answers to questions 17–19 on the diagrams at the bottom of the page, which show the apparent motions of the sun across the sky on June 21, at the locations indicated.

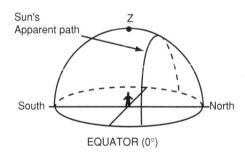

EQUATOR (0°)

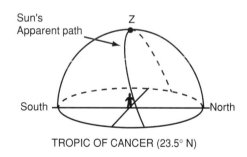

TROPIC OF CANCER (23.5° N)

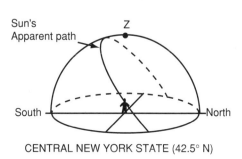

CENTRAL NEW YORK STATE (42.5° N)

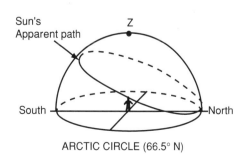

ARCTIC CIRCLE (66.5° N)

17. At which location will the noon shadow of a stick 1 meter high be the longest (1) Equator (2) Tropic of Cancer (3) central New York State (4) Arctic Circle

18. Which location will have the shortest period of sunlight on this date? (1) Equator (2) North Pole (3) central New York State (4) Arctic Circle

19. How often does the sun's path go through the highest point in the sky (marked "Z") for an observer in New York State? (1) every day (2) twice a year (3) once a year (4) never

20. The tilt of Earth on its axis is a cause of Earth's (1) uniform daylight hours (2) changing length of day and night (3) 24-hour day (4) $365\frac{1}{4}$-day year

21. The greatest difference in seasons would occur on a planet that has (1) a circular orbit (2) a slightly flattened shape (3) its axis of rotation perpendicular to the plane of its orbit around the sun (4) its axis of rotation inclined 45° to the plane of its orbit around the sun

FREE-RESPONSE QUESTIONS

(Answer the following questions on a separate sheet of paper.)

1. For thousands of years, people have looked at the stars in the night sky and have seen constellations. Name any constellation visible to an observer in New York.
(Name constellation, +1)

2. In a complete sentence, state one way in which constellations are useful.
(Complete sentence, +1; Common use, +1)

3. Make a sketch of a time exposure photograph of the stars made with the camera pointed due north and above the horizon. This should be a time exposure for several hours. Include Polaris and three other stars at different distances from Polaris. Also include an arrow to show the direction of the apparent motion of the stars.

(Polaris shown correctly, +1; Relative motion of 3 other stars, +1; Arrow shows correct direction of motion, +1)

4. Based only on what you can observe from Earth, explain why in the Northern Hemisphere it is colder in the winter than it is in the summer.
(Reasoning, +1 + 2; Complete sentence, +1)

5. The diagram below represents a mounted plastic hemisphere used to show the path of the sun through the sky. This view is from a direction directly above the model, and the letters indicate the four compass directions. Copy this diagram onto a separate sheet of paper. On your diagram, draw an arrow to show the path of the sun from sunrise to sunset at the equinoxes (March and September), as observed from New York State.
(Any line from sunrise to sunset, +1; Appropriate position of line relative to zenith, +1; Correct point for sunrise, +1; Correct point for sunset, +1)

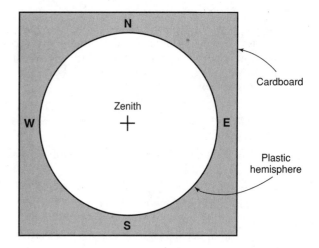

6. Sketch a simple, earthbound apparatus designed to prove that apparent motions of the sun and stars are in fact caused by Earth's rotation. On your sketch, label at least three of your device's essential parts.
(Correct device, +1; Essential parts, +1 each up to a maximum of 3 points)

Directions: The diagram below shows Earth's orbit as viewed from a position in space. On a copy of this diagram, label the features specified in problems 7 through 9.

7. The South Pole at position B.
(Correct answer, +1)

8. The position of New York State at position D.
(Correct answer, +1)

9. Earth's position in its orbit on May 1.
(Correct answer within one month, +1)

10. Explain why it's colder in the winter than the summer in terms of what we can easily observe right here on Earth.
(Complete sentence(s), +1; Quality of response, up to +2)

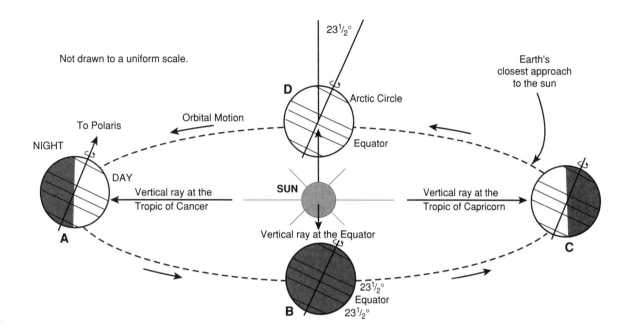

Not drawn to a uniform scale.

$23\frac{1}{2}°$

D   Arctic Circle

Earth's closest approach to the sun

Orbital Motion

To Polaris

Equator

NIGHT

SUN

DAY

Vertical ray at the Tropic of Cancer

Vertical ray at the Tropic of Capricorn

A

C

Vertical ray at the Equator

$23\frac{1}{2}°$
Equator
$23\frac{1}{2}°$

B

CHAPTER 10 Beyond Planet Earth

No other object in the night sky is as spectacular as Earth's moon. For thousands of years, the moon has inspired myths, songs, poems, and superstitions. Ancient ideas about the moon have been preserved in the English language. For example, the word *lunacy* comes from the belief that moonlight could drive a person insane, and *Monday* was once the day sacred to the moon goddess.

PHASES OF THE MOON

The apparent shape of the moon depends upon the changing relative positions of Earth, the sun, and the moon. As the moon completes one revolution around Earth each month, the growing and shrinking lighted area makes the moon appear to change in shape. When the moon and the sun are on the same side of Earth, the moon's dark side faces Earth, and the illuminated side of the moon is not visible from Earth. This is the new moon phase. See Figure 10-1. When the moon's position is opposite the sun, a fully lighted moon, the full moon, is seen. And if the positions of the moon and the sun are 90° apart, half of the moon is lighted and half is in shadow (the quarter moon). Apparent changes in the shape of the moon, caused by light and shadow, are called the phases of the moon.

Although one complete orbit of the moon around Earth takes about 27 days, a complete cycle of the moon's phases takes $29\frac{1}{2}$ days. This $2\frac{1}{2}$ day difference occurs because as the moon orbits Earth, Earth orbits the sun. When the moon gets back to its original position, it

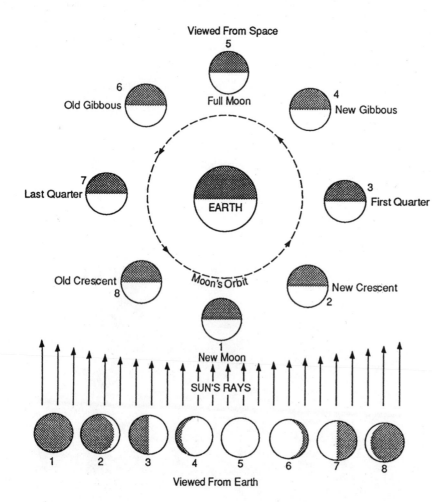

Figure 10-1. Phases of the moon. One half of the moon's surface is always illuminated as it orbits Earth. Viewed from Earth, the moon's phases are seen as different portions of the illuminated half. When the moon is in position 1, an observer on Earth cannot see any part of the moon because the lighted half of the moon is facing the sun.

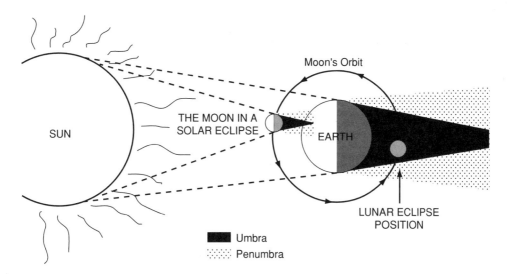

Figure 10-2. Eclipses of the sun and moon as observed from a position high above the North Pole. Eclipses of the sun fully darken a small area on Earth. Eclipses of the moon are visible from a much larger area of Earth. (Note that this diagram, like most astronomical diagrams is not to scale.)

must move through an extra angle of about 30° to compensate for Earth's orbital motion around the sun.

The moon's periods of rotation and revolution are equal. Because of this, the same side of the moon always faces Earth. Humans had never viewed the far side of the moon until the 1960s, when the Soviet Union (now Russia and the other members of the Commonwealth of Independent States) sent a rocket into orbit around the moon. As the discoverers of the moon's far side, the Soviets named the features found there.

ECLIPSES OF THE MOON AND SUN

When lighted from just one direction, all objects cast a shadow. A shadow has two parts: the umbra, the inner part, which is the darkest part, and the penumbra, the outer part, which is not as dark. Earth and the moon are lighted by the sun; they both cast shadows into space. See Figure 10-2. An eclipse of the moon occurs when the full moon moves into Earth's shadow. During a lunar eclipse, the moon turns a coppery red. You can still see the moon because sunlight is bent by Earth's atmosphere, which causes a weak illumination of the moon. If the orbits of Earth and the moon were in the same plane, there would be an eclipse of the moon every month. However, we know they are much more rare. This is because the moon's orbit is tilted at an angle of about 5° with respect to Earth's orbit. See Figure 10-3. As a result, the moon usually passes above or below Earth's shadow.

An eclipse of the sun occurs when the new moon briefly moves in front of the sun. At this time the moon casts its shadow on Earth. Because of the tilt of the moon's orbit, we do not have a solar eclipse at each new moon. Precise observations of the moon over hundreds of years have enabled astronomers to predict its orbit many years into the future. These predictions include

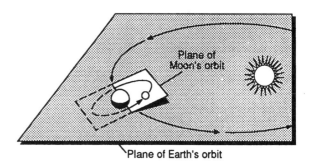

Figure 10-3. The moon's orbit is inclined about five degrees to the plane of Earth's orbit. Therefore, the moon is usually above or below the plane of the sun and eclipses are rare.

the timing of and best places to view eclipses of the sun and the moon.

It is a coincidence that as seen from Earth the apparent size of the moon is approximately equal to that of the sun. During many solar eclipses, the moon entirely covers the sun. However, during some eclipses the moon does not completely cover the sun and you can see a ring of light around the edge of the moon.

Angular Diameter of Celestial Objects.

If you hold a ping-pong ball at arm's length, it looks rather small. However, if the same ball is held close to your eye, it appears much larger. Although the size of the ball has not changed, the angular diameter of the ball has changed. Angular diameter is the angle formed between the sides of an object and your eye. The angular diameter of any object depends upon the actual size of the object and upon how far away the object is from the observer. The nearer an object is to an observer, the greater an object's angular diameter. For example, when you observe the sun, the moon, and the planets over a period of time, you will notice that they appear to change in size in a cyclic manner. The apparent change in size, or diameter, is due to a change in distance between each celestial object and Earth. The angular diameter of each celestial object changes periodically, but the real size, or diameter, of each celestial object stays the same.

Observations of the sun's angular diameter tell us that Earth is closest to the sun in January and farthest from the sun in July. Seasonal variations result from parallelism, the tilt of Earth's axis, and Earth's shape—not from Earth-sun distance. The sun's angular diameter is larger in winter and smaller in summer.

Angular Size and Shape of Orbit.

Variations in the appearance of solar eclipses are caused mostly by changes in the apparent size of the moon. Because the moon seems to change size more than the sun, we can infer that changes in the relative distance between the moon and Earth are greater than changes in the relative distance between the sun and Earth. Since both changes are small compared to the magnitude of the average distance, we can infer that the orbit of the moon around Earth and the orbit of Earth around the sun are nearly circular.

THE TIDES

People who live along the seashore are used to the twice daily rise and fall of the oceans we know as the **tides**. See Figure 10-4. In most places, the difference between high tide and low tide is less than one meter. The Bay of Fundy in eastern Canada has the world's greatest difference between high and low tide, which can exceed 15 meters. The cause of the tides is the gravitational attraction of the moon and the sun. The sun and the moon pull on the water in the oceans and on the solid part of Earth. The water of the oceans is pulled toward the moon, which causes a high tide. Another high tide occurs on the opposite side of Earth, where the solid part of Earth is pulled away from the oceans. The highest high tides and the lowest low tides, called spring tides, occur about twice a month near the full and new moon phases. See Figure 10-5. In that alignment, both the sun and moon pull in the same line. When the sun and moon are at right angles at the first and last quarter phases of the moon, the changes in water level are more

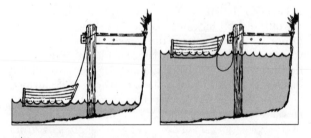

Figure 10-4. Every point along the ocean experiences two low tides and two high tides per day. The difference between high tide and low tide is generally less than a meter (about 3 feet), although it can be quite large in some places.

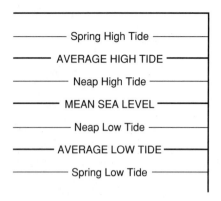

Figure 10-5. Levels of the tides. The height of the tides varies on a monthly cycle, although the distance to the moon, air pressure, and winds also affect these changes in sea level.

modest. These smaller tides are called the neap tides. Although the sun has many times the mass of the moon, the moon has more effect on the tides because it is so much closer to Earth.

QUESTIONS

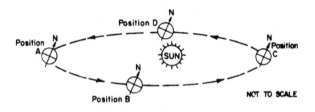

1. Which graph best shows the changing solar diameter as observed from Earth in the diagram above?

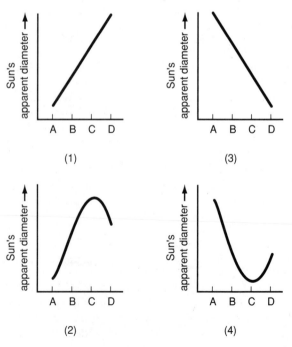

2. The angular diameter of an object depends upon (1) its distance only (2) its real size and distance (3) its angular velocity (4) its brightness

Directions: Base your answers to questions 3–5 on the diagram below.

3. At which position on the diagram below would the moon appear to be totally lighted as viewed from Earth? (1) A (2) B (3) C (4) D

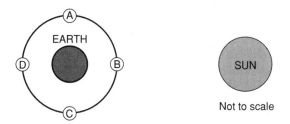

4. An eclipse of the sun can occur when the moon is at position (1) A (2) B (3) C (4) D

5. At which position would the left half of the moon appear lighted and the right half dark as viewed from Earth? (1) A (2) B (3) C (4) D

6. The moon takes approximately 27 days to orbit Earth. What is the smallest possible number of days from an eclipse of the sun to an eclipse of the moon? (1) about 7 days (2) about 14 days (3) about 27 days (4) about 60 days

7. An eclipse of the sun will darken the sky the most if (1) both the sun and the moon are relatively close to Earth (2) both the sun and the moon are relatively far from Earth (3) the sun is relatively close and the moon is relatively far away (4) the moon is relatively close and the sun is relatively far away

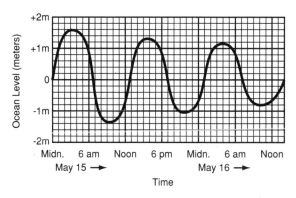

8. What causes the periodic change in sea level shown on the graph above? (1) changing winds and storm paths (2) motions of Earth and the moon (3) frequent earthquakes and tidal waves (4) the $23\frac{1}{2}°$ tilt to Earth's axis

9. A full cycle of the rise and fall of the tides usually occurs at intervals of (1) 6 hours (2) 12 hours (3) 24 hours (4) 48 hours

10. When the sun, moon, and Earth are in a direct line with each other, the tides that result are called (1) neap tides (2) full tides (3) ebb tides (4) spring tides

11. In one month, the number of times that the moon and sun are at right angles to each other in relation to Earth is (1) one (2) two (3) three (4) four

THE GEOMETRY OF ORBITS

The orbits of the planets that revolve around the sun look like flattened circles. The exact shape of an orbit, however, is an ellipse. An **ellipse** is defined by two fixed points called the foci (singular: **focus**) that lie on either side of the center of the *major axis*, a line through the widest part of an ellipse. See Figure 10-6. The orbits of the planets are ellipses with the sun at one focus. It is important to remember that the sun is *not* at the center of Earth's orbit.

If the two foci are located near the ends of the major axis, an ellipse is long and narrow, like the paths of many comets. At its most extreme elongation, an ellipse becomes a line. As the foci move closer together, the shape of an ellipse becomes circular. A circle is a special kind of an ellipse in which the two foci come together at a single point. See Figure 10-7. The orbits of the sun's planets are very close to circular, with the two foci close together.

You will find in the *Earth Science Reference Tables* the following formula that can be used to calculate the **eccentricity** (elongation) of an ellipse.

$$\text{eccentricity} = \frac{\textbf{distance between the foci}}{\textbf{length of the major axis}}$$

$$e = \frac{d}{L}$$

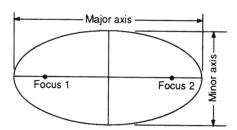

Figure 10-6. The major axis of an ellipse is a straight line that passes through the two foci.

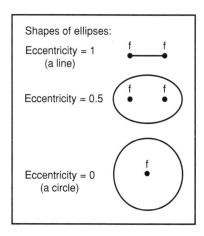

Figure 10-7. Shapes of ellipses

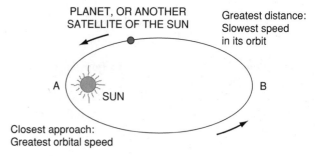

Sample Problem

Find the eccentricity of the ellipse in Figure 10-8. (The dots show the locations of the two foci. You will need a centimeter scale to measure the ellipse.)

Solution:

$$e = \frac{d}{L}$$

$$e = \frac{4 \text{ cm}}{5 \text{ cm}}$$

$$e = 0.8$$

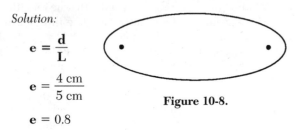

Figure 10-8.

Eccentricity is a ratio, so it has no units.

Figure 10-9. The speed of a planet varies with its distance from the sun. This is true for any satellite, including moons. When the satellite is closest, at position A, the gravitational attraction is the strongest, so the satellite moves the fastest in its orbit. The satellite slows as it moves toward B because its distance from the sun is increasing and the gravitational attraction is decreasing. This is a cyclic change.

THE FORCE OF GRAVITY

Gravity is a force of attraction between objects. This force depends on the masses of the objects and the distance between them. Increasing the mass of the objects increases the force while increasing the distance between them decreases the force. When you measure your weight, you are measuring the force of attraction between your body and Earth. If you want to lose mass you can eat less and exercise more so that there is less of you. This also would decrease your weight. If you could greatly decrease Earth's mass, this would also cause your weight to decrease. However, we do not have a way to significantly decrease Earth's mass. Another way to decrease your weight is to increase your distance from Earth. If you were to become an astronaut and travel into space, this would decrease the gravitational force between you and Earth (your weight). Go far enough away and you could become virtually weightless, but you would still have the same mass.

Gravity and the Planets.

Gravity is the force that holds the planets and other objects in the solar system in their orbits. Any object that orbits another object in space is known as a **satellite**. For example, Earth is a satellite of the sun, and the moon is Earth's satellite. Because orbits are not perfectly circular, the distance between Earth and the sun changes as Earth revolves around the sun. See Figure 10-9. We generally ignore the gravitational attraction of the planets, because most of the mass of the solar system is found in the sun. In their orbits, satellites move fastest when they are closest to the sun and slowest when they are farthest from the sun. Although Earth's orbit is not a perfect circle, it is so close that the changing orbital speed of planet Earth, while measurable is not noticeable to us.

The elliptical path of any satellite is a result of two factors, inertia and gravity. **Inertia** is the tendency of an object to remain at rest, or, if it is moving, to move with the same speed in the same direction. If a satellite has a circular orbit, inertia and the force of gravity are constant. There is no change in speed for this satellite, but there is a constant change in direction, allowing the

satellite to take a circular path. Gravity causes the direction to change continuously as the satellite moves in a circle. If the orbit is elliptical (eccentric), gravity also causes the speed to change; the satellite moves faster when it is near its primary, and slower when it is farther away.

With respect to the other planets in the solar system, the closer a planet is to the sun the faster it moves in its orbit. Mercury, the planet closest to the sun, travels about 1.6 times as fast as Earth and 10 times the speed of Pluto, which has the greatest average distance from the sun.

THE SOLAR SYSTEM

Through radiometric analysis, as discussed in Chapter 5, we know that the solar system is about 4.6 billion years old. Although this might seem extremely old, the solar system is in fact only about a third of the age of the universe. The "Big Bang," which created the universe, did not initially produce such heavy elements as carbon iron, silicon, and oxygen. These building blocks of the sun's planets (and of our bodies) originated in the explosive deaths of giant stars, for in nature only supernovae can create elements more massive than hydrogen or helium. As the late astronomer Carl Sagan noted, we are all made of "star-stuff."

Planets of the Solar System.

The planets can be divided into two groups: rocky (terrestrial) planets and gas giants. Earth, with a mean density of 5.5 g/cm^3, is the densest of the rocky planets. Figure 10-10 shows that of the other rocky planets, Mercury and Venus are most similar to Earth in density. Mars has a density that is about 70% that of Earth, and Pluto's density is about one fifth that of Earth.

Jupiter, Saturn, Uranus, and Neptune are known as the gas giants. This name is quite appropriate because they are mostly made up of compressed gases, with a tiny liquid and/or rocky core, and are roughly 4 to 11 times greater than Earth in diameter. The densities of

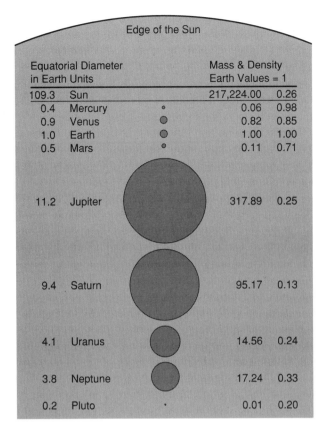

Equatorial Diameter in Earth Units		Mass & Density Earth Values = 1	
109.3	Sun	217,224.00	0.26
0.4	Mercury	0.06	0.98
0.9	Venus	0.82	0.85
1.0	Earth	1.00	1.00
0.5	Mars	0.11	0.71
11.2	Jupiter	317.89	0.25
9.4	Saturn	95.17	0.13
4.1	Uranus	14.56	0.24
3.8	Neptune	17.24	0.33
0.2	Pluto	0.01	0.20

Figure 10-10. A comparison of the other members of the solar system with Earth

these large planets range from 0.7 g/cm³ (Saturn) to 1.7 g/cm³ (Neptune).

The planet Mercury is similar to Earth's moon in several ways. Both the moon and Mercury are smaller than Earth. Like the moon, Mercury has a dark surface covered with craters left over from billions of years of collisions with meteorites. Unlike Earth, neither Mercury nor the moon has a significant atmosphere, thus they are not protected from meteor impacts and their craters do not erode quickly. Since they have almost no atmosphere, soil samples from both would show no chemical weathering. Both the moon and Mercury also show extremes in temperature that result from the lack of an atmosphere. Relatively slow rotation makes days and nights longer on Mercury and the moon than on Earth.

The surface temperatures on the planets are mainly the result of their distance from the sun. For example, the hottest surface temperatures occur on Mercury and Venus. Although Mercury is closer to the sun, Venus' surface temperatures are a little higher than those on the daylight side of Mercury. The hot temperatures on Venus are the result of a very dense atmosphere of carbon dioxide: a "greenhouse effect" run wild. Earth and Mars are cooler because of their greater distance from the sun. Although the atmosphere of Mars is mostly carbon dioxide, this atmosphere is very thin. Therefore, the greenhouse effect on Mars is minimal and temperatures are generally cooler than temperatures on Earth. The term "surface temperature" has little meaning on the gas giants, as these planets are primarily composed

of gases that increase in density with depth and pressure. Pluto, the outermost planet, is very cold, as it is about forty times as far from the sun as is Earth. See Figure 10-11.

Earth is Unique.

Our home planet is unique in several ways. Earth is the only planet that has abundant liquid water. Mars shows evidence of erosion by moving water, but liquid water is no longer present on the surface. The moons of Jupiter have abundant water, but only in the form of ice. From Chapter 5, you may remember how important liquid water was to the development of life on Earth. The presence of liquid water on Earth may be the principal reason why living organisms have not been detected elsewhere in the solar system. In addition, only our planet has an atmosphere with abundant free oxygen that is released when plants extract carbon from carbon dioxide by photosynthesis.

The federal government has established extensive programs to explore the solar system by means of satellites, probes, robots and, possibly, human visits to other planets. Scientists explore other planets to better understand our own planet, to investigate possibilities of establishing colonies on other planets, and to look for additional resources. Most likely, the cratered surface of Mars will be the next target for direct human exploration. Mars is relatively near Earth, its thin atmosphere is transparent and non-toxic, and it is probably the planet closest to the Earth in its physical conditions.

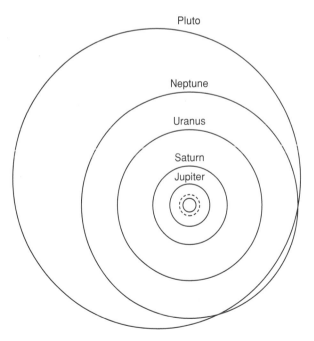

Figure 10-11. Orbits of the outer planets. The four outer planets have much larger orbits than the inner planets. The innermost circle is the orbit of Mars, with Mercury, Venus and Earth's orbits even smaller. The dots represent the orbits of the asteroids. Pluto and Neptune do not collide because of the inclination of Pluto's orbit.

Asteroids, Meteors, and Comets.

The nine planets are not the sun's only satellites. A number of smaller objects also orbit the sun, including asteroids, meteoroids, and comets.

Asteroids. Located for the most part in a belt between the orbits of Mars and Jupiter are tens of thousands of rocky objects known as **asteroids**. They range in size from roughly 600 miles (1000 kilometers) in diameter down to mere pebbles. Although asteroids are sometimes considered minor planets, all of the asteroids put together would form a body about half as big as Earth's moon.

A few asteroids have orbits that can cross Earth's orbit. There is evidence that a large asteroid approximately 10 kilometers in diameter struck Earth in the Yucatan region of Mexico about 65 million years ago. In addition to a buried crater, sedimentary deposits of that era are rich in iridium (a rare element on Earth), and fossils indicate that most living things suddenly became extinct (died out completely). Scientists think that this catastrophic collision might have thrown tons of dust into the atmosphere, blocking the sunlight, and dramatically cooling Earth's climates for many months. Without sunlight, plants could not make food, and died out. Without food, plant-eaters starved, which in turn caused meat-eaters to starve. Such a massive food shortage may have caused the extinction of the dinosaurs at the end of the Mesozoic era.

Meteors. Small solid particles from space can be caught by Earth's gravity and dragged down through the atmosphere. As the objects fall, they are heated by friction with Earth's atmosphere and burn up, producing streaks of light visible at night as **meteors**, or "shooting stars." (Potential meteors in space are called meteoroids.) Most meteors are vaporized during their fall through the atmosphere, although some of them are large enough to hit the ground. (Meteors that survive their fall and hit the ground are called meteorites.)

Each year, the orbiting Earth passes through thin clouds of meteoroids in early January, mid-August, and early December. During these times, meteors are particularly common. In 1992, a meteorite about the size of a football fell through the trunk of a car in Peekskill, New York. The most dramatic structure resulting from a meteor strike on Earth is probably Meteor Crater in northern Arizona, which is 4,150 feet (1,265 m) across and 570 feet (174 m) deep. Although Earth has been struck by meteors many times in its past, it is not covered with impact craters like the moon or Mercury. This is because only the largest meteors survive the fall through Earth's atmosphere, most of these strike the oceans, and impact craters on land are eroded away.

Meteor impacts were more common early in the history of the solar system. Over the past 4.5 billion years, most of the interplanetary debris (rocks, dust, and so on) has been swept up by the gravity of the planets.

Comets. Comets are icy objects, most of which originate in a region outside the planets. Some of them come close to the sun in highly elliptical orbits. Heating by the sun causes them to partially vaporize, producing a tail that can, in some cases, cross much of the night sky. Halley's comet is perhaps the best-known comet, and has a period of approximately 75 years. (By the way, the name Halley has a short *a* and rhymes with "tally.") Unlike meteors, which are visible for a few seconds and move rapidly, comets are visible for weeks and do not streak across the night sky.

QUESTIONS

12. Which of the following celestial objects usually have the most eccentric orbits? (1) planets (2) comets (3) asteroids (4) moons

13. What is the most likely way an asteroid impact caused the extinction of the dinosaurs? (1) The asteroid directly hit all the dinosaurs (2) The asteroid impact sent rocks into the air that hit the dinosaurs (3) The asteroid impact started catastrophic earthquakes all over the world (4) Dust raised by the impact changed the climate and food supply.

14. Which diagram below best shows the true shape of Earth's orbit around the sun?

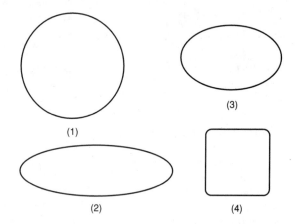

15. Earth moves fastest in its orbit when it is (1) closest to the sun (2) farthest from the sun (3) closest to the moon (4) farthest from the moon

16. Which celestial objects do not seem to show a cyclical, periodic motion? (1) planets (2) comets (3) meteors (4) moons

17. What is the eccentricity of the ellipse below? (1) 0.5 (2) 0.8 (3) 1.0 (4) 2.0

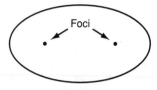

18. What does the tail of a comet show? (1) a trail of particles left by the comet flying through space (2) dust picked up by the comet from the vicinity of a planet (3) rapid motion of the comet though Earth's atmosphere (4) gases burned off the comet by solar radiation

19. Which of the following is *not* an ellipse? (1) line (2) circle (3) triangle

20. On which planet is a large portion of the surface covered by liquid water? (1) Mercury (2) Venus (3) Earth (4) Mars

21. The surface of Venus is much hotter than would be expected because it has (1) many active volcanoes (2) a slow rate of rotation (3) highly reflective clouds (4) a high percentage of carbon dioxide in its atmosphere

22. Earth has fewer impact craters than Mercury because of the (1) destruction of meteors in Earth's atmosphere (2) more rapid subduction of crustal plates on Mercury (3) slower weathering and erosion rates on Earth (4) faster rotational speed of Mercury.

Directions: Base your answers to questions 23–25 on the diagram below.

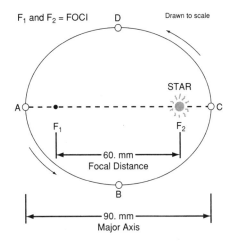

23. At what point in its orbit does the satellite shown above have the greatest velocity? (1) A (2) B (3) C (4) D

24. What is the eccentricity of this orbit? (1) 0.06 (2) 0.15 (3) 0.67 (4) 1.50

25. How does Earth's orbit around the sun compare with the planet shown above? (1) Earth's orbit is more flattened (2) Earth's orbit is more circular (3) Earth's orbit is exactly the same (4) Earth orbits the moon, not the sun.

26. When is the gravitational attraction between Earth and the sun the greatest? (1) when Earth is closest to the sun (2) when Earth is farthest from the sun (3) each day at 12 noon (4) each night at exactly midnight

Directions: Base your answers to questions 27–28 on the following diagram.

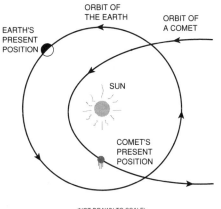

(NOT DRAWN TO SCALE)

27. The diagram shows the orbit of Earth and part of the orbit of a comet. Compared to the orbit of Earth, the orbit of the comet is (1) less eccentric (2) more eccentric (3) the same eccentricity

28. For the time shown in this diagram, an observer at Earth's equator at midnight (1) sees the comet straight overhead (2) sees the comet just rising (3) sees the comet just setting (4) cannot see the comet in the sky

The Sun.

The sun is by far the nearest star to Earth. A **star** is a large, self-luminous body in space that creates its own energy. Although the sun is smaller than most of the distant stars we see in the night sky, it is larger than most of the nearby stars, which are very dim. We may therefore conclude that the sun is fairly typical of the vast number of stars in the universe. Indeed, the sun, being a fairly average sort of star, appears near the middle of the simplified Hertzsprung-Russell diagram in Figure 10-12. The Hertzsprung-Russell diagram, named after the two astronomers who developed it, group stars by color (which is an indication of temperature) and how much light they give off. Using this diagram, most of the stars can be classified as white dwarfs, main sequence stars (like the sun), red giants, and supergiants.

Like all stars, the sun gets its energy from **nuclear fusion**, which you can think of as two hydrogen atoms fusing together to form a helium atom. This reaction produces a huge amount of energy. The nuclear energy that we use to generate electricity and to power some large ships is nuclear fission, in which large atoms such as uranium or plutonium split to form smaller atoms. Although fission does not produce as much energy as fusion and creates dangerous waste products, we have been unable to sustain controlled nuclear fusion because of the extremes in temperature and pressure that it requires. The only way we have been able to use fusion is in the form of hydrogen bombs.

If you look at a projected image of the sun, you may see dark spots on its surface. (Caution: never look at the

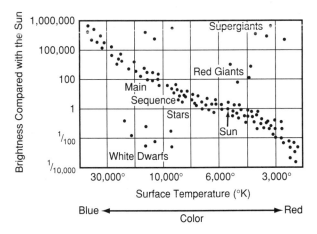

Figure 10-12. The Hertzsprung-Russell diagram is used to classify stars by temperature and size. In this scheme, our sun is a fairly typical star. Although the sun is brighter than most of the nearest stars, it is small compared with most of the stars we see at night.

sun directly through binoculars or telescope or without special protective equipment.) The sideways motion of these spots over time reveals that the sun rotates on its axis every 27 days. These **sunspots** are temporary storms on the visible surface of the sun. They are a little dimmer than the normal surface of the sun, and they often occur in pairs, each with opposite magnetic polarity. Sunspots come and go in cycles of about 11 years. The reason for this is not yet known.

GALAXIES OF STARS

When early astronomers looked at the clear sky on a dark, moonless night, they observed a dim band of light that winds across the sky. They named this band the Milky Way for its faint white color. Telescopic observations revealed that the Milky Way is actually a collection of distant stars that are too faint to be resolved by the unaided eye. When we observe the Milky Way, we are looking along the plane of our own galaxy. A **galaxy** is a huge body of stars and other matter in space. The sun is one of roughly 100 billion stars in the Milky Way.

The Milky Way is a spiral galaxy. Our solar system is located in a spiral arm well away from the galactic center. See Figure 10-13. Mapping the Milky Way galaxy had to be accomplished with radio telescopes because the view in visible light is blocked by clouds of dust. In addition to Earth's rotation on its axis and its orbital motion around the sun, the Earth moves along with the sun and other nearby stars in an orbit around the center of the Milky Way galaxy. Although it takes approximately 220 million years to complete this revolution, our velocity in this galactic rotation is nearly ten times as fast as our orbital motion around the sun.

On a clear, moonless night, you may be able to see the very small, faint patch of light that is our nearest galactic neighbor, a virtual twin of the Milky Way, the Andromeda galaxy. This galaxy is so distant that its light takes two million years to reach us. The Andromeda galaxy is one of about 30 galaxies in our local group. The galaxies are separated into groups with large, relatively empty spaces between them. Astronomers are now investigating super clusters as an even greater level of structure in the universe. Why matter in the universe, which formed from an explosion, is distributed so unevenly is one of the most perplexing questions facing astronomers today.

EVOLUTION OF THE UNIVERSE

One of the most important tools of astronomers is the spectroscope. A spectroscope is an instrument that separates light into its component colors, as does a glass prism. See Figure 10-14. The light given off by stars is marked by dark lines in certain colors. Each element in the stars adds it own unique signature of lines. However, since stars are primarily hydrogen and helium, the lines we usually see in a spectrograph are in the orange, yellow, green and blue areas that characterize these elements.

In the early part of the 20th century, Edwin Hubble discovered that light that reached Earth from distant galaxies shows spectral lines that are shifted toward the red end of the spectrum. He suggested that the **red-shifted** lines are evidence that distant galaxies are rushing away from us at a significant portion of the speed of light. In fact, observations of distant galaxies in all directions showed the red shift. And, the more distant the galaxies, the greater the red shift. The red shift is also known as the Doppler shift. See Figure 10-15. This and other observations have led scientists to the conclusion that the universe is expanding.

Computer models that reverse the expansion, taking us back in time, lead to the idea that at one time the universe was a primordial, concentrated object of incredible mass and density that exploded. This theory of the origin of the universe is now known as the "big bang." In addition, scientists can detect radiation remaining from the big bang.

Radio energy from the explosive origin of the universe, the **big bang**, was predicted but not observed

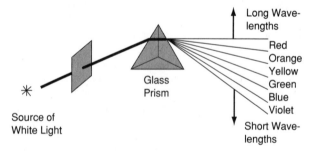

Figure 10-14. A glass prism can be used to separate white light into its component colors.

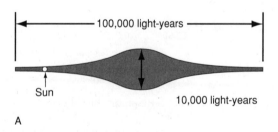

Figure 10-13. The Milky Way galaxy

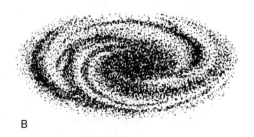

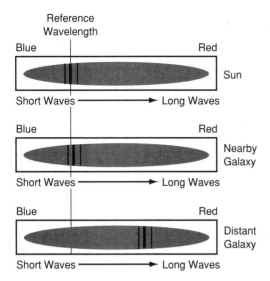

Figure 10-15. A method useful in estimating the distance to dim galaxies is to measure their red shift (Doppler shift). As the universe expands, the more distant a galaxy is the more its spectrum is shifted toward the red (longer wavelength) end of the spectrum.

until two American scientists working on long distance radio communications discovered it in the 1960s. They were unable to point a sensitive radio receiver in any direction in space without picking up annoying **background radiation**. They eventually realized that they were, in fact, "listening" to the original "noise" of the explosive birth of the universe.

Determining the age of the universe, that is, the time since the big bang, depends upon estimates of the distances to galaxies that show measurable red shifts. These estimates are difficult and uncertain. At present, scientists' best judgment indicates an age of the universe of about 10 to 15 billion years.

The Size of the Universe.
Perhaps the most significant thing for you to comprehend about the universe is its size. For those who think of a few kilometers, or even a few thousand kilometers, as a great distance, it is difficult to comprehend the size of the universe with a radius on the order of 10^{23} kilometers.

Perhaps this size is easier to comprehend if you understand how fast light travels. About 400 years ago, the Italian scientist Galileo tried to measure the speed of light, but he was unable to do it. Today, we understand why. Light travels so fast that it could circle Earth seven times in one second. Most scientists believe that the speed of light is the upper limit of all velocities. No object or energy can travel faster than light. Light takes about one and a half seconds to get to the moon, and light from the sun takes about eight minutes to reach Earth. Light from the nearest star (excluding the sun) takes about four years to reach us. The distance light can travel in one year is called a **light-year**, which is about 10 trillion kilometers. The universe is thought to be about 25 billion light-years in diameter.

The Future.
The long-term future of the universe is unclear. Some astronomers think that the expansion of the universe will continue forever. Others believe the force of gravity will eventually reverse the expansion and the universe will fall back together in the "big crunch." It is even possible that the universe pulsates between explosions and contractions.

An analogy may help you to understand this issue. If you throw a baseball upward, you expect gravity to slow its climb until the ball begins to fall back toward the ground. But if you could propel the ball fast enough, it would have enough speed to overcome the gravitational pull of the Earth. At a speed greater than its "escape velocity," the ball would continue into outer space, and never return. Therefore, the ultimate fate of the universe depends upon the balance between the rate of expansion and the escape velocity, which is determined by the mass and density of the universe. At present, these values are not known with enough accuracy to permit scientists to predict the fate of the universe reliably.

QUESTIONS

29. The four diagrams below show the Milky Way galaxy. In which diagram does the black area best represent the relative size of out solar system at this scale?

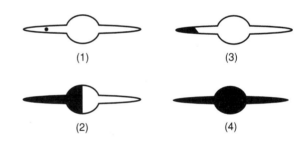

30. Which of the following choices lists these celestial objects in order of increasing size, from smallest to largest? (1) star, planet, galaxy (2) galaxy, star, planet (3) star, galaxy, planet (4) planet, star, galaxy

31. A comparison of the age of Earth obtained from radioactive dating and the age of the universe based on galactic red shifts suggests that (1) Earth is about the same age as the universe (2) Earth is immeasurably older than the universe (3) Earth was formed after the universe began (4) the two dating methods contradict each other

32. Which statement is correct about the most distant stars and galaxies we can observe with telescopes? (1) The stars and galaxies that are the most distant are the ones that look the brightest. (2) Large telescopes help us see very distant stars and galaxies with less time delay. (3) The more distant a star or galaxy, the faster it seems to be moving away from us. (4) The farther away stars and galaxies are, the larger they look in our telescopes.

The Scientist, Engineer, and Citizen

Research the likelihood of a large asteroid striking Earth with disastrous consequences for humans. Propose how we should discover large objects on a collision course with Earth. Devise a written plan that details how to minimize the human consequences of a major asteroid impact.

CHAPTER 10 REVIEW QUESTIONS

1. Why do we always see the same side of the moon? (1) The moon does not rotate on its axis. (2) The moon does not revolve around Earth. (3) The periods of the moon's rotation and revolution are equal. (4) The moon's revolutionary period is just half of the moon's period of rotation.

2. The tides are caused by (1) only the sun (2) only the moon (3) both the sun and the moon (4) the most distant stars

3. The day and the year, as units of time, are based upon the motions of (1) the moon (2) the sun (3) Earth (4) the distant stars

Directions: Base your answers to questions 4–6 on the diagram below, which shows the positions of the sun, moon, and Earth on two different occasions.

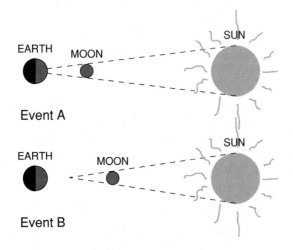

4. In which of the two diagrams above will a person on Earth see the greatest darkening of the sky? (1) event A (2) event B (3) both are the same

5. As observed from Earth, what is the moon phase in both of these diagrams? (1) Full (2) Quarter (3) Crescent (4) New

6. In which event does the moon have the largest angular diameter as measured from Earth? (1) event A (2) event B (3) both are the same

7. Which diagram below best shows the positions of the sun, the moon, and Earth when the sky is made dark by an eclipse of the sun?

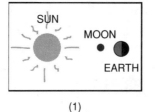

(1)

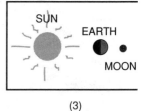

(3)

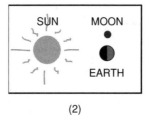

(2)

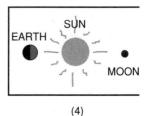

(4)

Directions: Base your answers to questions 8 and 9 on the *Earth Science Reference Tables*.

8. Which of these planets travels the fastest in its orbit around the sun? (1) Mercury (2) Venus (3) Earth (4) Pluto

9. Which planet has an orbit that is closest to a perfect circle? (1) Mercury (2) Venus (3) Earth (4) Pluto

10. Which statement best describes how galaxies generally move? (1) Galaxies move toward one another. (2) Galaxies move away from one another. (3) Galaxies move randomly. (4) Galaxies do not move.

Directions: Base your answers to questions 11 through 13 on the *Earth Science Reference Tables*, the diagram below, and your knowledge of earth science. The diagram represents a model of the orbit of a moon around a planet. Points *A, B, C,* and *D* indicate four positions of the moon in its orbit. Points F_1 and F_2 are focal points of the orbit.

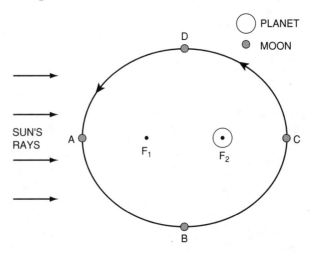

11. When viewed from the planet, the moon has the greatest apparent diameter at point (1) A (2) B (3) C (4) D

174

Reviewing Earth Science: Chapter 10

12. For an observer on the planet, at which position in the moon's orbit does the full-moon phase occur? (1) A (2) B (3) C (4) D

13. As the moon moves in its orbit from point *D* to *B*, the force of gravitational attraction between the moon and the planet (1) increases, only (2) decreases, only (3) increases, then decreases (4) decreases, then increases

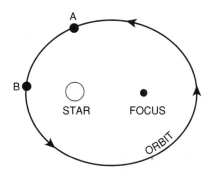

14. What is the eccentricity of the orbit shown above? (1) 0 (2) 0.2 (3) 0.4 (4) 0.8

15. What is the satellite in this star/planet system? (1) the planet (2) the star (3) the focus (4) the ellipse

16. The diagram below represents the orbit of a comet around the sun. In which position is the comet moving the fastest? (1) a (2) b (3) c (4) d

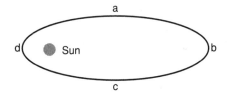

Answer the following questions on a separate sheet of paper.)

1. Draw a labeled diagram that shows the positions of Earth, the sun, and the moon during an eclipse of the moon. You must show the relative sizes of the three objects, their relative distances, and the correct positions of the three objects. They do not have to be drawn to a uniform scale.

(Correct labels and sizes, +1; Correct positions, +1; Correct distances apart, +1)

2. Define galaxy.

(Correct definition, +1)

3. Make a sketch of the Milky Way galaxy and indicate the position of our solar system.

(Correct shape, +1; Approximate position, +1)

4. Briefly tell how the universe began and give one example of experimental evidence to support your answer. Respond in one or more complete sentences.

(Complete sentence(s), +1; Correct beginning, +1; Correct evidence, +1)

5. Why were scientists *not* aware of the surface features of nearly half of the moon until the start of the space age (middle of the twentieth century)?

(Explanation, +1; Complete sentences, +1)

CHAPTER 11 Environmental Awareness

HOW ARE EARTH SYSTEMS LINKED?

Our planet may be unique. As far as we know, it is the only place where life exists and where humans can live without the constant use of artificial life-support systems. The other planets that orbit our sun are too hot or too cold to support human life. They have atmospheres that are too dense or too thin, from thick atmospheres that would be poisonous to humans, to practically no atmosphere at all to provide oxygen or to act as a shield against the harmful radiation that permeates outer space. As far as we can determine with our present technology, planet Earth seems to be unique as a place where life as we know it can develop and thrive.

Balance of Nature.

A principle of chemistry states: if part of a system in balance (**equilibrium**) is changed, other parts of the system will also change to establish a new equilibrium. With regard to pollution, this principle has special meaning for environmentalists. **Pollution** is any substance or form of energy in sufficient concentration to harm living things or the natural environment. It means that when we pollute the environment, other changes are likely to occur as the environment adjusts itself.

For example, when you fertilize your lawn, some of the fertilizer will be washed away by rainfall. It will be carried into nearby streams and lakes. But the result is likely to be more significant than just a little fertilizer in the water. The fertilizer provides nutrients for bacteria that multiply in polluted waterways. The bacteria, in turn, reduce the oxygen content of the water, which leads to the growth of different bacteria that thrive in low oxygen conditions. Fish such as trout, which require clean, well-oxygenated water, die. Less desirable species, such as catfish and carp, take their place.

Adding too many nutrients to water is called organic pollution. Organic pollution is especially severe in farming areas where animal wastes and fertilizers are left on the land. In short, the simple act of fertilizing your lawn can contribute to major changes in a nearby ecosystem, and you may never be aware of all the changes even a small action causes.

HOW DOES TECHNOLOGY IMPACT THE ENVIRONMENT?

As new technologies are developed, new sources of pollution may be created. When they were first invented, chlorofluorocarbons (CFCs) were thought to be miracle substances. These inexpensive compounds are excellent at carrying away heat, and they are also relatively stable. Chlorofluorocarbons made air conditioning affordable in homes, businesses, and modes of transportation. However, in the early 1990s, satellite-based measurements showed that chlorofluorocarbons were drifting into the upper atmosphere where they were destroying Earth's ozone layer. **Ozone** (O_3), is a form of oxygen that protects us from harmful radiation from outer space. CFCs convert ozone into normal oxygen (O_2), which does not protect us from ultraviolet and other high-energy radiation from space.

Other pollutants are contaminating our waterways. Electrical transformers convert high voltage electricity, which can be transmitted long distances, into the lower voltage used in our homes. Although transformers are efficient, some of the electrical energy is lost as heat. Water could be used to cool the transformers. However, water evaporates easily, leaving the wires exposed. The exposed wires could cause a fire. Polychlorinated biphenyls (PCBs) disperse waste heat, and do not evaporate. In addition, PCBs are chemically inactive. Unfortunately, large amounts of PCBs were dumped into the environment near factories where they were manufactured and installed in electrical devices. These wastes settled into river sediments downstream from these factories. Fish from the Great Lakes and many rivers in the United States have been found to have low levels of PCBs. Initially, there was little concern because PCBs were thought to be relatively harmless. Subsequently, PCBs were shown to cause cancer, even when they are eaten in very low concentrations. PCB contamination of the Hudson River in New York State has led to debates among scientist about how to best remove the dangerous chemicals from the river sediments.

HOW CAN WE CLASSIFY POLLUTION?

We sometimes classify pollution by the part of the environment it affects: air, water, or ground. Pollutants are also classified according to their source. Pollution is created by individuals, by communities that collect and dispose of pollutants improperly, and by industries, some of which use a wide range of poisonous chemicals. See Figure 11-1.

Air Pollution.

Carbon dioxide is a natural component of our atmosphere. It is a waste gas given off by all living organisms that take in oxygen for respiration. See Figure 11-2. We know that the use of fossil fuels

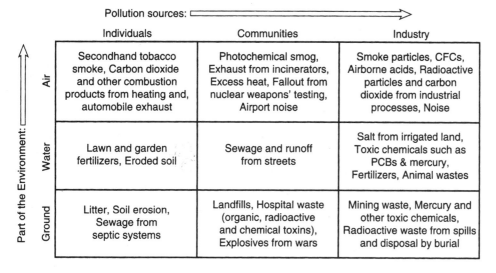

Figure 11-1. Classification of common pollutants. Pollution can be classified by the source of the pollutants and the part of the environment affected. Many forms of pollution belong to more than one category. For example, buried toxins may enter the groundwater and streams or they can escape into the air.

Pollution sources:	Individuals	Communities	Industry
Air	Secondhand tobacco smoke, Carbon dioxide and other combustion products from heating and, automobile exhaust	Photochemical smog, Exhaust from incinerators, Excess heat, Fallout from nuclear weapons' testing, Airport noise	Smoke particles, CFCs, Airborne acids, Radioactive particles and carbon dioxide from industrial processes, Noise
Water	Lawn and garden fertilizers, Eroded soil	Sewage and runoff from streets	Salt from irrigated land, Toxic chemicals such as PCBs & mercury, Fertilizers, Animal wastes
Ground	Litter, Soil erosion, Sewage from septic systems	Landfills, Hospital waste (organic, radioactive and chemical toxins), Explosives from wars	Mining waste, Mercury and other toxic chemicals, Radioactive waste from spills and disposal by burial

adds carbon dioxide to Earth's atmosphere. See Figure 11-3. Carbon dioxide is a "**greenhouse gas.**" The high temperatures found on the planet Venus are largely a result of the greenhouse effect caused by Venus's thick atmosphere of carbon dioxide that lets in sunlight, but retards the escape of heat. If the increase in the level of carbon dioxide in our atmosphere causes climatic change, it is not clear how it would affect any particular location on Earth. Some locations would probably experience more warming than others. In some places, a reduction in rainfall might cause greater problems than the expected increase in temperature.

Metropolitan Los Angeles is one of the fastest growing areas in the United States. Los Angeles sits in several valleys located between the San Gabriel Mountains and the Pacific Ocean. The surrounding mountains prevent the free flow of winds from the ocean. Exhausts from motor vehicles, homes, and power plants are trapped and changed by sunlight into the brown haze known as photochemical smog. One component of pho-

tochemical smog is ozone. The same ozone we need in the upper atmosphere, becomes a pollutant at ground level, especially for people who have respiratory problems.

When fossil fuels are burned without proper pollution controls, oxides of nitrogen and sulfur are released into the atmosphere. They may be carried hundreds of kilometers downwind. When these oxides mix with water in the atmosphere, they form acids. Although rain is naturally slightly acidic, acid contamination has produced rain that is as much as 40 times more acidic than normal precipitation. Acid precipitation is a special problem in locations such as New York's Adirondack Mountains where the bedrock has little calcite (limestone or marble), which can help neutralize acidity in the water. The accumulation of acidic winter snow is a special problem because it produces a rush of acid water in the spring, when the snow melts. Unfortunately, fish spawn (mate and lay eggs) in the spring. Acid precipitation harms fish in their early stages of

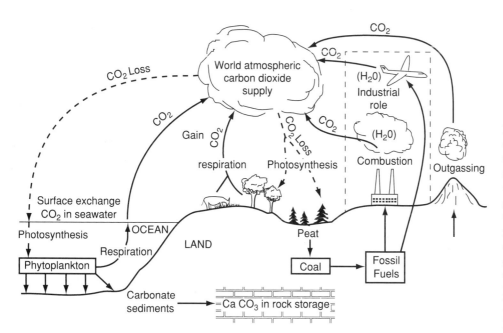

Figure 11-2. The carbon cycle. Carbon dioxide, CO_2, is taken from the atmosphere by photosynthesis and absorbed by seawater. Respiration and volcanoes are the primary natural sources of carbon dioxide. When they burn fossil fuels, humans add CO_2 to the atmosphere. Large amounts of CO_2 are held in carbonate rocks, primarily limestone.

Environmental Awareness

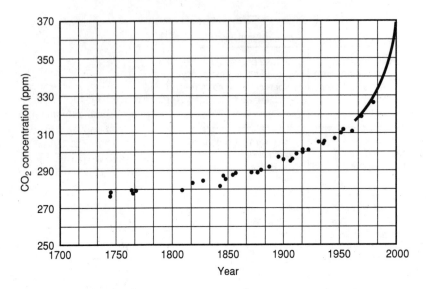

Figure 11-3. Carbon dioxide concentrations in the atmosphere in parts per million (ppm). The solid line, which begins in 1958, shows continuous measurements of CO_2; the dots represent ice core data. Scientists know the CO_2 content of Earth's atmosphere is increasing, and this is likely to produce global warming. However, it is not clear how global warming will affect the climate of any particular location.

development when they are especially sensitive to acidified water. Figure 11-4 shows the most important sources of air pollution. As you can see, what starts as air pollution can sometimes end up polluting our water.

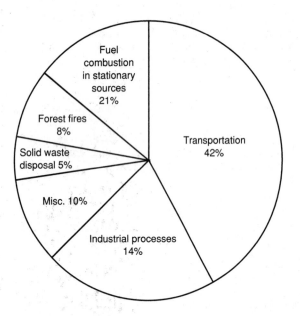

Figure 11-4. Sources of air pollution in the United States (percent by mass)

Water Pollution.

The sunny climate and infrequent frosts in Southern California and Arizona make this area an excellent place to grow fruits and vegetables. This is especially true in the winter when fruits and vegetables are not available from other Northern Hemisphere regions because of the cold. However, water is in short supply in the Southwest. The Colorado River is used and re-used for irrigation as it flows through this region. During its passage through this desert area, the water picks up salts from the soil. By the time the river reaches Mexico, very little water is left, and that water is seriously polluted with salts washed from the irrigated fields.

In the late 1950s, many people living in the southern part of Japan along Minamata Bay developed serious health problems. They ate fish from the bay into which nearby industries discharged wastes that contained mercury. Even in very low concentrations, mercury, like other heavy metals, is capable of causing permanent nerve damage. During the early 1970s in the United States, some tuna and swordfish sold in stores were found to contain dangerous levels of mercury. The government had the fish removed from the stores and issued a warning to the public. Since that time, the governments of the United States and Canada have prohibited the dumping of industrial wastes that contain mercury. Figure 11-5 describes some modern ecological disasters.

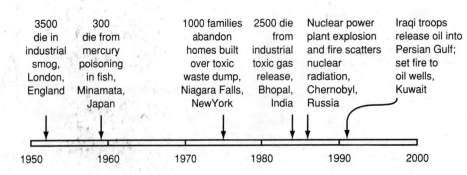

Figure 11-5. Recent environmental disasters. Although advances in technology can make our lives better, they can also cause environmental disasters.

Ground Pollution.

We are constantly trying to find better ways to dispose of our household and community garbage. At one time garbage was taken to dumps where it was burned. When it became clear the open burning of trash was creating unacceptable levels of air pollution and that these dumps were infested with rats that carried disease, many communities developed "sanitary landfills." In a sanitary landfill, the garbage was covered each day by a layer of soil. However, rainwater and groundwater that ran out of the landfills carried dangerous chemicals into nearby streams. Large cities are now unable to find safe places to build landfills. Today, increasing numbers of communities are building high-temperature incinerators that burn hot enough to decompose most of the dangerous substances that were once released by outdoor burning. But even modern incinerators produce toxic ash. Although the garbage has been reduced in volume by burning, the ash must be buried with even stronger safeguards than those needed at old landfills. This often means a site with a thick, plastic liner both above and below the ash.

In Niagara Falls, New York, zoning officials allowed the construction of a large housing development and a school on land where toxic chemicals had been buried. After they moved in, the families noticed elevated incidences of cancer and birth defects. In addition, heavily polluted water was found seeping out of the ground. About 1000 families were forced to move from their homes. These homes had to be abandoned when the government declared the site to be unfit for human habitation.

Energy Pollution.

When we think of pollution we usually think of substances in the environment, but pollution can also be in the form of energy. We are surrounded by sources of low-level natural radioactivity. See Figure 11-6. Except in a few places where the decay of natural uranium in the ground releases radioactive radon gas into homes or other buildings, scientists generally consider the level of radioactivity in the natural environment acceptable.

Nuclear power plants, hospitals, and some industries, on the other hand, produce high-level radioactive nuclear waste. The radioactivity given off by these substances is capable of causing cancer, birth defects, and even death. Some of these waste products will continue to give off lethal quantities of radiation for thousands of years. Some scientists have suggested burying these high-level radioactive wastes in deep underground storage areas. We have yet to find a method of disposing of high-level radioactive wastes that is universally accepted as safe.

HOW HAS THE HUMAN POPULATION GROWN?

The human population increased gradually, from the time of the earliest civilizations until the industrial revolution in the 1800s. As a result of the technological

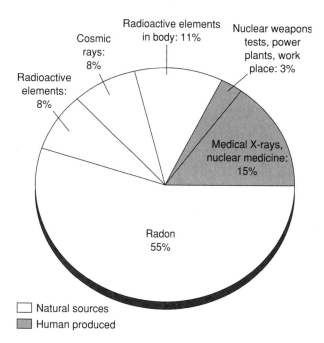

Figure 11-6. Sources of nuclear radiation exposure. For the average person, more than 80% of the exposure to nuclear radiation is thought to be from the natural environment. Large numbers of X rays or radiation from medical procedures can change these proportions.

innovations that occurred during the industrial revolution, farmers were able to produce more food at lower cost than ever before. At the same time, advances in medicine reduced infant mortality and greatly reduced the occurrence of such diseases as tuberculosis, pneumonia, and smallpox. By about 1850, Earth's population reached a billion people. In 1930, less than a hundred years later, the world's population had doubled to two billion. The next population doubling took place in only 45 years. Now, as we enter the 21st century, there are more than 6 billion people on planet Earth. See Figure 11-7. This is the "population explosion" that worries many ecologists. If Earth's population continues to increase at this rate, there will be more people than the planet can support. When we consider our use of energy, the picture is even more alarming. We use many times more energy per person than our ancestors did before the industrial revolution. Our supply of fossil fuels is limited; some scientists predict that we could run out of oil early in the 21st century.

Clearly, Earth's human population cannot continue to increase at an accelerating pace. In fact, the populations of the wealthier nations of Europe and North America have stabilized. In these places, parents no longer have large families to insure that someone will care for them in their old age. That responsibility can be assumed by government. The expense of providing an education for their children also helps keep families small in these nations. As wealth spreads from privileged nations to the rest of the world, it is likely that the population of the planet will stabilize at a sustainable number.

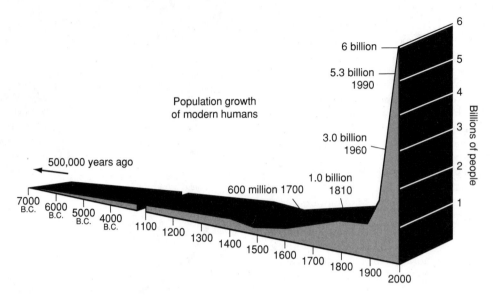

Figure 11-7. The population explosion. Since the industrial revolution, Earth's human population has grown very quickly.

HOW CAN WE BEST MANAGE OUR RESOURCES?

We depend upon Earth for all of our physical needs. Many of our resources are renewable. Renewable resources circulate through the environment and are replenished as we use them. For example, as we use groundwater, it can be replenished by precipitation and inflow from surface water sources. Trees are cut to make paper and building materials. When we plant trees at the same rate at which they are cut, our wood reserves remain constant. Wise management will lead us to use our renewable resources no faster than they can be regenerated by natural cycles.

Other resources, such as mineral ores, fossil fuels, and soil, are nonrenewable because they take so long to form that there is little or no hope of replacing them once they are used. Most of the world's deposits of iron ore formed billions of years ago before oxygen became abundant in the atmosphere. As we mine iron ore, there is little chance of replacing it through natural cycles. We need to plan wisely so that we can make the best use of these nonrenewable resources. Recycling or reusing nonrenewable resources will help prolong Earth's limited supply of these materials.

Will We Run Out?
What happens when we run out of resources? History provides us with several examples. In the 1800s whale oil was burned in lamps as a clean-burning source of indoor lighting. As the number of whales decreased, normal effects of "supply and demand" took over, the price of whale oil increased. But this did not mean that people had to live without interior lighting. At first whale oil was replaced by kerosene, which was less expensive to produce. The next step was gaslight. In 1878, Thomas Edison invented the electric light bulb. With the development of production technology and a network to carry electrical energy to even the most remote homes, electricity is used for lighting and many other energy needs.

In many places where wood had been used as fuel, so many trees have been cut that the land has been nearly cleared of trees. This is true of some parts of England and in parts of Europe. Some of these areas now get most of their energy from fossil fuels, such as coal, oil, and gasoline. Eventually sources of coal and petroleum will be depleted, then a new source of energy must be found. Other areas rely on nuclear power plants for energy. But nuclear power plants generate high-level radioactive wastes that must be stored safely for thousands of years. Throughout history, as one source of energy has been depleted, another has been developed to take its place. Solar technology, which is nearly pollution free, may provide our energy in the future.

Topsoil, needed for growing crops, is another resource that is being lost. While it is difficult to imagine how we could survive if we ran out of topsoil, historical examples of resource depletion have not necessarily led to the kinds of disasters that some scientists have predicted.

The Future.
We need to think of our resources as investments in our future. Investments provide the greatest benefit when they are managed properly. If we squander our resources, they will be gone before we can fully appreciate their value. The object is to use our resources, but to do so with the greatest possible awareness of our future needs. This is a three-step process. First, we need to conduct scientific research to find the best ways to use and conserve resources. Second, we must explore alternate ways to provide for future needs. Third, we need to educate those who will harvest our resources and those who consume them.

We can learn to become better citizens of our planet if we understand and appreciate the Native American quotation, "We do not inherit the Earth from our ancestors, we borrow it from our children."

The Scientist, Engineer, and Citizen

Identify a real pollution problem in your community. Devise a plan of action to minimize its effect or eliminate the problem.

CHAPTER 11
REVIEW QUESTIONS

1. The climates of densely populated industrial areas tend to be warmer than similarly located sparsely populated rural areas. From this observation, what can be inferred about the human influence on local climate? (1) Local climates are not affected by increases in population density. (2) The local climate in densely populated areas can be changed by human activities. (3) In densely populated areas, human activities increase the amount of natural pollutants. (4) In sparsely populated areas, human activities have stabilized the rate of energy absorption.

2. Which of the sources of energy listed below is most nearly pollution free? (1) nuclear (2) solar (3) coal (4) natural gas

3. Which pollutant is *not* usually produced or added to the environment by human activities? (1) sound (2) pollen (3) radiation (4) smoke

4. Which is the *least* probable source of atmospheric pollution in heavily populated cities? (1) human activities (2) industrial plants (3) natural processes (4) automobile traffic

5. The data table below shows the average dust concentrations in the air over many years for selected cities of different populations.

Population in Millions	Dust Particles/Meter³
less than 0.7	110
between 0.7 and 1.0	150
greater than 1.0	190

Based on this data table, which graph best represents the general relationship between population and concentration of dust particles?

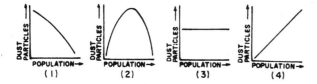

6. As the human population density along a shore of a lake increases, the pollution of the lake usually (1) decreases (2) increases (3) remains the same

7. Which graph (top right column) generally represents the relationship between the quality of river water and the density of human population along the river?

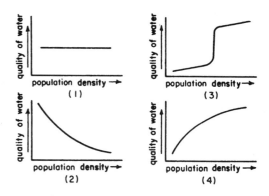

8. A major argument against the construction of nuclear-powered electric generation stations is the claim that they pollute bodies of water by discharging large quantities of (1) noise (2) heat (3) organisms (4) chemicals

9. What is the main reason that a high concentration of bacteria is harmful to a lake? (1) They release large amounts of oxygen. (2) They use up large amounts of oxygen. (3) They cause excessive cooling of the water. (4) They provide food for predators.

Directions: Base your answers to questions 10–13 on the map below.

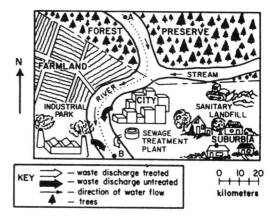

10. Which landscape region has probably been altered *least* by the activities of humans? (1) suburbia (2) sanitary landfill (3) farmland (4) forest preserve

11. Which graph best represents the probable number of bacteria long line *A-B* in the rivers?

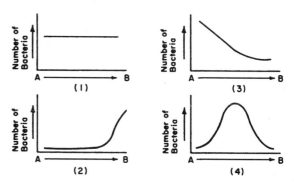

12. If light rains occurred for one hour, which area would most likely experience the greatest amount of surface

runoff per square kilometers? (1) farmland (2) suburbia (3) forest preserve (4) city

13. Which diagram best illustrates the probable *air pollution field* of this area at an elevation of 100 meters on a windless spring afternoon?

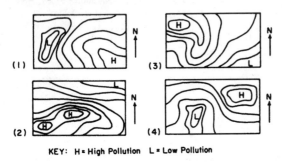

KEY: H = High Pollution   L = Low Pollution

14. Which graph best represents human population growth?

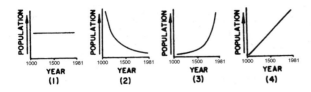

15. Earth's human population is (1) decreasing (2) increasing (3) remaining the same

16. When humans' careless activities decrease the amount of plant life, the amount of runoff usually (1) decreases (2) increases (3) remains the same

17. Many landscapes in New York State are presently being altered by (1) glacial activity (2) volcanic action (3) potential evapotranspiration (4) human activities

18. Which statement is best supported by the graph shown below? (1) From 1960 to 2000 there was a decrease in the use of fossil fuels. (2) From 1900 to 1960, the average person continuously used a greater quantity of fossil fuels. (3) By 1980 the world population was approximately 400 million. (4) From 1970 to 2000 the world population remained relatively constant.

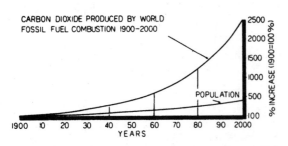

19. Legislation by federal, state, and local governments dealing with the problem of pollution has come about mainly as a result of (1) people's ability to solve this problem with technology (2) nature's ability to clean itself, given enough time (3) people's belief that natural resources are inexhaustible (4) people's action because of their needs, awareness, and attitudes

20. Which graph (top right column) best shows the relationship between atmospheric transparency and the concentration of pollution particles in the air?

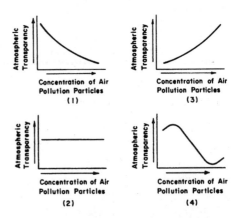

Directions: Base your answers to questions 21–25 on your knowledge of earth science and the air pollution field map shown below. The isolines represent the concentration of pollutants measured in particles/cm³.

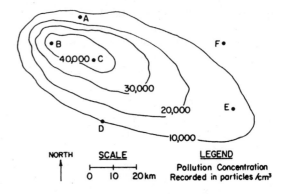

21. The major source of air pollution is most likely at point (1) A (2) B (3) E (4) D

22. The winds responsible for this air pollution pattern are most likely blowing from the (1) northeast (2) northwest (3) southeast (4) southwest

23. The most rapid increase in air pollution would be encountered when traveling between points (1) A and B (2) A and F (3) C and D (4) D and E

24. The air pollution field illustrated by the map is located in a heavily populated area. Which is the *least* probable source of the pollution? (1) human activities (2) industrial plants (3) automobile traffic (4) natural processes

25. Which graph best represents the relationship between the pollution concentration and distance from point B toward point E?

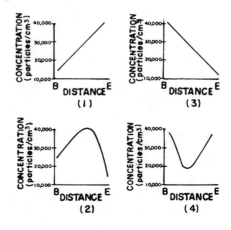

Directions: Base your answers to questions 26–30 on your knowledge of earth science, the *Earth Science Reference Tables*, and the diagrams and map below. The graphs in diagram I show the sources of nitrogen and sulfur dioxide emissions in the United States. Diagram II gives information about the acidity of Adirondack lakes. The map shows regions of the United States affected by acid rain.

26. Which pH level of lake water would not support any fish life? (1) 7.0 (2) 6.0 (3) 5.0 (4) 4.0

DIAGRAM I

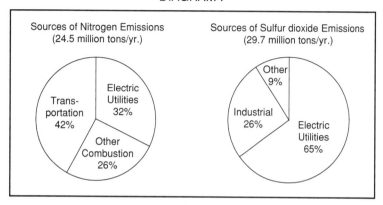

Sources of Nitrogen Emissions
(24.5 million tons/yr.)

Electric Utilities 32%
Transportation 42%
Other Combustion 26%

Sources of Sulfur dioxide Emissions
(29.7 million tons/yr.)

Other 9%
Industrial 26%
Electric Utilities 65%

DIAGRAM II

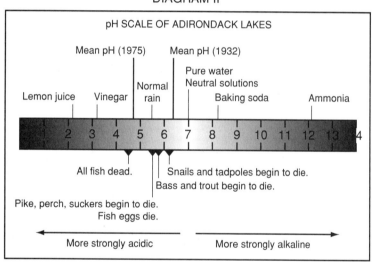

pH SCALE OF ADIRONDACK LAKES

Mean pH (1975)
Mean pH (1932)
Pure water
Neutral solutions
Lemon juice   Vinegar   Normal rain   Baking soda   Ammonia

1 2 3 4 5 6 7 8 9 10 11 12 13 14

All fish dead.
Snails and tadpoles begin to die.
Bass and trout begin to die.
Pike, perch, suckers begin to die.
Fish eggs die.

More strongly acidic ← → More strongly alkaline

REGIONS OF THE UNITED STATES SENSITIVE TO ACID RAIN

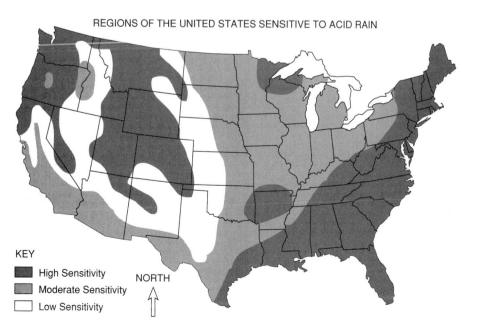

KEY
■ High Sensitivity
▨ Moderate Sensitivity
□ Low Sensitivity

NORTH ↑

27. Which graph best shows the change in acidity in Adirondack lakes since 1930?

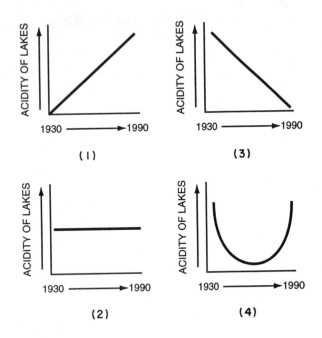

(1)

(2)

(3)

(4)

28. The primary cause of acid rain is the (1) weathering and erosion of limestone rocks (2) decay of plant and animal organisms (3) burning of fossil fuels by humans (4) destruction of the ozone layer

29. Acid rain can best be reduced by (1) increasing the use of high-sulfur coal (2) controlling pollutants at the source (3) reducing the cost of petroleum (4) eliminating all use of nuclear energy

30. In addition to its effects on living organisms, acid rain may cause changes in the landscape by (1) decreasing chemical weathering due to an increase in the destruction of vegetation (2) decreasing physical weathering due to less frost action (3) increasing the breakdown of rock material due to an increase in chemical weathering (4) increasing physical weathering of rock material due to an increase in the circulation of groundwater

FREE-RESPONSE QUESTIONS

(Answer the following questions on a separate sheet of paper.)

1. Identify a form of pollution that primarily affects the ground.
(Response, +1)

2. Name and define three types of air pollution.
(Name and definition, +1 each)

3. Describe the most common relationship between the human population and the amount of environmental pollution in an area.
(Relationship, +1; Complete sentence(s), +1)

4. How can pollution of the ground result in water pollution?
(Explanation, +1, Complete sentence(s), +1)

5. Explain how air pollution from a factory in Pennsylvania can kill the fish in an Adirondack lake.
(Explanation, +1; Complete sentence(s), +1)

6. The graph shows the present sources of energy used in New York State. Give one reason this graph is likely to change in the future.
(Reasoning, +1; Complete sentences, +1)

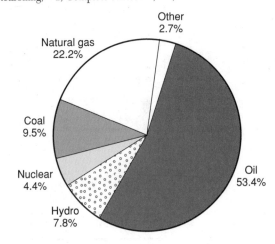

Science, Technology, and Society

The SETI Project: Anyone Out There?

In 1982, a group of the world's foremost astronomers issued the following statement.

"Intelligent organisms are as much a part of the universe as stars and galaxies. It is hard to imagine a more exciting astronomical discovery or one that would have greater impact on human perceptions than the detection of extraterrestrial intelligence."

Ten years later, at 3:00 P.M. on October 12, 1992, the most ambitious hunt for such organisms was launched when astronomer Jill Tarter flipped a switch at Arecibo, Puerto Rico, the site of the world's largest radiotelescope. Tarter is the Project Scientist, or director, of NASA's SETI program. And SETI stands for the pulsequickening phrase: Search for Extra-Terrestrial Intelligence.

When Tarter threw the switch, the 300-meter-wide aluminum dish at Arecibo began to collect radio waves zipping to Earth from outer space. Scientists expected that most of the radio waves would be irregular and random. Such waves are generated naturally by stars. But what if the telescope, or others that are part of the 10-year SETI project, picked up a signal that was not irregular or random?

Scientists would then set in motion a series of actions to check, recheck, and check again the nature and source of the signals. After careful analysis and confirmation by researchers around the world, a spokesperson for NASA would announce to the world, "We are not alone."

But what would be the significance of such a discovery? According to Arthur C. Clarke, who wrote the best selling novel *2001: A Space Odyssey*, a message from extraterrestrials (or ETs) might "contain answers to almost all the questions our philosophers and scientists have been asking for centuries, and solutions to many of the practical problems that beset mankind."

If this event comes to pass, a great deal of credit will have to go to Cornell University scientists Frank Drake, Giuseppe Cocconi, and Philip Morrison who, in the late 1950s and early 1960s, suggested that a survey of space might turn up signals produced by ETs. Although many other scientists considered this idea far-fetched, the Cornell researchers continued to press for the establishment of a hunt for ETs. As Cocconi and Morrison put it in an article published in 1959, "The probability of success is difficult to estimate, but if we never search, the chance of success is zero."

In the beginning, the search, undertaken by Drake in 1960, was limited to only two stars that were very similar to the sun. Their names were Tau Ceti and Epsilon Eridani and they lay 11 light-years from Earth.

Drake had chosen the stars because he reasoned that sunlike stars would be most likely to possess a planetary system with Earthlike planets. And, as far as he or anyone else knew, life similar to that on Earth could only evolve on a planet like Earth. The logic was sound. But after a short 150-hour search, the results were negative.

Although Drake's search had ended in failure, he and other scientists knew that in the Milky Way galaxy—our home family of stars— there were millions of stars like the sun. Did intelligent beings inhabit one or more of these? To find the answer would require advanced technology, time, money, and very persuasive arguments.

By the late 1970s, such arguments had persuaded officials at NASA to seek funds to launch a search. Many members of Congress were reluctant to allocate money for what they considered foolish endeavors. But the scientists persisted and, finally, $100 million dollars was made available to launch a 10-year full-scale search for ETs.

The money was there. So was the time. What's more, technology not available to Drake three decades earlier was now available. For example, Drake had had

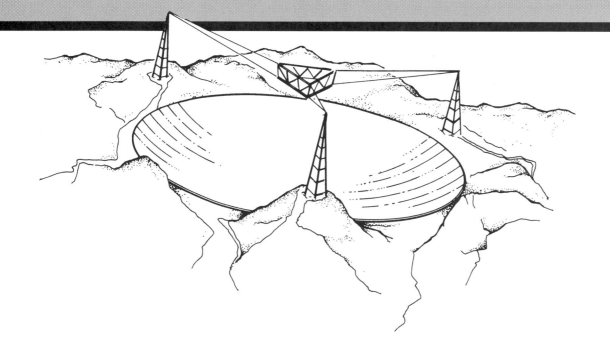

to painstakingly analyze radio wave data to determine whether it might represent messages from ETs. Today, modern computers can do the job in seconds

SETI is really a two-part project. One part, the "targeted search," will be carried out by huge radio-telescopes, like the one at Arecibo. Since these telescopes provide a narrow view, they will focus on individual, sunlike stars. These stars—1000 of them—will all be within about 80 light-years of Earth. (Because radio waves travel at the speed of light, and since a light-year is the distance light travels in a year, a message from an ET 80 light-years away would take 80 years to reach us.) The other part, the "sky survey," will be carried out by many smaller radiotelescopes that can scan larger areas of space. These radiotelescopes will systematically survey the rest of the sky.

Should we spend $100 million on the remote chance that we will be able to carry on century-long conversations with ETs or receive descriptions of their civilization? Is $100 million possibly "the biggest bargain in history," as Drake claims. What do you think?

Questions

1. An early pioneer in the search for ETs was
a. Jill Tarter. c. Frank Drake.
b. Arthur C. Clarke. d. SETI.

2. The "target search" will focus on about
a. 2 stars. c. 100 stars.
b. 10 stars. d. 1000 stars.

3. If we receive a message from ETs that live 40 light-years from the Earth, that message was sent
a. 20 years ago. c. 80 years ago.
b. 40 years ago. d. 160 years ago.

4. Distinguish between each part of the SETI project.

5. Explain why you agree, or disagree, with Frank Drake's characterization of SETI as possibly "the biggest bargain in history."

The Ozone Hole: What Made It?

News item:
Washington April 14, 1993—Satellite measurements indicate an abundance of ozone-destroying chemicals remained in the atmosphere over the Northern Hemisphere much longer this winter than last, researchers said today.

These words, written by Warren E. Leary for *The New York Times*, sent ripples of alarm through the scientific community. The news meant that a phenomenon first sighted over the sparsely populated Antarctic was now lurking over the highly populated regions of North America and Europe, where hundreds of millions of people live. What was the phenomenon? What had caused it? And what could be its consequences'?

The answer to the first question is easy. Concentrated in Earth's stratosphere (a layer of atmosphere that extends from 10–50 km above Earth's surface) is a layer of ozone. And something is punching a hole through that ozone layer. But why should anyone care? And what is ozone anyway?

Ozone is a form of oxygen. But unlike oxygen you breathe, which consists of two atoms of oxygen bonded together, a molecule of ozone consists of three atoms of oxygen. This oxygen triplet possesses a unique and important property. It absorbs ultraviolet (UV) radiation streaming in from the sun. So what? you might ask. So this: UV radiation can kill living things. It can also cause skin cancer in humans.

For a number of years, scientists had known that substances called chlorofluorocarbons (CFCs) were at least partly responsible for destroying ozone high in the sky. And this meant that humans were also responsible. That's because CFCs are chemicals we use as coolants in refrigerators and air conditioners. They were also used in various kinds of aerosol cans and in the manufacture of products such as insulating foams.

When CFCs escape into the air—and they do—they rise into the stratosphere where they can survive for 50 to 100 years. During that time, the CFCs break up, releasing free chlorine. The highly reactive chlorine atoms can do two things. They can react with ozone— thinning out the ozone layer—to form a new compound called chlorine monoxide (ClO) or they can react with nitrogen—leaving the ozone layer in one piece—to form chlorine nitrate ($ClONO_2$).

Obviously, as far as people are concerned, a reaction with nitrogen is preferable to one with ozone But this doesn't happen to a great enough extent, even though there is plenty of nitrogen in the stratosphere. As a matter of fact, about 80 percent of the stratosphere consists of nitrogen. So why doesn't the nitrogen hook on to the chlorine? That's the question many scientists tried to answer.

Initially, researchers investigated strange clouds found in the stratosphere that were tens of kilometers long and a few kilometers thick. They looked like huge red eyes with green pupils. But a study of these clouds revealed that they were made of pure water. They had no effect on the nitrogen in the stratosphere. There were, however, other clouds in the stratosphere, so thin and so spread out that they were invisible to the unaided eye. What were they made of?

The answer was as startling as it was revealing. These unseeable clouds contained a mixture of water and . . . nitric acid (HNO_3)! The nitrogen that might otherwise have neutralized the chlorine set loose from CFCs was already tied up, which left the chlorine free to break up ozone molecules.

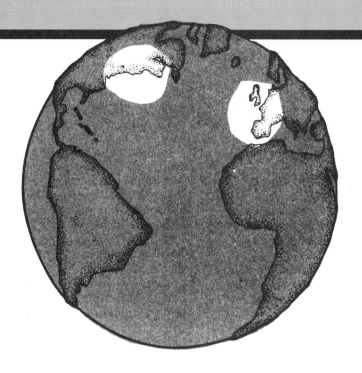

There is general agreement, however, that if we did not pump CFCs into the atmosphere to begin with, no harm would come to the ozone layer. So the ultimate responsibility rests with us, not the clouds above our heads.

What then, can we do to save the ozone layer? What is being done about it? What do you think?

Questions

1. The stratosphere extends above Earth's surface from
   a. 0-10 km.   c. 10-50 km.
   b. 10-20 km.   d. 10-100 km.

2. The ozone layer absorbs
   a. ultraviolet radiation.   c. CFCs.
   b. nitrogen.   d. water.

3. CFCs are used in all the following devices except
   a. refrigerators.   c. aerosol cans.
   b. televisions.   d. air conditioners.

4. Describe how nitrogen might protect the ozone layer and why its effect is limited.

5. On a separate sheet of paper, express your views on what people—or society—might do to protect the ozone layer. Include measures already undertaken by various governments, and a discussion of the impacts of your proposals.

The Gaia Controversy

arly in the 1960s, NASA scientists were eagerly working on one of the most dramatic explorations of space. They were planning the two Viking missions to Mars, which they hoped would answer the question of whether life did exist—or had ever existed—on the rosy-colored planet.

Many experts were consulted to help design the instruments that would hunt for signs of life after the Vikings had settled on the Martian surface. Among these was a British scientist and inventor by the name of James E. Lovelock.

Before Lovelock tackled the problems of instrumentation, he studied data about Martian chemistry that had been gathered by NASA's infrared telescopes. The chemistry of Mars turned out to be very stable. This, concluded Lovelock, was a clear sign that living things did not inhabit Mars. Living things, Lovelock pointed out, constantly change the environment in which they live, as happens on Earth.

The Viking spacecraft, which landed on Mars in 1976, supported Lovelock's conclusion. Instruments aboard the vehicles detected no signs of life. But why were there no living things on Mars? There were a number of answers to that question, the most obvious of which was that it was simply too cold to support life as we know it. Could there be life on Venus, our other planetary neighbor? No, concluded Lovelock. That planet was too hot.

This led Lovelock to ask himself an intriguing question and, in answer, to propose a startling hypothesis. Why, he asked, was Mars too cold, Venus too hot, but Earth just the right temperature to support life?

Lovelock proposed that living things actually controlled the environment of Earth so that it remained supportive of life. Since this kind of control is a property of life—like the way your body automatically controls its temperature—Lovelock further suggested that Earth as a whole behaved as if it were a living organism. Lovelock called this idea the Gaia (GUY-ah) hypothesis, after the Greek goddess of Earth.

Scientists did not dispute the fact that organisms affected Earth's environment. After all, through photosynthesis green plaints released oxygen into the air and soaked up carbon dioxide. As a matter of fact, green plants had been responsible for producing the oxygen-rich atmosphere that had made the evolution of oxygen-breathing animals possible.

Just so, Lovelock and his supporters argued. However, they went a step further, one that critics could not accept. The supporters of the Gaia hypothesis proposed that living things on Earth work together to promote an enviromnent that is good for them. Lovelock assigned a kind of *purpose*—almost a consciousness—to the activities of Earth's living community. That is, they act *symbiotically*, or cooperatively, to alter their environment so as to improve their chances of survival. And this the critics could not accept. Among other things, they argued that survival was promoted by competition rather than cooperation.

To get a better idea of what the Gaia hypothesis is all about, consider the following statements, which present currently accepted assumptions about Earth:

- About 3.8 billion years ago, when life began to evolve, the average temperature of Earth was about 23 degrees Celsius.
- The average temperature of Earth today is about 15 degrees Celsius and, within a relatively small range, has remained so for the past 3.8 billion years.
- The sun has burned hotter as time has passed.
- Earth now receives 25–30% more heat and light from the sun than it did 3.8 billion years ago.

Question: How could the temperature of Earth remain relatively constant while heat from the sun increased?

Question: Did the evolution of life somehow keep Earth cooler than it otherwise would have been?

According to the Gaia hypothesis, the questions can be answered as follows. We have evidence that about 4 billion years ago—prior to the evolution of

life on Earth—the atmosphere held great amounts of carbon dioxide, perhaps up to 98%. Today, Earth's atmosphere is only 0.03% carbon dioxide. Since this gas is known to allow sunlight to pass through to Earth's surface, but to limit heat from escaping from the surface, an abundance of carbon dioxide in Earth's early atmosphere should have caused Earth's temperature to rise.

According to the best evidence we have, the first living things to evolve on Earth were bacteria. And, like living things to follow, bacteria required carbon atoms to build chemicals vital to their survival, like proteins and enzymes. Where did the bacteria get the carbon they needed? From the carbon dioxide in the atmosphere. What's more, the green algae that were soon to evolve also pulled carbon out of the air. By doing this, these organisms lowered the percentage of carbon dioxide in the atmosphere and, therefore, reduced the average temperature of Earth, making it a better place for more complex living things to evolve.

Thus, the chemical activities of early forms of life made possible the evolution and survival of later forms of life. But if the bacteria and algae used up all the carbon dioxide they could not survive. How, then, was carbon dioxide kept in the air? Animals, whose existence had been made possible by the bacteria and algae, cooperated by exhaling carbon dioxide into the atmosphere.

Can living things regulate Earth's environment for their own benefit? Have they done so in the past? And if they've done so, need we worry about such things as pollution? Or can we count on living things to automatically set our environment right? What do you think?

Questions

1. About 3.8 billion years ago, the average temperature of the Earth was
a. 2°C.   c. 23°C.
b. 15°C.   d. 72°C.

2. The percentage of carbon dioxide in the Earth's atmosphere today is about
a. 0.   c. 0.3.
b. 0.03.   d. 98.

3. The first living things to evolve on Earth were
a. bacteria.   c. animals.
b. green algae.   d. humans

4. What led James Lovelock to assume no life existed on Mars?

5. On a separate sheet of paper, give your views of the Gaia hypothesis. Do library research to find data and arguments to support your position. Include references to these data and arguments.

Doomsday Rocks: Cause for Concern?

Its name is Swift-Tuttle. It's 10 km wide. It's a comet that sweeps by Earth about every 130 years. And, like a few other comets and some asteroids, it crosses Earth's orbit from time to time. The next time Swift-Tuttle is scheduled to do this is sometime in July of the year 2126. If the date turns out to be July 26, look out! Why? That's the date when Earth will be near the same point in its orbit where the comet would cross. Result? Collision!

However, according to comet and asteroid expert Brian G. Marsden of the Smithsonian Astrophysical Observatory in Cambridge, Massachusetts, Swift-Tuttle should cross Earth's orbit on July 20, 2126 not on July 26. If Marsden's prediction is accurate, your great-great-grandchildren will have nothing to worry about. Earth will be about 24 million kilometers away when Swift-Tuttle visits.

But the paths of comets are not always easy to predict. Swift-Tuttle itself gave Marsden a hard time. In 1973, he had predicted its return to the vicinity of Earth in 1981 or 1992, depending on the effects of different variables.

The year 1981 came and went and Swift-Tuttle failed to show up. Time passed as Marsden and other astronomers kept an eye on the sky in search of the tardy Swift-Tuttle. Then, on September 27, 1992, the comet was spotted against the background of the Big Dipper's stars. Marsden recalculated the date the comet would reach a point closest to the sun, or *perihelion* which is a kind of landmark for comets. According to Marsden's best estimate, the date would be November 25, 1992.

But as Swift-Tuttle whizzed through space, something unseen happened. Perhaps it may have been one or more bursts of gas from the comet, triggered by heat from the sun. Like the effects of rockets on a space vehicle, these bursts of gas altered the path of Swift-Tuttle. Result? The comet reached perihelion on December 12 instead of November 25.

Marsden was unconcerned. As he put it, "A 17-day error out of 130 years is good enough for me." But if a similar error occurs in the year 2126, will it be good enough for Earth's inhabitants of that time?

This brings up a key question. Why should we worry about a comet or asteroid hitting Earth? Scientists explain that a collision with even a small comet or asteroid, say one-half kilometer across, would cause an explosion with a force equal to more than one million tons of TNT!

Has such a natural explosion ever rocked Earth? Yes, say many scientists, about 65 million years ago. If the scientists are correct, and there is mounting evidence to support their view, such a collision and explosion may have caused the extinction of thousands of species including the dinosaurs.

But we don't have to go back millions of years to find evidence of such explosions. On June 30, 1908, vast areas of forest along the Tunguska River in Siberia were leveled and charred, along with the animals who lived there. Evidence points to a "rock from space" as the culprit.

In fact, impacts like this happen every 100 years or so. What's more, near misses occur even more frequently. In January, 1991, an asteroid zipped past Earth only about 160,000 km away. What's disturbing is that the asteroid was discovered only a few hours before its brush with our planet.

For all of these reasons, many astronomers are urging that a comet and asteroid watch system be set up. This would consist of five special telescopes positioned around the world. These telescopes would be designed to spot comets and asteroids. The orbits of these objects would be quickly determined to find out whether they were headed our way. Such a system of observatories might give us a few year's warning of a comet or asteroid whose path led directly to Earth. Armed with this information we might be able to head off the collision. How?

A number of ideas have been proposed. Among these would be sending a space vehicle to the comet or asteroid. The vehicle could deposit a rocket on the "rock" which, when fired, would alter its orbit so it

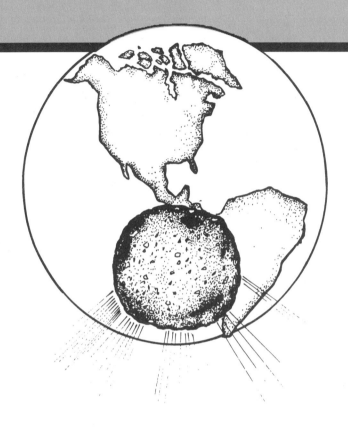

would miss Earth. Another idea is to explode a nuclear bomb on one side of the space rock, again pushing it out of its path toward Earth.

Setting up a tracking system to spot doomsday rocks would take millions of dollars—your family's tax dollars. Should we spend the money to possibly avoid an event that might not occur in your lifetime, or in the lifetime of your children, or grandchildren? What do you think?

Questions

1. Swift-Tuttle crosses Earth's orbit about once every
   a. 13 years.
   b. 130 years.
   c. 1300 years.
   d. 2126 years .

2. Perihelion is the point in space when a moving object like a comet is
   a. closest to Earth.
   b. farthest from Earth.
   c. closest to the sun.
   d. farthest from the sun.

3. Scientists estimate that a collision between a "rock from space" and Earth, like the one that occurred in Siberia in 1908, occurs on average every
   a. 10 years.
   b. 100 years.
   c. 1000 years.
   d. 10,000 years.

4. What do many scientists believe happened 65 million years ago?

5. On a separate sheet of paper, express your views on whether an expensive comet and asteroid watching system should be installed around the world. Back up your views with appropriate data

Electricity From Space: A Bright Idea?

Electricity provides energy to light homes and cities and to run factories and businesses. In a real sense it is the energy of progress—the energy that improves our standard of living. Yet we pay a price for that energy. And the price involves more than dollars and cents.

According to many scientists, the price we pay is the pollution of our environment. That's because much of our electricity is generated in a process that starts with the burning of coal or oil. The by-products of this burning include carbon dioxide, which may cause Earth to heat up, and gases that contain sulfur, which irritate people's eyes and skin, and cause acid rain.

Although there are sources of "clean" electricity, such as flowing water used to run hydroelectric power plants, windmills that run electric generators, and arrays of solar panels that convert sunlight into electricity, none of these sources has been able to satisfy the energy needs of the world's people. And as the population of our planet grows, the problem of providing people with the energy they need will grow also.

As engineer Peter Glaser puts it, "In 2030 there will be 8 billion people in the world" who will be seeking a standard of living like the one we now enjoy and "the only thing stopping them will be energy," or the lack of it.

But if this energy will not be available on Earth, will the world's people have to settle for lower standards of living? No, says Glaser. There's plenty of energy in space. All we have to do is find a way to collect it and transport it to Earth.

The energy is contained in sunlight. If you had a bucket whose bottom had a surface area of one square meter, you could gather 1400 joules per second of solar energy in space. And if you could transmit that power continuously to your home, you could run your stereo and every other appliance in your house—not to mention its lights—indefinitely.

That's one of the reasons why Peter Glaser advocates putting solar power satellites (SPSs) in space. If an SPS were positioned 36,000 km above Earth in a stationary orbit, it would be in almost constant sunshine. Photovoltaic solar cells could convert that sunlight into electricity. In turn, the electricity would be converted into microwaves, like those produced in a microwave oven. Like all electromagnetic waves. microwaves could be beamed down to an antenna on Earth. Once down there, the microwaves can be reconverted into electricity and fed into power grids serving large areas of Earth.

Although the principle is simple, the engineering feats required to make it work in practice are considerable. For example, engineers estimate that for an SPS to be a practical source of electricity for Earth dwellers it would have to have a surface area of about 55 square kilometers, or about the area of Manhattan Island. Moreover, by the time the spreading beam of microwaves reached Earth, it would cover an area the size of a medium-sized city. A receiving antenna would have to be the same size. And land would have to be set aside for the device, which would look like a huge oval dish.

Regardless of the problems, Glaser believes that SPSs will end up being a major source of electricity in the 21st Century. He proposes that the development of the technology should advance in steps. A first step might be to design an SPS that would provide electricity for the planned space station, *Freedom*. And if people go back to the moon, a second step might be to build an SPS to provide the moon colony with electricity. Along the way, engineers would have opportunities to solve SPS problems as they arise.

This idea of clean energy from the sky may sound good—and it may be good—but it is not without its detractors. At least three concerns have been expressed by critics: (1) When the microwaves knife through Earth's upper atmosphere they will heat it up. What effects would this have? (2) How will beams of microwaves affect television and radio signals on Earth? (3) How would the incoming microwaves affect living things, including people, near the receiving antennas?

Should we spend millions of dollars on building SPSs in space? Do the problems and concerns associated with such a project outweigh its potential benefits? Or do the potential benefits to the world's people and their environment make going ahead with such a program worthwhile, even essential? What do you think?

Questions

1. In the year 2030, the number of people on Earth will be about
    a. 8 million.   c. 80 million.
    b. 8 billion.   d. 80 billion.

2. Each square meter just above Earth's atmosphere receives about
    a. 140 joules per second of solar energy.
    b. 1400 joules per second of solar energy.
    c. 14,000 joules per second of solar energy.
    d. 140,000 joules per second of solar energy.

3. As it approaches Earth from space, a beam of microwaves
    a. spreads out.
    b. narrows down.
    c. is unchanged.
    d. first spreads out and then narrows down.

4. What are three concerns expressed by critics of SPSs that beam microwaves to Earth?

5. On a separate sheet of paper, give your views on whether we should invest tax dollars in the development of SPSs. Give reasons for your position.

Turning Darkness to Dawn: Should We?

"It was nothing I'd ever seen before. First, there was a pulsating object that flashed very bright every one and a half seconds, which I'm sure was the *Banner* spacecraft tumbling through space." The words were those of astronomer Terence Dickinson of Saint. Lawrence College in Kingston, Ontario, as reported in *The New York Times* on February 5, 1993.

The spacecraft, called *Znamya* by its Russian builders—*Banner* in English—was basically nothing more than an aluminum disc 20 meters in diameter, equipped with a motor. Originally folded up like a Japanese fan, it had been part of the space cargo ship *Progress,* which had been sent on a resupply mission to Russia's *Mir* space station.

After the two cosmonauts aboard the *Mir* unloaded the supplies they needed, the *Progress* separated from the space station and deployed *Banner. Banner's* motor unfolded the "fan" and, through commands from Earth, rockets aboard *Progress* positioned *Banner* so it would reflect sunlight to Earth's surface. And that's what Terence Dickinson reported seeing in the early morning sky.

If that were all *Banner* was about, you might shrug your shoulders and think, "So what?" What good is a mirror in space anyway? After all, you could hardly use it to make sure your hair was combed.

That's true. However, *Banner* was not put in space for cosmetic purposes. It was put there to test a concept that could literally change the face of Earth, or, at least, part of its face. As project engineer Nikolai N. Sevastyanov put it: "The reflector was a big success because it proved the concept was right." But to what concept was the Russian engineer referring?

The concept was as dramatic as it was simple. Its aim was to turn night into day or, at least, a kind of twilight. But for what purpose? To illuminate ballparks? To shed light on high crime areas in big cities? To make night driving safer on interstate highways'? Although these ideas may have merit, the Russian designers of *Banner* had something else in mind.

They envisioned a reflector many kilometers in diameter; one which would be controlled by a guidance system that would allow it to throw a huge beam of sunlight onto a given spot on the nightside of Earth. For the chosen spot, this would bring daylight saving time on a grand scale.

The advantages? Energy use in the area would plummet because people would not have to use as much electricity to light homes, businesses, and factories. Crops would get higher doses of sunlight. They would grow faster and yield more food. Growing seasons would also be stretched out, and perhaps more than one crop could be harvested a season. Food would be more plentiful and more of the world's people would be better fed.

So what's the downsides? First of all, what parts of the world will be chosen for the night-to-day treatment? Who would do the choosing? And what would be the criteria for the choices? How would the local environment be affected by fiddling with nature's day-night cycle? And what would be the effect on the behavior of people robbed of regular periods of darkness? Would the change affect their behavior in some unwanted way?

The Russian experiment seems to indicate that the technology to turn night into day is likely to be available soon. Their next step is to put a 200-meter-diameter mirror into space, provided they can raise the millions of rubles needed to do so.

But will the ultimate goal do more good for society than harm? What factors should be considered before

investing more money in the program—part of which the Russians are seeking from western companies, including some in the United States? What do you think?

Questions

1. The *Banner* space vehicle was used to
   a. bring supplies to a space station.
   b. carry two cosmonauts.
   c. reflect sunlight to Earth.
   d. send TV signals to Earth.

2. When deployed the *Banner* space vehicle's diameter was
   a. 2 m.   c. 200 m.
   b. 20 m.   d. 2000 m.

3. The goal of the program pioneered by *Banner* is to
   a. increase crop production and energy use.
   b. decrease crop production and energy use.
   c. increase crop production and decrease energy use.
   d. decrease crop production and increase energy use.

4. What problems would have to be investigated before the *Banner* concept was put into effect?

5. On a separate sheet of paper, describe the actions you would propose be taken before making a commitment to build and launch a huge version of the *Banner* space vehicle.

Can a Little Child Help Predict The Weather?

Meteorologists call him El Niño, or "little boy" in Spanish, and her La Niña, or "little girl." Both grow up in the Pacific Oceans. And, if scientists are correct, detecting the growth of one or the other can lead to weather predictions months, or even a few years, in advance.

As you might guess, El Niño and La Niña are not human. To find out what they are and how they affect the weather, you've got to take a long journey to the western part of the Pacific Ocean. Let's say you did this in the spring of 1991. You would have found a huge patch of warm water above Australia that stretched eastward for a few thousand kilometers.

As weeks passed, you would have noticed that the winds that normally blow from east to west over the Pacific were becoming weaker. Result? You would have observed the patch of warm water slowly drifting eastward. By June, waters to the east that only a few months earlier had been relatively cool would have become 1°C to 1.5°C warmer.

You might well have predicted that the ominous patch of warm water would arrive off the coast of South America by December, 1991. If you had done this, your prediction would have agreed with that of a number of scientists who call such an event, which occurs every four to seven years, an El Niño.

Was El Niño really on the way in the spring of 1991? To scientists, this was a very important question, since in the past the coming of an El Niño heralded dramatic changes in weather patterns in different parts of the world including the United States. Two years earlier, computers at Columbia University's Lamont-Doherty Geological Observatory in Palisades, New York, had predicted that an El Niño would indeed arrive in late 1991. Computers at other institutions had, however, come up with other predictions .

Then in November of 1991 great thunderstorms began to rumble over the eastern Pacific Ocean. El Niños are thought to trigger such atmospheric disturbances. The storms prompted Chester Ropelewski of the National Meteorological Center in Camp Springs, Maryland, to venture, "From the observations, it looks as though we're in the middle of a warm event," or an El Niño.

You might think that a "warm event" is something to look forward to. Certainly, beaches bathed in warm water are attractive to surfers and other lovers of sand and sea. But an El Niño brings more than warm water to a nearby coastline. And what it brings may not be welcome at all.

First of all, El Niño's thunderstorms change the atmosphere in predictable, but troubling ways. The storms transport heat from the ocean's surface into Earth's atmosphere. As the heat rises it runs into great streams of air that constantly move around Earth from west to east. These rivers of air are called jet streams. And the heat changes the course of their flow.

This might be of little consequence except for the fact that jet streams control the movements of large masses of air across the world. Some of these masses are wet and warm. Others are dry and cold. As you know from personal experience, the arrival of a wet and warm air mass over your head brings different kinds of weather than the arrival of a dry and cold air mass. So El Niño affects local weather. What's more, since jet streams circle the globe, the effects of El Niño are felt all over the world.

Although by Thanksgiving of 1991, El Niño had not yet arrived off the coast of South America, weather forecasters of the National Weather Service became convinced it was on its way. Based on this conviction, the agency issued a long-range weather forecast for the coming few months. The prediction included heavy rains along the Gulf Coast and southeast sections of the United States. The northern part of the continent, the forecasters said, would be abnormally warm. What happened?

During the winter, heavy rains drenched parts of the southern United States. For example, between December and February, 63.5 cm of it poured down on south-central Texas. As a matter of fact, the amount of rain that fell on Texas was double what it would normally be. And "sunny California" seemed

also to be a victim of El Niño. Within 10 days in February, three storms dumped 20 cm of rain on Los Angeles. Reports of still heavier rains came from the mountains to the east of the city.

Up north—from Alaska east through Canada—people were enjoying an unusually warm December. Many inhabitants of these usually cold regions tapped thermometers to make sure the instruments were recording correct temperatures, which were 3°C to 7°C above average.

People in other parts of the world were also feeling the effects of El Niño. Australia and India were abnormally dry. So was southeastern Africa. But wet weather drenched the usually dry northwest coast of South America. El Niño had turned the weather in these places upside down. The predictions of scientists had turned out to be correct.

But of what benefit are such long-range weather forecasts? Ropelewski suggests that farmers who normally plant crops that thrive in relatively dry weather could switch to waterloving crops when an El Niño is scheduled to deliver torrents of rain. And people who live in areas slated for unusually dry weather could take measures to lessen the effects of droughts.

By now you're probably wondering about the other "child" in this story, La Niña. What is "she?" La Niñas pop up when winds from the east blow more and more strongly, pulling up cold, deep water off the coast of South America and driving it toward the west. By late June 1992 this was exactly what was happening. What kind of weather does La Niña bring to Australia, India, southeast Africa, and the northern and southern parts of the United States? What do you think?

Questions

1. When El Niño arrives in parts of the Pacific Ocean, the temperature of the water
   a. stays the same.
   b. increases by 1°C–1.5°C.
   c. decreases by 1°C–1.5°C.
   d. increases by 3°C–7°C.

2. El Niños occur every
   a. 1-3 years.   c. 3-5 years.
   b. 2-4 years.   d. 4-7 years.

3. You would expect a La Niña to bring weather that is
   a. the same as that brought by an El Niño.
   b. opposite to that brought by an El Niño.
   c. similar but less severe than that brought by an El Niño.
   d. similar but more severe than that brought by an El Niño.

4. How do El Niños affect weather over land?

5. On a separate sheet of paper, explain how knowledge of El Niños and La Niñas may be used to benefit society.

The Greenhouse Effect: Is It Black and White?

The greenhouse effect, that global warming due to an increase of carbon dioxide and certain other gases in the atmosphere, is coming! Or is it?

Arguments rage on both sides of this issue. And since the effects of global warming could be devastating to life on our planet, the issue has to be carefully examined so that the world's citizens can make informed decisions—decisions that could have far-reaching environmental, social, and economic impact.

To evaluate the dangers of a greenhouse effect, you must take into consideration three basic factors: (1) the causes of the greenhouse effect; (2) data that supports or refutes the idea that the greenhouse effect is actually happening; and (3) the evaluation of feedback processes, or events that tend to increase or decrease global warming.

First of all, we can agree—along with all scientists—on two facts: primarily due to the burning of fossil fuels, greenhouse gases (mostly carbon dioxide) are building up in the atmosphere, and these gases trap heat near the planet's surface, which *tends* to increase Earth's temperature. But has the temperature actually increased and, if so, has the increase been because of the greenhouse effect?

There's no question that the amount of carbon dioxide in the atmosphere has increased since the beginning of the Industrial Revolution in the 19th century. As a matter of fact, the amount of carbon dioxide in the air has jumped 25 percent by mass in the last 100 years. And the concentration of other greenhouse gases has also gone up.

According to some scientists, this should have produced an increase in average global temperatures of between 0.75°C and 1.5°C. The actual figure is 0.5°C. Nevertheless, some researchers say, any increase in global temperatures is a concern because such increases could trigger positive feedback processes that would speed the warming trend. But what's a feedback process and how does it work?

You don't have to look farther than your own body for examples. For instance, one feedback process in your body stimulates perspiration as your body's temperature increases above normal, say, when you are exercising on a hot day. This is a *negative* feedback because it tends to reverse, or work against, the warming trend.

In this example, a negative feedback is healthy. If the feedback was *positive*, however, your temperature would soar and you would be in danger of passing out from heat stroke. This is the kind of feedback that worries scientists who believe a dangerous greenhouse effect is coming.

Let's examine some positive feedback processes that might aggravate the greenhouse effect. As carbon dioxide builds up in the atmosphere, temperatures would begin to increase near Earth's surface. Water from the world's oceans begins to evaporate at an increasing rate. This water vapor traps more heat, and global temperatures would get a boost upward.

Vast sheets of glistening white ice begin to melt in the Arctic and Antarctic, reducing the amount of heat and light they reflect away from Earth's surface. The uncovered land and water absorb more heat and grow still warmer.

As the frozen arctic tundra warms, the water trapped in its soil melts. Under these conditions, organic matter in the soil begins to oxidize. In the process, huge amounts of methane gas are produced and released into the air. Methane is a powerful greenhouse gas. The temperature climbs still higher.

The heat begins to dry out other parts of the world, including areas where great numbers of green plants thrive. These plants don't grow as well, and insect pests gobble up many that are weakened by drought. Fires devastate vast parched forests and grasslands. Since plants remove carbon dioxide from the air during photosynthesis, this reduction in plant life allows even more of the gas to build up in the atmosphere.

What could be the result of all these positive feedbacks? An uncontrollable, runaway greenhouse effect that, according to a report of Japan's Advisory Panel on Environment and Culture, could ". . . cause the destruction of the entire planet and every living thing on it." But will nature and people conspire to hold back or reverse the greenhouse effect?

Certainly, people can help by doing such things as regulating the use of fossil fuels, by preventing the cutting down of forests for lumber, by controlling population growth, and by limiting the growing of rice and the raising of cattle (two activities that add methane to the atmosphere). But critic S. Fred Singer of the Science and Environmental Policy Project in Washington, D.C., says that such activities could condemn "billions [of people] to continued poverty, starvation and misery." This would be especially tragic if the greenhouse effect were never to happen. More studies and much patience are needed before such measures should be undertaken, urge the critics.

Of course, scientists and environmentalists who see the greenhouse effect as becoming uncontrollable if something is not done to check it soon say we can't wait. What do you think?

Questions

1. Since the beginning of the Industrial Revolution, the amount of carbon dioxide in the atmosphere has
   a. increased by 25%. c. remained unchanged.
   b. decreased by 25%. d. become zero.

2. During the past 100 years, the average global temperature has
   a. been unchanged. c. increased 0.75°C.
   b. increased 0.5°C. d. increased 1.5°C.

3. Perspiring on a hot day is an example of
   a. positive feedback.
   b. negative feedback.
   c. neither positive nor negative feedback.
   d. the greenhouse effect.

4. Explain how the shrinking of polar ice caps produces positive feedback.

5. On a separate sheet of paper, describe those governmental policies you would support concerning the greenhouse effect. Explain why you would support those policies.

Beaches: Should We Leave Them Alone?

In the winter of 1992-93, a series of powerful storms battered the east coast of the United States. Thundering waves unleashed tremendous torrents of energy on beaches along the coasts of New Jersey and New York. Beaches vanished. Homes were swept away. Pounding seas driven by ferocious winds cut new inlets where none had existed before.

Homeowners, merchants, and local politicians called for relief. Many asked that protective barriers be erected to hold back the sea when future storms strike. To many people, placing such barriers on beaches made sense. To others, including some geologists who specialize in beach erosion, putting up barriers was an invitation to disaster. How come?

Beaches, like other landforms, are changed by *erosion*, or wearing away by wind and moving water. Some of the changes are triggered by natural events like storms, the ebb and flow of tides, and the steady lapping of waves. These forces often strip away sand in one place only to deposit it somewhere else.

In most cases, such erosion and deposition tends to preserve beaches over time. But when people interfere with these natural processes, an unbalanced erosion can occur that destroys beaches, perhaps forever.

What kinds of human activities speed up erosion of beaches? Anything that interferes with the movement of sand along or onto a coastline.

This happens, for instance, when people build rock jetties that jut into the sea. Although the jetties produce relatively calm water for harbors and vacationers, they block the migration of sand along a coastline, say, from north to south. Beaches to the north still lose their sand but beaches to the south that would ordinarily gain this sand are blocked from getting it by the jetties.

Similarly, any kind of construction, such as a home or parking lot, that is built too close to the water of a beach may keep the sands from migrating naturally.

Sometimes sand robbers are located far from beaches. For example, some beaches get their sand from rivers and creeks that constantly sweep *silt*, fine grains of eroded rock, toward the sea. When such rivers are dammed to produce hydroelectricity, or the bottoms and sides of creeks are paved with concrete to inhibit flooding, the flow of silt is interrupted. The sand of the beaches that is carried away by natural forces is not replenished and the beaches shrink.

Clearly, we need electricity, we can't put up with flooding rivers and creeks, and we should have the right to build homes near the shoreline. But what about a beach's right to *its* sand? Should that be protected too? Put another way, don't the beaches belong to all of us and, if so, shouldn't something be done to protect our right to have beaches?

A beach's right to its sand and our right to enjoy unspoiled beaches is a concern of Los Angeles lawyer Katherine E. Stone. Ms. Stone suggests that "certain kinds of resources are held in common for everyone under a trust. Those resources include the air, the sea, fish swimming in the sea, and the shore of the sea as well."

In recent years, local, state, and federal governments have recognized such rights by passing laws or instituting regulations that require builders not to interfere with the natural flow of sand or, if they do, to replace the sand at their own expense. This, of course, increases the cost of construction, electricity and flood control, which people have to pay for when they buy products or pay taxes.

What's more, some people say such laws and regulations are unconstitutional. What happens, they say, if a person buys a piece of oceanfront land and then is not permitted to build on it. The value of the land plummets and the person loses a lot of money. Isn't this the same as the government taking land

and not compensating the owner for it, which is a violation of the Fifth Amendment to the U.S. Constitution?

No, say supporters of beach erosion control. The government isn't taking the land. It is only regulating how the land can be used.

Clearly, this is a complex issue with reasonable arguments on both sides. Which arguments make more sense? What do you think?

Questions

1. A rock jetty causes erosion by
 a. wearing away a beach.
 b. protecting a harbor.
 c. controlling floods.
 d. preventing the movement of sand.

2. One source of sand is silt from
 a. rivers.   c. jetties.
 b. dams.   d. storms.

3. Katherine E. Stone believes
 a. people should build homes where they want.
 b. a beach has a right to its sand.
 c. builders should not have to replace sand.
 d. the Fifth Amendment is unconstitutional.

4. With regard to beaches, what are some causes of natural and unnatural erosion?

5. Look up the Fifth Amendment to the U.S. Constitution. On a separate sheet of paper identify the part that applies to the protection of beaches. Then look up the Supreme Court decision of 1992 in the case of *Lucas* v. *South Carolina Coastal Commission.* Explain why you do or do not agree with the Supreme Court's decision.

Ice Ages: What Gets Them Started?

They've come before. They're scheduled to come again—and soon. But this time something will be different. This time great civilizations, billions of people, and some of the world's finest cities will be in the way.

"They" are 3000-meter-thick tongues of ice that, although they creep along the ground at a snail's pace, can level everything in their paths. Last time, that meant grass, shrubs, and trees. Next time it could mean the twin spires of the World Trade Center in New York City, the soaring Sears Tower in Chicago, and all the other buildings in between.

These tongues of ice are the shock troops of an ice age. By about 20,000 years ago they had advanced almost halfway from Earth's polar regions toward the equator. They never got that far. But in the Northern Hemisphere they did not stop their march until they had reached points a third of the way down the East Coast and as far down in the Midwest as the Ohio River. What gave them the order to march? Can we countermand that order?

About 70 years ago, a Serbian astronomer by the name of Milutin Milankovitch proposed a hypothesis which suggested that ice ages are caused by motions of Earth in space. The motions, said Milankovitch, affect how intensely sunlight falls on the northern and southern hemispheres of Earth and, hence, the temperatures of these hemispheres. When the temperatures drop, ice ages follow. Conversely, when the temperatures rise, ice ages end.

Milankovitch identified three motions of Earth that could cause such fluctuations in temperature. The first is a change in the angle of Earth's tilt on its axis. It's now about 23.5 degrees. But it varies from 21.5 degrees to 24.5 degrees, making one complete cycle every 41,000 years. The greater the tilt, the greater the difference in winter and summer temperatures.

The second motion involves a change in the shape of Earth's orbit from more elliptical to almost circular. When the orbit becomes more elliptical—which happens every 100,000 years— the distance between Earth and the sun in one season, say winter in the northern hemisphere, is greater than when the orbit is more circular. This would make for colder winters.

Finally, the third motion is a kind of wobble that affects Earth as it spins. A complete wobble takes 23,000 years. Taken together, the wobble and the shape of Earth's orbit either maximize or minimize the amount of sunlight that strikes the northern and southern hemispheres.

As geologists Wallace S. Broecker and George H. Denton put it in an article in the January, 1990 issue of *Scientific American:* "When these . . . controllers of seasonality reinforce each other in one hemisphere, they oppose each other in the opposite hemisphere." That is, there would be times when winter and summer temperatures in North America would vary more greatly than they would in South America. At such time, winter snows could pile up to great depths in North America and would not melt over the summer. As time passed, the weight of the snow would compress it into ice that would spread south-ward in a new ice age.

These three factors, suggested Milankovitch, produced the ice ages. What's more, Milankovitch proposed that the timing of these factors should produce ice ages at regular intervals of 23,000, 41,000, and 100,000 years. Based on the analysis of sediments brought up from the ocean bottom—which provide clues concerning when Earth was covered with the most and least ice—Broecker and Denton report: "Over the past 800,000 years, the global ice volume has peaked every 100,000 years . . . In addition, 'wrinkles' superimposed on each [100,000-year] cycle . . . have come at intervals of roughly 23,000 and 41,000 years...."

The Milankovitch hypothesis, as it had come to be known, seemed to be supported by the ocean-bottom data. Then in October of 1992 came evidence that questioned the validity of this hypothesis.

The evidence had been gathered by a team of scientists at an open, water-filled fault zone called Devils Hole in south-central Nevada. The team, lead by Isaac T. Winograd of the United States Geological Survey, had obtained a core of a mineral called calcite from underwater rock, deep in Devils Hole. Scuba divers had brought the 36-centimeter-long core, a cylinder about the size and shape of the

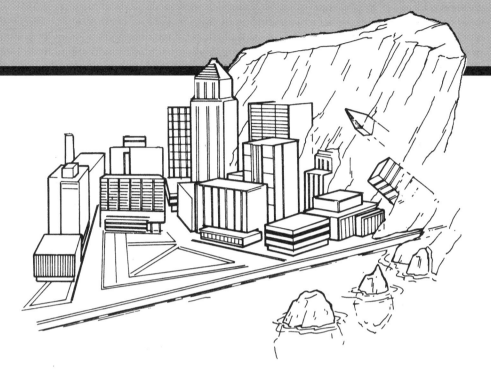

cardboard tube in a roll of paper toweling, from about 30 meters under the water.

The core held deposits of calcite that had been laid down between 60,000 and 560,000 years ago. By analyzing 285 samples of the core taken every 1.26 mm along its length, the researchers were able to date increases and decreases in ice that had occurred on Earth's surface over the 500,000-year period. (Each slice of the core represented a period of about 1,800 years.)

Result? Oddly, some northern hemisphere ice ages appeared to end at times when sunlight was *weakest* in that region. According to the Milankovitch hypothesis, that should have been a time when the ice ages were beginning. Moreover, the length of the ice ages did not follow the cycles of Earth's motions in space.

Whose data was correct? And what did they mean? The scientific jury is still out on both questions. However, Winograd suggests that the data gathered by his team points to a complex interaction of Earth's atmosphere, oceans, and other factors as the cause of ice ages. If this is true, then human activities, such as those that pump greenhouse gases into the atmosphere, may bring on or prevent the next ice age.

Could we interfere with nature by deliberately creating a greenhouse effect? Should we? What do you think?

Questions

1. The tilt of Earth's axis varies between
   a. 0 and 21.5 degrees.
   b. 21.5 and 23.5 degrees.
   c. 21.5 and 24.5 degrees.
   d. 45.0 and 90.0 degrees.

2. A complete cycle in Earth's "wobble" takes
   a. 100,000 years.   c. 23,000 years.
   b. 41,000 years.   d. 500,000 years.

3. Data gathered at Devils Hole
   a. supported the Milankovitch hypothesis.
   b. refuted the Milankovitch hypothesis.
   c. had nothing to do with ice ages.
   d. was gathered from the ocean bottom.

4. What is the Milankovitch hypothesis?

5. On a separate sheet of paper, suggest what could be done to avert the next ice age. Discuss other implications of your suggestion.

Nuclear Waste: Where Should It Go?

By the year 2000, 48,000 tons of nuclear waste will have piled up in temporary storage areas around the United States. These wastes are by-products of both the military weapons industry and the civilian nuclear industry. Among other things, the wastes contain radioactive plutonium, one of the deadliest chemical poisons on Earth.

For decades, the United States government has been searching for a "permanent" resting place for these "hot" substances. And permanent means a lot of years. Why a lot of years'? The isotope of plutonium that is used in nuclear bombs and in nuclear power plants—Pu-239—has an extremely long half-life of 24,100 years. That means that half of the Pu-239 placed in storage today will still be producing lethal radioactivity 24,100 years from now.

By the early 1990s, the search had narrowed down to a barren hump of land in southwestern Nevada called Yucca Mountain. The site was picked for a number of reasons.

For one thing, the mountain—really a long ridge—is fairly far from a populated area. The nearest city, bustling Las Vegas, is 90 miles to the southeast, and hardly anyone lives in between.

For another thing, the area is extremely dry. On average, only 15 cm of rain fall on the dusty slopes of Yucca Mountain each year. And almost all of that evaporates in the blazing Nevada sun. Very little of the precipitation soaks into the soil. Since moisture would tend to corrode the barrels in which the wastes were stored, its absence increases the likelihood of the containers staying in one piece.

Finally, Yucca Mountain rock is rich in a family of minerals called zeolites. And zeolites possess a property that make them ideal as a safe-deposit "box" for radioactive materials. The zeolites bind, or hang on to, such materials.

Okay, so let's start shipping all those tons of radioactive waste to Yucca Mountain. Not so fast, say critics of the plan, as well as four out of five citizens of Nevada. What gives these people cause for concern? Among other things the geology of the regions

If you visited the area around Yucca Mountain, a number of geologic features would catch your eye. One would be Busted Butte, a strange hill rising out of the desert to the southeast. Why strange? It's only half a hill. Long ago the other half was destroyed by an earthquake. In addition, to the west you would spot four old volcanoes.

All this might lead you to conclude that Yucca Mountain lies in an active geological region, and you would be correct. But would this pose a danger to the storage facility and, in turn, to the people of Nevada?

Yes, declares engineering geologist Jerry Szymanski, Yucca Mountain's most vocal critic. Szymanski points to veins of a mineral called calcite that snake up and down through the rock of Yucca Mountain. These veins, insists Szymanski, were deposited by groundwater rising from below the mountain through cracks caused by earthquakes and other geologic activity.

Says Szymanski, "Groundwater will rise again in the next 10,000 years. It is as certain as death." And when the groundwater floods the storage areas in the mountain, the plutonium-containing barrels would corrode, eventually leaking their deadly contents into the environment.

Not likely, say other scientists who point to evidence that the calcite veins were deposited top to bottom, probably by rainwater. According to a report issued in April, 1992 by a 17 member panel of scientists, "…There is no evidence to support the assertion [by Szymanski] that the water table has risen periodically hundreds of meters from deep within the crust. In fact, the evidence strongly supports a surface process origin from rainwater…"

One piece of evidence supporting a "surface process" is that calcite deposits caused by the upwelling of groundwater usually form mounds on the surface. There are no such mounds on Yucca Mountain. In addition, water moving upward produces relatively pure deposits. But water moving downward

produces deposits that are full of sand, clay, and volcanic cinders— which is what is found in Yucca Mountain. Finally, at least some of the calcite veins don't go all the way down through the mountain. If they rose from beneath the mountain they would be almost bottomless.

Nevertheless, some people are not convinced that Yucca Mountain is a safe depository for nuclear wastes. Seismologist Charles Archambeau of the University of Colorado believes it's Szymanski's aggressive personality, not his science, that turns people off to his ideas. Says Archambeau: "People get irritated by Szymanski's style, but what matters is the science . . . My own conclusion is that [Yucca Mountain]. . . is a dangerous place."

Nevada officials, including Governor Bob Miller and U.S. Senator Richard Bryan see the villain as the nuclear industry, which is overloaded with nuclear wastes and which mounted a television and radio advertising campaign to convince Nevadans that Yucca Mountain was a safe haven for the wastes. Governor Miller views the industry's media blitz as an attempt "to brainwash Nevadans." Senator Bryan calls it nothing less than "a declaration of war against the people of Nevada."

Should Yucca Mountain be chosen as the storage site for the country's nuclear wastes? Should the objections of Nevadans outweigh the needs of the nuclear industry? Should other factors be considered? What do you think?

Questions

1. By the year 2000, the number of tons of nuclear waste in the United States will be about
   a. 4800.
   c. 480,000.
   b. 48,000.
   d. 4,800,000.

2. The half-life of Pu-239 is
   a. 2410 years.
   c. 10,000 years.
   b. 239 years.
   d. 24,100 years.

3. Zeolites are
   a. radioactive chemicals
   c. buttes
   b. minerals
   d. critics of Szymanski

4. What evidence exists to support the idea that Yucca Mountain is in a geologically active area?

5. On a separate sheet of paper, discuss the pros and cons of placing a nuclear waste facility in Yucca Mountain. Express your own view and support it with data provided in this article and/or with library research.

Earthquake Prediction: On Shaky Ground?

The Parkfield Cafe looks like many others of its kind until you notice the words painted on a large water tank next to the building. First of all, who would want to be there "when it happens"? Most people would go out of their way to avoid an earthquake.

But seismologists trying to find ways to predict earthquakes are not "most people." Like mountain climbers who head for the craggiest peaks "because they're there," seismologists trek to earthquake country because that's where the earthquakes are. And the California town of Parkfield is a virtual treasure chest of earthquakes.

Perched atop a segment of the infamous San Andreas Fault, Parkfield has attracted scores of seismologists bent on finding ways to predict earthquakes so that people can be warned of the coming of a temblor in time to seek safety. These scientists come with a wide variety of instruments designed to detect signs that precede an earthquake.

For example, instruments can detect effects of stress that build up as two sides of a fault press more and more forcefully against each other. Some of these devices measure bulges or tilts in the land. Others are used to detect slight movements as one side of a rocky fault creeps past the other side.

But, besides the fact that the Parkfield area is a particularly active earthquake region, there was something else that lured instrument-packing seismologists to this spot. That something was a prediction made in 1985 by the United States Geological Survey (USGS) that a major earthquake would strike the area before the end of 1992. Moreover, this was the first long-range earthquake prediction ever officially made by American seismologists. And the scientists wanted to be there not only when it happened but during the period before, too. Why?

They hoped to discover changes that precede earthquakes. In other words, they wanted to uncover the signs of coming quakes, signs that would allow for accurate quake predictions.

Why had Parkfield been chosen for what turned out to be a $19 million, seven-year experiment? Put another way, what had led seismologists to believe a big earthquake would strike at or near Parkfield before 1992? The answer: history!

Records revealed that since 1857 the region had been rocked six times by earthquakes whose magnitudes were between 5.5 and 6.0 on the Richter scale. More significantly, the earthquakes had occurred at remarkably regular intervals, once about every 22 years, with the last one in 1966. This was one factor that led the seismologists to make their prediction

What happened? In early October of 1992, a series of small earthquakes shook the town of Middle Mountain, 10 km north of Parkfield. But none scored higher than 3.1 on the Richter scale. Then, on October 19, a 4.7-level quake rumbled through the ground halfway between Middle Mountain and Parkfield. This prompted the state of California to announce what is called an A-level earthquake alert.

There are five levels of alert, ranging from A to E. An E essentially means little or no chance of a major earthquake. An A means the chances are very good that one is about to strike. The A-level alert translated into a prediction by the California Office of Emergency Services that there was a 33 percent probability that a 6.0-magnitude earthquake would shake the area within three days.

But the predicted earthquake never struck. Nor had it struck by mid-1993. Both the long-range and short-range predictions had missed the mark. Did this mean that earthquake prediction was impossible? No, said John O. Langbien of the USGS, pointing out that: "Scientifically . . . if the earthquake doesn't come now, but in three years, we'd be pretty happy with the results.

Langbien and other seismologists emphasize that many factors. some of them yet to be identified, affect the occurrence of earthquakes. For example,

seismologists Robert Simpson of the USCS and Terry Tullis of Brown University suggest that the 6.5 quake that struck Coalinga, 30 km northeast of Parkfield, in 1983 might have relieved some of the stress that had built up in the San Andreas Fault under Parkfield. This, they hypothesize, could cause a delay of a few years in the arrival of the originally predicted Parkfield quake.

The main problem with predicting earthquakes based on history, says Harvard University's Yehuda Ben-Zion, is that, "If you think in terms of a simple [historical] clock, you have no hope of predicting earthquakes," because the crust is too complex and too many factors interact to cause temblors.

Does that mean that the Parkfield experiment was a waste of money and scientific time? No, declares Ben-Zion, adding "you have to work on details" to understand how an earthquake is triggered, and "Parkfield is essential to that." Do you agree with Ben-Zion? Should we spend more money to discover whether earthquakes can be predicted? What do you think?

Questions

1. The San Andreas Fault is located in
   a. Nevada.
   b. California.
   c. Arizona.
   d. New Mexico.

2. The USGS predicted that a major earthquake would strike the area around Parkfield, CA, before the end of
   a. 1966.
   b. 1985.
   c. 1992.
   d. 1995.

3. Historically, the period between earthquakes at Parkfield has been about
   a. 2 years.
   b. 12 years.
   c. 22 years.
   d. 40 years.

4. What kinds of "signs" do seismologists look for before an earthquake?

5. On a separate sheet of paper, explain why you would or would not favor spending money on continued earthquake prediction research.

Diamond Dust and Dinosaurs

If our modern society had flourished some 65 million years ago and you had been alive at the time, you might have tuned into the weather segment of a local newscast to hear: "Today's forecast: cloudy as usual with steady diamond-dust showers, heavy at times."

Since humans would not evolve for at least another 63 million years, no such broadcast ever occurred. But the event apparently did. In 1991, diamond dust was found in 65 million-year-old rocks. What's more, this particular discovery provided still another clue to the solution of one of science's most intriguing mysteries: what caused the extinction of the dinosaurs?

The mystery began with the discovery that a great many species, including virtually all of the dinosaurs, did not survive beyond what geologists call the Cretaceous-Tertiary, or K-T, boundary. This is a boundary in time which marks the end of the Cretaceous Period and the beginning of the Tertiary Period. The date of the boundary is roughly 65 million years ago. What prevented so many living things from crossing this boundary? Put another way, what happened 65 million years ago to kill off the dinosaurs and a horde of other animals and plants?

No single event, said many scientists who contended that the living things that died out did so gradually over millions of years. But at least two scientists did not agree. They were a father and son team, geologist Walter Alvarez and his Nobel-Prize-winning physicist father, Luis.

Walter Alvarez had made a curious discovery in the late 1970s. He had found a layer of rock holding extraordinarily high concentrations of the element iridium. That in itself might not have caused Alvarez's pulse to quicken, save for the fact that iridium in high concentrations is not generally found in earthly rocks. It is, however, among the elemental passengers of space rocks: meteorites and asteroids. But even more astounding was the uncovering of a startling coincidence. The layer of rock was just about 65 million years old. It marked the K-T boundary.

Like most scientists, Walter and Luis Alvarez did not believe in coincidences in nature. They were sure that the iridium level and the extinction of the dinosaurs were connected, and proposed what turned out to be a very unpopular hypothesis. Their premise? A large object from space crashed into Earth 65 million years ago. The impact from the collision threw vast amounts of dust into the air. This dust shrouded the sun for many years, changing Earth's climate. The change disrupted the life cycles of plants and animals, setting loose a chain of events that led to the abrupt extinction of the dinosaurs and other living things.

The controversy raged through the 1980s. Critics pointed out that the fossils of certain dinosaurs and other animals seemed to vanish in layers of rocks that were older than 65 million years. This was evidence, the critics said, that these creatures died out gradually, starting before 65 million years ago.

The Alvarezes and a growing band of supporters felt they should look harder for dinosaur fossils near the K-T boundary. Soon paleontologists were scouring the rocks in such places as the Hell Creek Formation along the border of Montana and North Dakota, one of the richest treasure chests of dinosaur fossils.

A team of fossil hunters led by Peter M. Sheehan of the Milwaukee Public Museum spent three summers systematically hunting for dinosaur fossils in the rocks of the Hell Creek Formation. Their painstaking work was rewarded with the discovery of dinosaur fossils in all layers of rock near the K-T boundary but not in layers above it. This suggested that the extinctions had not been gradual but sudden. The asteroid-impact hypothesis had gained supporting evidence.

But skeptics were hard to convince. If the extinctions were caused by an asteroid impact, where, they asked, was the telltale crater? Tiny bits of glass found around the Caribbean Sea provided a clue to the answer to this question. The bits of glass, called *tektites*, are produced when large objects from space crash into Earth. Tektites start out as molten bits of rock that are sprayed into the sky when a large object

from space hits the ground. As the drops of molten rock fall, they solidify into glass.

The discovery of tektites around the Caribbean led some scientists to believe that, if they looked hard enough, they might find a crater in or near the Caribbean Sea. Sure enough, in February of 1991, *The New York Times* reported: "Scientists . . . have identified a buried crater near Merida, Yucatan, that is more than 100 miles wide, extending out under the Gulf of Mexico." The crater was the largest ever found on Earth. And how old was the crater? About 65 million years!

Some scientists are still not convinced that an asteroid smashing into Earth was responsible for the extinction of the dinosaurs. They suggest that slower changes in climate may have been responsible. What do you think? (By the way, before you tackle this question, you might be wondering just what diamonds might have to do with dinosaur extinctions. Diamonds are a form of carbon that has been transformed by extreme heat and pressure. Could an asteroid impact have produced the 65-million-year-old diamond dust found in 1991?)

Questions

1. The K-T boundary is how many years old?
   a. 6.5 million
   b. 65 million
   c. 650 million
   d. 6.5 billion

2. The significance of the iridium find is that
   a. dinosaur bones are rich in the element.
   b. Earth rocks are rich in the element.
   c. objects from space are rich in the element.
   d. diamonds are rich in the element.

3. Tektites are
   a. fossils.
   b. bits of glass.
   c. objects from outer space.
   d. diamonds.

4. Describe the reasoning that led Walter and Luis Alvarez to develop their hypothesis.

5. On a separate sheet of paper, discuss and evaluate the evidence presented to support the argument that an impact by an object from space caused the extinction of the dinosaurs .

Runoff: A Runaway Problem?

Huge thunderheads glide ominously across the land. Within minutes the sky turns from bright blue to a deep charcoal-gray. Lightning bolts streak to the ground. Thunder rumbles, and torrents of rain pour down.

The storm sweeps over a forest and then over vast farmlands. It rushes over a small city. In past years, much of the water dumped on the region would have seeped slowly into the soil. The flow of the water into streams, rivers, and lakes would have been controlled by carpets of grass and shrubs and great stands of trees—the living inhabitants of a *watershed*, a large area of land that receives water from rain or snow and feeds it into local bodies of water.

But great areas of the forest have been cut down for lumber. Farmers have cleared the land to plant crops. And cement and asphalt have replaced vegetation in cities and suburbs. Result? The water runs off the land like spilled milk off a glass tabletop. As it rages along, this run-off water picks up dirt, fertilizers, pesticides, and various metals, only to deposit them later in streams, rivers, and lakes.

The fresh water that came from the sky is now polluted water. And the pollution can clog bodies of water with choking silt and contaminate them with poisonous chemicals. The toll in dead fish will be large. Moreover, people will be robbed of sources of clean, fresh water for drinking and for recreation.

Runoff due to the destruction of watersheds is not just a local problem. In June of 1989, the Environmental Protection Agency (EPA) reported that no fewer than 17,000 bodies of water in the United States had been degraded, most of them by uncontrolled runoff. Yet, according to some scientists and engineers, few governmental agencies—local or federal—were doing much to correct the problem.

As environmental engineer Diane M. Cameron put it in an article published in the magazine *Environment* in March of 1990: ."...runoff is at the bottom of our priority list." But what's it doing down there? you might ask.

For one thing, we need the products whose production adds to the runoff problem. For example, we need the corn and wheat from such states as Iowa and Nebraska. There's no question that land has to be cleared to make room for such food crops. What's more, to grow healthy and bountiful crops farmers apply fertilizer and pesticides to the soil and plants.

Unfortunately, when rain splashes onto farmland, it picks up some of the fertilizers and pesticides and sweeps them into nearby streams, rivers, and lakes. In her article, Cameron states that, "In Iowa . . . agricultural runoff is blamed for more than 95 percent of the water-quality problems in the state. . ."

Farms are not the only contributors to the problem. Developers of suburban homes and city dwellers also contribute. For example, an area in Maryland near Washington, D.C., called the Anacostia watershed is now one-third paved over or covered with buildings. In the summer, rain falling on the sizzling pavement has been known to warm to an astounding 33°C. When this hot water pours into the Anacostia River, the lives of fish and other inhabitants of the river are seriously threatened.

14

Logging, especially a practice called *clear-cutting*—the cutting down of all the trees in a particular part of a forest—also promotes uncontrolled runoff and the accumulation of silt in rivers. In some parts of the country, sheep and cattle that munch away grass set the stage for rampant runoff. In other areas, mining practices may allow acids and heavy metals to escape into rainwater.

So what's to be done? Many states rely on education and voluntary programs to control runoff and its problems. The federal government also has programs to do this. However, ". . . federal programs lack statutory muscle, regulatory clout, and adequate funding. . . ," says Diane Cameron. How come? Cameron explains that, ". . . the particular groups who cause runoff. . . are not politically palatable targets for regulation . . . [Nevertheless] the consequences of this neglect are staggering."

How can we curb runaway runoff and restore watersheds without infringing on the rights of farmers, city folk, loggers, and miners, or giving up the products we need? What do you think?

Questions

1. In 1989, the EPA reported that the number of degraded bodies of water in the U.S. was
   a. 7000.
   c. 70,000.
   b. 17,000.
   d. 170,000.

2. Agricultural runoff is thought to account for what percent of the water-quality problems of Iowa?
   a. none
   c. 95%
   b. 10%
   d. 100%

3. Mining practices may contaminate rainwater with
   a. fertilizers.
   c. hot water.
   b. pesticides.
   d. acids and heavy metals.

4. How does farming contribute to water pollution ?

5. Pick one cause of uncontrolled runoff and, on a separate sheet of paper, recommend how it might be controlled. Consider and describe the economic and social effects of your proposal.

Glossary of Earth Science Terms

Abrasion: A form of physical weathering caused by friction between rock particles.

Absolute age: The age of a rock unit, a fossil, or an event expressed in units of time, such as years.

Absolute humidity: The moisture content of the air more commonly expressed as a vapor pressure in millibars .

Absolute zero: The coldest possible temperature, −273°C. At absolute zero, molecules have no energy of vibration (heat).

Absorption (energy): The taking in of energy.

Abyssal plains: The flat regions of the ocean basins.

Actual evapotranspiration: The amount of water that is lost by the soil in evaporation and transpiration within a given period of time.

Adiabatic temperature change: The change in the temperature of a gas caused by expansion (cooling) or compression (warming).

Aerobic bacteria: Microscopic organisms that must live in water with dissolved oxygen.

Aerosol: Tiny particles or droplets suspended in a gas.

Agent of erosion: A medium, such as water, wind, or glacial ice, that transports weathered sediments.

Air mass: A large body of air that has relatively uniform conditions of temperature and pressure. The character of an air mass depends upon its origin.

Air pressure: The effect of the weight of the atmosphere pressing on a given surface area.

Alpine glacier: A glacier that forms in high mountains where snow accumulates to sufficient depth that it is compressed and recrystallized into ice.

Altitude: The height, measured in degrees, of an object above the horizon of an observer.

Anaerobic bacteria: Bacteria that can live without oxygen. See **aerobic bacteria.**

Anemometer: A device that measures wind speed.

Angle of insolation: The angle of the sun above the horizon.

Angular diameter: The angle formed between opposite sides of an object and an observer's eye.

Annular drainage pattern: A stream pattern of concentric circles formed on a mountain whose rocks have differing competence.

Anticyclone: A high-pressure system that usually brings cool, clear weather as its winds rotate clockwise and away from the center; a zone of divergence.

Aphelion: The farthest approach of a satellite to its primary; where a satellite moves the slowest in its orbit.

Apparent diameter: How large an object looks, which depends upon its size and distance from an observer.

Apparent motion: The way celestial objects *appear* to move through the sky.

Apparent solar day: The time required for the sun to go from its highest point in the sky on one day to its highest point the next day.

Apparent solar time: Time based upon the position of the sun in the sky. It is usually a few minutes ahead of, or behind, clock time (mean solar time).

Arc: A uniformly curved line that is a part of a circle; the path of the sun or a star through the sky.

Arctic air mass: An extremely cold air mass.

Arid: Dry; a climate in which there is little precipitation or a climate in which the potential evapotranspiration exceeds the precipitation

Asthenosphere: The part of the Earth's interior below the lithosphere that is plastic in response to stress.

Astronomy: The study of the motions and properties of objects in space.

Atmosphere: The shell of gases that surrounds the Earth.

Atmospheric pressure: A measure of the force exerted by the atmosphere.

Atmospheric variables: The observable or measurable characteristics of the air, such as temperature, pressure, humidity, wind speed, and wind direction.

Axis: The imaginary line around which an object rotates.

Banding: A type of layering (foliation) found in some metamorphic rocks that is caused by the movement or growth of minerals into homogeneous layers.

Barometer: An instrument used to measure air pressure.

Basaltic: Igneous rock composed mostly of dark-colored, dense minerals containing compounds of iron and magnesium.

Base level: The lowest level to which streams can erode.

Basic unit: A unit of measure, like mass, length, or time, that cannot be expressed in terms of a combination of other units.

Bedrock: The solid layer of rock that extends into the Earth. Bedrock can always be found beneath the soil.

Bench mark: A metal disk, or other marker, placed in rock or concrete that shows a location or surveyed position and known elevation above sea level.

Big bang: The theory that the universe began in an explosion of a primordial, concentrated object of incredible mass and density.

Big crunch: The theory that gravity will reverse the expansion of the universe so that it contracts.

Boiling temperature: The temperature at which a substance changes from a liquid to a gaseous phase.

Bonding: Attachments; the way that atoms are connected to adjacent atoms.

Calorie: The amount of heat energy needed to raise the temperature of one gram of pure water one Celsius degree; a common measuring unit of heat energy.

Calorimeter: A closed energy system used to determine the specific heat of a substance.

Capillarity: The ability of a soil to draw water upward into tiny pores.

Capillary water: Water held within the aerated zone of the soil above the water table.

Carbon 14: A radioactive form of the element carbon that has been used to find the absolute age of recent fossils and geologic events.

Celestial object: An object in the sky outside the Earth's atmosphere; the sun, moon, stars, and planets.

Celestial sphere: An imaginary sphere encircling the Earth on which all objects in the night sky appear.

Cement (natural): A mineral or another fine matrix that fills the pores between the grains of sediments, forming sedimentary rock.

Chemical weathering: A change in the chemical composition of a rock caused by adjustment to conditions at the surface of the Earth.

Circumference: The distance around a circle, or the straight-line distance around a sphere.

Classification: The organization of objects, ideas, or information into groupings.

Cleavage: The way that a mineral splits between layers of atoms that are joined by weak bonds.

Cleavage planes: The flat surfaces along which some minerals break naturally.

Climate: The average weather conditions over many years of observation.

Cloud: A large mass of water droplets or ice crystals suspended in the air.

Coalesce: Combine. Cloud droplets must coalesce to fall as precipitation.

Colloid: Tiny particles or droplets suspended in a gas or a liquid indefinitely.

Color: Typically used in Earth science to describe the characteristic color of a mineral.

Competent rock: Hard rock that resists weathering and erosion.

Compression: A reduction in the volume of a substance through the application of a force.

Compressional waves: See **P-waves.**

Condensation: The process by which a gas changes into a liquid; a way in which clouds form.

Condensation nuclei: See **condensation surface**.

Condensation surface: A surface on which water vapor may change into a liquid.

Conduction: The way in which heat energy is transferred through matter by the direct contact of molecules.

Conglomerate: A sedimentary rock composed of cemented gravel, pebbles, or cobbles.

Constellations: The patterns people have observed that mark the positions of stars in the sky.

Contact metamorphism: Chemical and physical changes in a rock, caused mostly by heat, next to an intrusion or extrusion of molten liquid rock.

Continental air mass: A body of arid air that is low in humidity because it formed over a land area.

Continental climate: A climate in which there are large seasonal changes in temperature due to the absence of nearby bodies of water to moderate the climate.

Continental crust: Rocks within the continents, usually a thin layer of sedimentary rocks over granitic rocks, that are lighter than oceanic crust.

Continental drift: The idea that the continents move over the surface of the Earth like rafts on water.

Continental ice sheet: A glacier that spreads over a wide geographic area.

Continental margin: The transition zone made up of the continental self and the continental slope.

Continental shelf: The gently sloping region at the edge of a continent that extends from the shore toward the ocean basin.

Continental slope: The region at the edge of the continental shelf towards the ocean basin; its slope is much steeper than that of the continental shelf.

Contour interval: The difference in height between two adjacent contour lines.

Contour line: A line on a map that connects places with the same elevation and shows the shape of the land.

Contour map: A map that shows the shape of the land with contour lines; a map showing an elevation field.

Convection: The circulation of a heated fluid (a liquid or a gas) caused by density currents; a form of heat flow in which the heated material moves.

Convection cell: The circular path of convection flow.

Convergence: The coming together of winds as they blow into a cyclone (low-pressure system); the coming together of tectonic plates.

Convergent boundary: A boundary at which crustal plates collide.

Coordinate system: A grid in which each location has a unique designation defined by the intersecting of two lines. Latitude and longitude are the most common coordinates used on the Earth.

Core: The innermost layer of the Earth, thought to be composed mostly of iron and nickel.

Coriolis effect (force): The apparent curvature of the winds, ocean currents, or objects moving long distances along the Earth's surface; caused by the rotation of the Earth on its axis.

Correlation: A matchup of rock layers in different locations by age or by rock types.

Crust: The thin, outermost layer of the solid Earth.

Crystal: The solid form of a mineral with regular shape caused by the internal arrangement of atoms.

Crystallization: The formation of intergrown crystals as a liquid cools to form a solid.

Cyclic change: A change that repeats itself, like the annual cycle of the seasons or the apparent daily motion of the sun through the sky.

Cyclone: A low-pressure system in which the winds rotate counterclockwise in the Northern Hemisphere and converge to the center.

Decay product: The element produced by the decay of a radioactive isotope.

Decay product ratio: The ratio between the mass of a radioactive element and its decay product.

Deficit: Within the water budget, a shortage of water because there is not enough water available from precipitation and storage to satisfy the potential evapotranspiration.

Dendritic: A pattern resembling tree branches.

Density: The mass per unit volume of a substance.

Deposition: The settling out or release of sediments by an agent of erosion.

Derived units: Units of measure that consist of combinations of basic units.

Dew point: The temperature at which the air would be saturated with moisture.

Direct rays: Sunlight that strikes the Earth from straight overhead; vertical rays.

Discharge: The quantity of water flowing past a certain point in a stream per unit of time.

Distorted structures: Bedding, fossils, or other features of a rock that have been warped or otherwise changed by metamorphism.

Divergence: The outward movement of winds from a high-pressure zone (anticyclone).

Divergent boundary: A plate boundary at which the plates move apart; an upwelling of material that forms new crust that moves away from the boundary.

Doppler shift: See **redshift**.

Double refraction: The property of transparent crystals that forms a double image of objects viewed through the crystals.

Drainage pattern: The arrangement of adjoining streams as seen from above.

Drumlin: An oval-shaped mound of unsorted glacial till.

Duration of insolation: The length of time that the sun is in the sky from sunrise to sunset.

Dynamic equilibrium: A state of balance in which something is changing, but the amount remains constant.

Earthquake: Natural vibrations, sometimes destructive, that radiate from a sudden movement along a fault zone within the Earth or from sudden movements of magma (molten rock) under a volcano.

Earth science: The study of Earth's systems and our setting in the universe

Eccentricity: The degree of elongation of an ellipse.

Eclipse: A shadowing of a celestial object. A lunar eclipse occurs when the Earth lies between the moon and the sun. A solar eclipse occurs. when the moon passes between the Earth and the sun.

Electromagnetic energy: A form of energy, such as heat waves, visible light, and X rays, that can radiate through empty space.

Electromagnetic spectrum: The complete range of electromagnetic energy from long-wave radiowaves to short-wave gamma rays.

Ellipse: A closed curve around two fixed points known as the foci. All orbits are ellipses.

Energy: The ability to do work.

Energy sink: See **sink**.

Energy source: See **source**.

Epicenter: A location along the Earth's surface that is directly above the focus of an earthquake. An earthquake is felt most strongly at its epicenter.

Equator: An imaginary line that circles the earth halfway between the North and South Poles.

Equilibrium: A state of balance between opposing forces in a system.

Equinox: The time at which the sun is directly above the equator, and all places on the Earth have 12 hours of daylight and 12 hours of darkness. The equinoxes are near the end of March and September, and they mark the beginning of spring and autumn.

Era: A large division of geologic time.

Erosion: The transportation of weathered material (sediments) by water, wind, or ice away from their place of origin and the deposition of them elsewhere.

Erosional-depositional system: A river system within which energy transformations from potential energy to kinetic energy are constantly occurring.

Escarpment: A steep slope or cliff where resistant layers of sedimentary rock overlie weaker layers.

Esker: A winding ridge of sand and gravel deposited by a stream confined to a tunnel under a glacier.

Evaporation: A change in phase from a liquid to a gas (vapor); also known as vaporization.

Evaporite: A sedimentary rock that is deposited as minerals in a saturated solution settle out of an evaporating body of water.

Evapotranspiration: A combination of evaporation from the ground and evaporation from plants (transpiration). Within the water budget, water enters the air by evapotranspiration.

Event: A change or series of changes in the Earth's environment.

Evolution (organic): The principle that living things have changed in form through the history of the Earth from a few simple organisms to a great diversity of organisms.

Extrusion: Molten, liquid rock (lava) flowing out onto the surface of the Earth; a fine-grained igneous rock formed by the rapid crystallization of lava at or near the surface of the Earth.

Extrusive rocks: Rocks formed from lava that solidifies quickly at Earth's surface.

Fault: A break in the rock of the Earth's crust along which there has been displacement (movement).

Felsic: Light-colored rocks composed mostly of feldspar and silica.

Field: A region of space in which a similar quantity can be measured at every point or location.

Flotation: The transportation of sediments along the surface of a stream.

Fluid: A substance that can flow; liquids and gases.

Focus: One of two fixed points that determine the shape and position of an ellipse; an earthquake's point of origin within the Earth.

Folded strata: Layers of rock that have been bent by forces within the Earth.

Foliation: The alignment or segregation of minerals in a metamorphic rock, giving it a layered appearance.

Formation: A mappable unit of rock of uniform age or composition.

Fossil: Any preserved remains or traces of life.

Fossil fuels: Fuels, such as coal, oil, and natural gas, that were formed millions of years ago from the remains of ancient organisms.

Foucault pendulum: A swinging weight that is free to rotate as it swings back and forth. The slow change in direction of a swinging Foucault pendulum is proof of the rotation of the Earth.

Fracture: The uneven splitting of a mineral sample.

Freezing temperature: The temperature at which a liquid will start to change to a solid.

Front: A boundary, or interface, between different air masses.

Frost action: A form of physical weathering in climates with seasonal temperature changes alternately above and below 0°C.

Galaxy: A huge body of stars and other matter in space.

Gas: A phase of matter in which molecules or atoms flow freely and are not bound closely together.

Geocentric model: An early model of the solar system and universe in which the Earth is a stationary object located at the center of the universe around which all celestial objects revolved.

Geologic time scale: Divisions of the history of the Earth originally based upon observations of fossil evidence. Through the use of radioactive isotope measurements, it has changed from a relative scale to an absolute scale.

Glacial erratic: A large rock that has been transported by a glacier.

Glacier: A large mass of moving ice.

Graded bedding: Layers of sediment that change from coarse particles at the bottom of each layer to progressively finer particles toward the top.

Gradient: The rate of change in field values between two points in a field; the average slope.

Grains: The particles of which rocks are made.

Granitic: Rocks composed mostly of light-colored, low density minerals like quartz and feldspar.

Gravity (gravitational force): An attractive force between objects that is directly proportional to the product of their masses and inversely proportional to the square of the distance between the centers of their masses; gravity holds objects on the Earth.

Greenhouse effect: A process in which infrared heat waves are trapped in the Earth's atmosphere by gases like carbon dioxide.

Greenwich Mean Time: Time based upon observations of the sun along the prime meridian.

Groundwater: Water that infiltrates the ground.

Half-life: The time required for half of a radioactive element's atoms in a sample to change to the decay product.

Hardness: In geology, the ability of a mineral to resist scratches.

Heat energy: The total potential and kinetic energy that can be released as heat from an object.

Heat of fusion: Latent potential energy absorbed when a solid melts and released when a liquid freezes.

Heat of vaporization: Latent potential energy absorbed when a liquid vaporizes and released when a gas condenses.

Heliocentric model: The modern model of the solar system and universe in which the planets revolve around the sun and the Earth undergoes daily rotation.

High-pressure system: An anticyclone; a dense mass of air in which the atmospheric pressure is the highest at the center; a zone of divergence.

Horizontal sorting: A gradual change in the size, density, and shape of particles deposited when a stream slows down as it reaches calm water. The largest, most dense, and roundest particles settle first while the smaller, least dense, and flatter particles are carried farther out into the calm water.

Humid: Moist; describes a climate in which there is abundant precipitation or in which the precipitation exceeds the potential evapotranspiration.

Humidity: A measure of the moisture, or water vapor content, of the air.

Humus: Organic remains that are in the soil.

Hydrosphere: The liquid water part of the Earth including the oceans, lakes, streams, and groundwater.

Ice age: A long period of Earth's history when ice sheets cover large areas of the continents.

Igneous rock: Rock formed by the cooling and crystallization of molten rock (magma or lava).

Index fossil: A fossil that can be found over a large geographic area but existed for a brief period of geologic time. An index fossil is useful in determining the geologic age of the rock in which it is found.

Inference: A scientific conclusion based upon observations and experiences; something that is thought out, but not directly observed; an interpretation.

Infiltration: Water seeping into the ground.

Infrared waves: Long-wave heat radiation.

Inner core: The central portion of the Earth's core that is thought to be composed mostly of iron and nickel in the solid state.

Insolation: A contraction of the words, "*in*coming *sol*ar *radi*ation." Electromagnetic energy that the Earth receives from the sun.

Insolation-temperature lag: The time delay between maximum or minimum insolation and maximum or minimum air temperature.

Instrument: A device that makes observations or measurements easier to perform or more precise.

Intensity: Strength.

Interface: A boundary between different materials or systems.

Intrusion: Molten, liquid rock (magma) being pushed into cracks within the Earth; a body of coarse-grained igneous rock formed by slow cooling in the Earth.

Intrusive rocks: Rocks that crystallize slowly inside the Earth.

Isobar: A line on a weather map connecting places with the same atmospheric pressure.

Isoline: A line connecting points of the same value within a field.

Isostasy: The theory that the Earth's crust floats on the denser rock beneath it in a state of equilibrium.

Isosurface: A surface in which all points have the same measured value.

Isotherm: A line connecting places of the same temperature within a temperature field or on a weather map.

Isotope: A form of an element with more or fewer neutrons than other forms of the same element.

Joint: A crack in a rock produced by shrinkage or uneven pressure. Unlike a fault, no displacement along a joint surface occurs.

Kame: A delta deposited by a stream at the end of a glacier.

Kettle: A lake left when a block of glacial ice melts.

Kinetic energy: Energy of motion.

Landscape: The general shape of a region on the Earth's surface.

Latent heat: Energy absorbed or released in a change in state. Latent heat is so named because it does not show up as a temperature change.

Latitude: The angular distance in degrees north or south of the equator. It varies from 0° at the equator to 90° at the poles.

Lava: Molten rock at the surface of the Earth.

Leaching: A process in which groundwater carries dissolved minerals deeper into the soil as the water infiltrates farther into the ground.

Leeward: The downwind side of a mountain range. Usually the side with less precipitation.

Length: The distance between two points, measured in meters or other units of length.

Light-year: The distance light travels in one year.

Liquid: A phase of matter in which the molecules or atoms are close together but are free to move about.

Lithosphere: The solid portion of the Earth below the atmosphere and hydrosphere; a solid layer that includes the crust and the upper portion of the Earth's mantle.

Longitude: The angular distance in degrees east or west of the prime meridian. Longitude varies from 0° at the prime meridian to 180° near the middle of the Pacific Ocean.

Low-pressure system: A weather system in which the atmospheric pressure is lower than surrounding areas; a cyclone.

Luster: The way that the surface of a mineral reflects light.

Mafic: Composed of dark minerals rich in iron and magnesium.

Magma: Molten rock within the Earth.

Magnitude: The total energy released by an earthquake, measured by the Richter scale.

Mantle: The portion of the Earth below the crust and above the core.

Marine (maritime) air mass: A body of air that is relatively moist because it formed over an ocean.

Marine climate: A climate in which seasonal temperature changes are moderated by large bodies of water.

Mass: The quantity of matter in an object, measured in grams or other units of mass.

Maturity: A relative measure of the development of a landscape as either young, mature, or old.

Meander: A natural looping bend, or S-shaped curve, in a stream.

Mean solar day: The average length of the day as measured from noon to noon (24 hours).

Measurement: An observation, made with an instrument, of a quantity.

Melting temperature: The temperature at which a substance starts to change from a solid to a liquid phase.

Meridian: An imaginary semicircle, drawn around the Earth from the North Pole to the South Pole, that represents a constant longitude.

Metamorphic rock: A sedimentary or igneous rock that has been changed in texture or composition by heat or pressure, or both, without melting.

Meteorite: A natural object that has fallen to the Earth from space.

Meteorologist: A scientist who studys the weather.

Meteorology: The study of the changing conditions of the atmosphere, or weather.

Mid-ocean ridges: A system of submerged mountain ranges that encircles the Earth and often connects with mountain ranges on the continents, new crust forms here.

Millibar: A metric unit of atmospheric pressure.

Minerals: The natural, crystalline inorganic substances of which rocks are made.

Model: A representation of an object or natural event. Maps, graphs, and mathematical formulas are models.

Moho: The interface between the Earth's crust and mantle.

Mohs scale: A series of ten minerals used as a scale of hardness.

Moisture: The presence of water or water vapor, particularly in the atmosphere.

Monomineralic: Describes a rock composed of a single mineral.

Moraines: Irregular, hilly, unsorted deposits formed at the end of an advancing glacier when the melting ice front stays at the same position for a period of time; ridges deposited along the sides of a glacier.

Mountain: A landscape region characterized by non-horizontal rock structure and great topographic relief; a landscape feature usually characterized by high elevation and steep slopes.

Navigation: The science of locating your position on the Earth.

Nonrenewable resources: Resources that cannot be replenished for millions of years, if at all.

Nonsedimentary rocks: Igneous or metamorphic rocks that were not formed directly by sedimentary processes.

North Star: Polaris; the star located almost directly above the North Pole. It is often used for navigation or to find the local latitude.

Oblate spheroid: The nearly spherical shape of the Earth, slightly flattened at the poles and slightly bulging at the equator.

Observation: Information obtained directly from the senses.

Occluded front: A type of weather front that is produced when a cold air mass overtakes a warm air mass, isolating the warm air above the ground.

Ocean-floor spreading: The theory that the oceanic crust has been constructed by material from deep within the Earth that rises and spreads apart at the mid-ocean ridges.

Oceanic crust: The relatively thin, dense layer of basaltic rock that underlies the ocean sediments and lies on top of the mantle layer.

Oceanography: The study of the characteristics and dynamics of the blanket of water that covers most of our planet.

Orbit: The path (usually an ellipse) of any satellite around its primary.

Orbital speed: The measure of a satellite's orbital motion.

Organic evolution: See **evolution.**

Organic sedimentary rock: Rock formed by the accumulation of plant or animal remains.

Origin time: The time when an earthquake occurs at its epicenter.

Orogeny: The process of mountain building.

Outcrop: Bedrock that is exposed at the surface because it is not covered by soil.

Outer core: The outside portion of the Earth's core that is thought to consist mostly of iron and nickel in the liquid state because S-waves can not go through it.

Outwash: Layered deposits left by water from a glacier.

Ozone: A form of oxygen (O_3) that in the upper atmosphere protects the Earth from harmful radiation from outer space. At ground level ozone is a pollutant.

Ozone layer: A layer in the upper atmosphere that has a high ozone content.

Pangaea: The ancient supercontinent that broke apart millions of years ago to form the present continents.

Parallel: An imaginary line, drawn around the Earth and parallel to the equator, that represents a constant latitude.

Percent error: A mathematical method of comparing a measurement with the commonly accepted value for that measurement; percent deviation from accepted value.

Perihelion: The closest approach of a satellite to its primary; where a satellite moves the fastest in its orbit.

Period: The amount of time required for a complete cycle; in geologic time, a subdivision of an era.

Permeability: The ability of a soil to transmit water.

Phase: The physical state of matter; solid, liquid, or gas; the shape of the lighted portion of a celestial object, like the phases of the moon.

Physical weathering: The mechanical breakdown of rocks without any change in chemical composition.

Piedmont glacier: The part of an alpine glacier that flows into a flat area below the mountain.

Plains: A landscape region characterized by horizontal rock structure and low topographic relief.

Planetary wind belts: Latitude zones of prevailing wind conditions caused by uneven heating of the Earth and the Earth's rotation; the mid-latitude westerlies, the polar easterlies, the trade winds, and the doldrums.

Plate boundaries: The lines along which crustal plates meet and interact.

Plate tectonics: A unified theory of crustal motions that incorporates continental drift and ocean-floor spreading; the theory that the Earth's surface is composed of about a dozen large, rigid plates that carry the continents with them as they diverge and converge.

Plateau: A landscape region characterized by horizontal rock structure and high topographic relief. A plateau is usually a relatively flat or rolling uplands area deeply cut by stream valleys.

Polar air mass: A cool air mass.

Polaris: See **North Star.**

Pollution: Any substance or form of energy in sufficient concentration to harm living things or the natural environment.

Polymineralic: Describes a rock composed of more than one mineral.

Porosity: The portion or percentage of empty space within a soil; the number of pores in a material compared with its volume.

Potential energy: Energy in storage, energy of position, or energy involved in a change in state.

Potential evapotranspiration: The demand of the atmosphere for moisture; the amount of water that could be lost by the soil in evaporation and transpiration within a given period of time, if plenty of water were available.

Precipitation: Water, in the form of rain, snow, or sleet, falling from the sky; a sedimentary process that involves substances settling out of a water solution that is saturated.

Prediction: An inference made about future events.

Pressure gradient: The rate of change in air pressure between two points on a map.

Primary: An object (lying along the major axis of an ellipse) around which a satellite moves. The sun is the primary of the orbiting Earth, and the Earth is the primary of the moon.

Primary waves: See **P-waves.**

Prime Meridian: An imaginary line (semicircle) that runs through Greenwich, England, from the North Pole to the South Pole.

Probability: The likelihood of an event.

Profile: A side view of the elevations along a baseline crossing contour lines on a topographic map.

P-waves: Compressional (longitudinal) waves that are the fastest form of seismic waves to radiate from an earthquake and can travel through solids and liquids; also known as primary waves.

Radial drainage: A pattern of streams that runs away from a central mountain, like a volcano.

Radiation: The emission and transfer of heat energy by means of electromagnetic waves, and the only way that energy can travel through empty space; rays or particles given off by an unstable radioactive substance.

Radiative balance: An equilibrium between absorbed radiant energy and radiant energy given off.

Radioactivity: The emission of energy rays or nuclear particles from the breakdown of an unstable isotope.

Recharge: In the water budget, infiltrating water that enters storage in the root zone of the soil.

Redshift: The displacement of spectral lines of distant stars toward the red end of the spectrum; Doppler shift.

Reflection: The process by which energy waves bounce off a surface or interface.

Refraction: The way that energy waves change direction as they move from one medium to another.

Regional metamorphism: The process by which large masses of rock are changed by deep burial within the Earth.

Relative age: A comparative age; age expressed as before or after other events without specifying the age in units of measure.

Relative humidity: The ratio between the actual amount of water vapor in the air and the maximum amount of water vapor the air can hold at a given temperature.

Relief (topographic): Changes in elevation from one place to another.

Renewable resources: Resources that can be replaced by nature after they have been used.

Residual soil: Soil that remains on top of the bedrock from which it forms.

Retrograde motion: The apparent backward motion of planets, such as Mars, through the stars. Retrograde motion is in a direction opposite to the more common direction of motion.

Reversed magnetic polarity: Refers to an igneous rock that was formed at a time in the geologic past when the north and south magnetic poles of the Earth had the opposite polarity that they have at the present.

Revolution: The orbital motion of a satellite around its primary. The Earth revolves around the sun in an annual cycle.

Rift: A linear feature of the Earth where new crust is being created.

Ring of Fire: The zone of volcanoes, earthquakes, and mountain building that surrounds the Pacific Ocean.

Rock: A natural piece of the solid Earth, usually composed of one or more minerals.

Rock cycle: A model of natural changes in rocks and sediment.

Rotation: The spinning of a body around an internal axis. The Earth's rotation causes day and night.

Runoff: Precipitation that is unable to infiltrate the soil, so it moves overland into streams. In the water budget, runoff is surplus water.

Satellite: An object that moves elliptically around another object. The Earth is a satellite of the sun. The moon is a satellite of the Earth.

Saturation: A weather condition in which the air holds as much water vapor as it can at a given temperature; a saturated solution is one that can hold no more of a particular substance dissolved in it.

Saturation vapor pressure: The portion of air pressure that could be caused by the weight of water vapor alone, if the air were saturated with water vapor.

Scalar: A measured quantity that has magnitude (size), but no direction. Temperature is a scalar quantity because it has no direction.

Scattering: Random reflections from irregular surfaces.

Scientific notation: A mathematical shorthand in which numbers are written in the form $M \times 10^n$, where M is a number between 1 and 10, and 10^n is a power of 10.

Seamount: An isolated volcanic island located on the bottom of the ocean.

Seasons: The annual cycle of weather conditions as the Earth orbits the sun.

Secondary waves: See **S-waves.**

Sediment: Accumulations of particles of weathered rock, organic remains, or both; rock fragments.

Sedimentary rock: Rock formed by the compression and cementation of particles of sediment.

Seismic waves: Vibrational energy that radiates through the Earth from an earthquake.

Seismograph: An instrument designed to measure and record the magnitude of an earthquake.

Seismologist: A scientist who studys earthquakes.

Seismometer: An instrument that detects vibrations of the ground.

Senses: Any of the five means by which we directly observe our environment; sight, hearing, smell, taste, and touch.

Shear waves: See **S-waves.**

Silica tetrahedron: A four-sided pyramid formed by four oxygen atoms bonded to one silicon atom in the center; the structural unit of silicate minerals.

Silicates: The large family of minerals that has the silicon-oxygen tetrahedron as its basic structure.

Sink (energy): An object or region that absorbs energy because it is cooler than its surroundings.

Slope: See **gradient.**

Soil: Weathered rock mixed with organic remains at the top of the lithosphere.

Soil association: Soils that are similar and found together.

Soil horizon: A layer within the soil showing a particular stage of soil development.

Solar noon: The time when the sun is at its highest point in the sky.

Solar system: The Earth and eight other planets that revolve around the sun.

Solid: A state of matter in which the molecules or atoms are rigidly held together in a three-dimensional network known as a crystal lattice.

Solstice: The longest or shortest day (hours of daylight) of the year when the sun is directly above the Tropic of Cancer or the Tropic of Capricorn. The solstices occur about December 21 and about June 21, and they mark the beginning of winter and summer.

Sorted: Separated by particle size or other characteristics.

Source (energy): An object or region that gives off energy because it is hotter than its surroundings.

Source region: The place where an air mass originates.

Species: A group of living organisms with similar characteristics, a common name, and the capability to interbreed.

Specific gravity: The ratio of a substance's density to the density of water.

Specific heat: The amount of heat energy required to raise the temperature of one gram of a substance by one Celsius degree. Water, with a specific heat of 1, is the common standard.

Spectrum: See **electromagnetic spectrum.**

Sphere: A round object on whose surface all points are equidistant from its center.

State of matter: See **phase.**

Static equilibrium: A state of balance in a system in which no movement or change occurs in any of the system's components.

Stationary front: An interface between two air masses that is not moving.

Storage: Within the water budget, water held in the root zone that can be used for evapotranspiration.

Strata: Layers or beds of rock, usually sedimentary.

Streak: The color of the powder of a mineral revealed by rubbing the mineral along a white, unglazed porcelain plate.

Streambed: The bottom of a stream.

Stream discharge: See **discharge.**

Striations (glacial): Parallel scratches on a rock surface caused by the movements of a glacier.

Subduction zone: The region in which the Earth's crust is destroyed as it is pulled down into the mantle.

Sublimation: A direct change in phase from a solid to a gas or from a gas to a solid without the liquid phase occurring.

Submarine canyons: The V-shaped valleys that cut across the continental shelf and the continental slope.

Subsidence: The gradual sinking of a portion of the Earth's crust.

Superposition (law of): The principle that the lowest layers in a sequence of rock strata must have been deposited before the layers above, unless the rock strata have been turned upside down. The oldest rocks are generally found at the bottom of an outcrop.

Surplus: In the water budget, water that becomes runoff or sinks below the water table when precipitation is greater than potential evapotranspiration and storage is full.

Suspension: A fluid containing large particles that can be filtered out but are too small to settle out on their own. A cloud is a suspension of tiny water droplets in the sky.

S-waves: Transverse earthquake waves that arrive after the P-waves and that cannot travel through a liquid such as the outer core of the Earth; also known as secondary or shear waves.

Synoptic weather map: A map showing a variety of field quantities, like temperature, pressure, and sky conditions, at a particular time and over a large geographic area.

Talus: Rock fragments that accumulate at the base of a cliff.

Tectonics: The study of large-scale deformations of the Earth.

Tectonic structures: Rock structures formed by faulting and folding.

Temperature: A measure of the average vibrational kinetic energy in a substance.

Terrace (marine): A series of flat areas, cut by wave or stream action, that go up from a shoreline like steps.

Tetrahedron: See **silica tetrahedron.**

Texture: The shape or feel of a surface; particularly the shape, arrangement, and size of mineral crystals on a rock surface.

Thermal energy: See **heat energy.**

Tides: The rise and fall of the oceans that usually occurs twice a day.

Till: Unsorted sediments deposited directly by glacial ice.

Tilted strata: Beds of rock (usually sedimentary), thought to have been deposited flat and level, that have been pushed into a different inclination (angle), usually by motions of the Earth's crust.

Time: A measurable period in which an event or process occurs.

Topographic map: See **contour map.**

Topography: The shape of the land surface.

Track: The route followed by a weather system.

Traction: The transportation of large particles along a streambed by rolling and bouncing.

Transform boundary: A plate boundary at which crustal plates slide past one another.

Transition zone: Rock adjacent to an igneous intrusion that has been altered by the heat of the intrusion; a region of contact metamorphism that gradually intensifies toward the contact.

Transparency: The quality of a mineral that determines how it transmits light.

Transpiration: The process by which living plants release water vapor to the atmosphere.

Transported soil: Soil eroded and deposited away from its parent bedrock.

Transverse wave: An energy wave that vibrates perpendicular to the direction of travel, like S-waves and electromagnetic energy.

Trellis drainage: A drainage pattern in which most of the streams occupy parallel valleys; usually develops on folded strata of rocks with differing competence.

Trench (ocean): An ocean floor depression that marks the zone where crust is being subducted.

Tropic of Cancer: The farthest north that the vertical ray of sunlight ever gets (at the June solstice), $23\frac{1}{2}°$ north of the equator.

Tropic of Capricorn: The farthest south that the vertical ray of sunlight ever gets (at the December solstice), $23\frac{1}{2}°$ south of the equator.

Tropical air mass: A warm air mass.

Troposphere: The lowest layer of air, from the surface of the Earth up to about 12 km, that contains most of the mass of the atmosphere.

Tsunami: An ocean wave or a series of waves usually associated with undersea earthquakes.

Turbidity current: A down-slope underwater flow of a dense mixture of sediment and sea water that can deposit a layer of graded bedding.

Unconformity: A gap in the geologic record caused by the erosion of sediments or rock before they are protected by layers above.

Uniformitarianism: The principal that most of the geologic events of the past are similar to processes that we can observe in the present.

Uplift: The rising of the Earth's crust from forces within the Earth, generally related to motions of the tectonic plates.

Usage: Within the water budget, water from storage that is used for evapotranspiration because there is not enough precipitation to satisfy the potential evapotranspiration.

Vaporization: See **evaporation.**

Vapor pressure: The portion of the total air pressure caused by the weight of water vapor.

Vector: A quantity that has both magnitude (size) and direction. Wind is a vector quantity because the wind is specified by both a speed (magnitude) and a direction.

Vein: A small inclusion of crystalline rock within a preexisting rock; formed by intrusion, partial melting, or deposition in cracks by mineral-laden groundwater.

Vertical ray: Sunlight that strikes the Earth from directly overhead (the zenith). At any given time, the vertical ray of sunlight strikes the Earth at a single location.

Vertical sorting: The sorting of particles from bottom to top in a layer, with the roundest, largest, and densest particles settling at the bottom and the flattest, smallest, and least dense particles at the top.

Visibility: A measure of the transparency of the atmosphere. Fog, haze, precipitation, and pollution reduce the visibility of the air.

Volcanic ash: Cinders that are blown into the air by a volcano, and that are useful in correlating rock outcrops in different locations.

Volume: The amount of space that matter occupies.

Walking the outcrop: A method of following rock layers to correlate layers within the same outcropping.

Water budget: An accounting procedure that models the annual movement of water through the soil for any given location.

Water cycle: A model of the circulation of water between the oceans, atmosphere, and land.

Water table: A boundary at the top of the saturated zone within the soil.

Water vapor: Water in the form of a gas.

Wavelength: The distance between corresponding points on two successive crests or two successive troughs of a wave. For visible light, the wavelength determines the color. Heat radiation (infrared) and red light have longer wavelengths than violet, ultraviolet, or X rays.

Weather: The short-term condition of the atmosphere and the changes that occur within hours or days.

Weathering: The breakdown of rock due to physical or chemical changes.

Weight: A measurement of the pull of gravity on an object.

Wind: The natural movement of air along, or parallel to, the Earth's surface; convection within the atmosphere.

Windward: The side of a mountain range where warm, moist air is forced to rise, leading to cloud formation and precipitation.

Year: The time required for a planet (the Earth) to complete one orbit around its primary (the sun).

Zenith: The point on a celestial sphere that is directly overhead with respect to an observer (90°).

Zone of aeration: The part of the soil above the water table in which most of the interconnected pores are filled with air.

Zone of crustal activity: An area around an ocean ridge or continental mountain range where volcanoes and earthquake epicenters are concentrated.

Zone of saturation: The portion of the soil below the water table, in which the pores are filled with groundwater.

Index

Reference Tables and Charts

Surface Ocean Currents

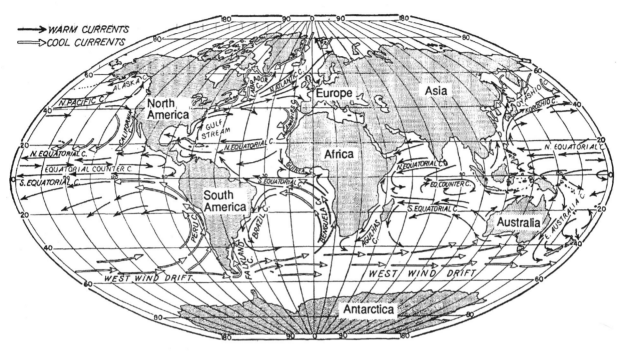

Earth Science Reference Tables — 2001 Edition

Tectonic Plates

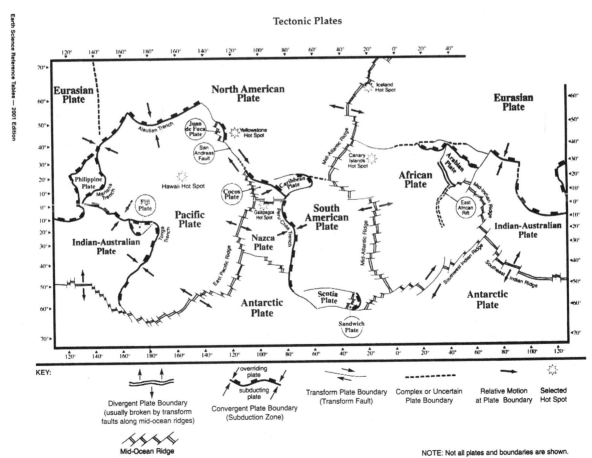

KEY:

Divergent Plate Boundary
(usually broken by transform
faults along mid-ocean ridges)

Convergent Plate Boundary
(Subduction Zone)

Transform Plate Boundary
(Transform Fault)

Complex or Uncertain
Plate Boundary

Relative Motion
at Plate Boundary

Selected
Hot Spot

Mid-Ocean Ridge

NOTE: Not all plates and boundaries are shown.

Generalized Landscape Regions of New York State

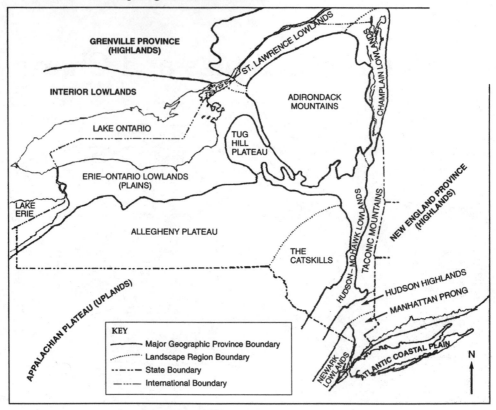

KEY
- —— Major Geographic Province Boundary
- ········ Landscape Region Boundary
- —·—·— State Boundary
- —··—··— International Boundary

Generalized Bedrock Geology of New York State

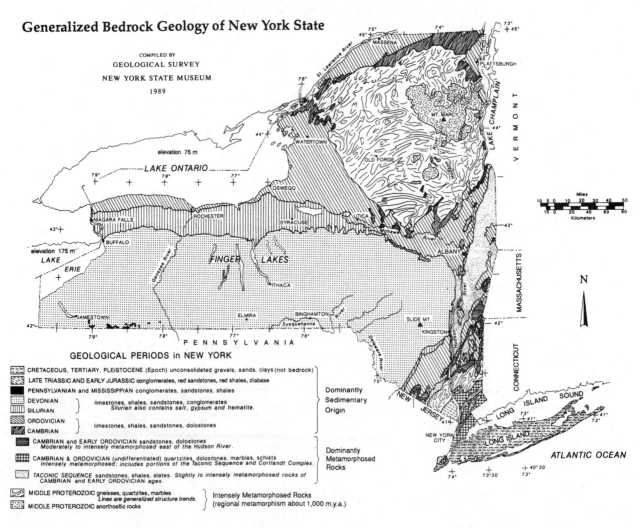

COMPILED BY
GEOLOGICAL SURVEY
NEW YORK STATE MUSEUM
1989

GEOLOGICAL PERIODS in NEW YORK

CRETACEOUS, TERTIARY, PLEISTOCENE (Epoch) unconsolidated gravels, sands, clays (not bedrock)

LATE TRIASSIC AND EARLY JURASSIC conglomerates, red sandstones, red shales, diabase

PENNSYLVANIAN and MISSISSIPPIAN conglomerates, sandstones, shales

DEVONIAN
SILURIAN
limestones, shales, sandstones, conglomerates
Silurian also contains salt, gypsum and hematite.

ORDOVICIAN
CAMBRIAN
limestones, shales, sandstones, dolostones

Dominantly
Sedimentary
Origin

CAMBRIAN and EARLY ORDOVICIAN sandstones, dolostones
Moderately to intensely metamorphosed east of the Hudson River.

CAMBRIAN & ORDOVICIAN (undifferentiated) quartzites, dolostones, marbles, schists
Intensely metamorphosed; includes portions of the Taconic Sequence and Cortlandt Complex.

TACONIC SEQUENCE sandstones, shales, slates. Slightly to intensely metamorphosed rocks of
CAMBRIAN and EARLY ORDOVICIAN ages.

Dominantly
Metamorphosed
Rocks

MIDDLE PROTEROZOIC gneisses, quartzites, marbles
Lines are generalized structure trends.

MIDDLE PROTEROZOIC anorthositic rocks

Intensely Metamorphosed Rocks
(regional metamorphism about 1,000 m.y.a.)

Rock Cycle in Earth's Crust

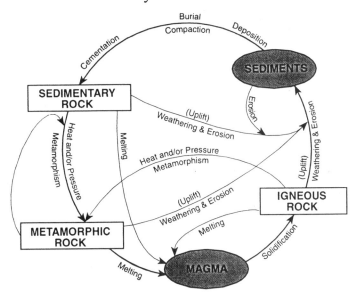

Relationship of Transported Particle Size to Water Velocity

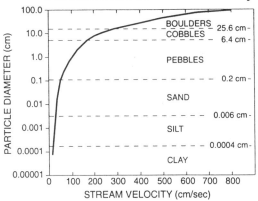

*This generalized graph shows the water velocity needed to maintain, but not start, movement. Variations occur due to differences in particle density and shape.

Scheme for Igneous Rock Identification

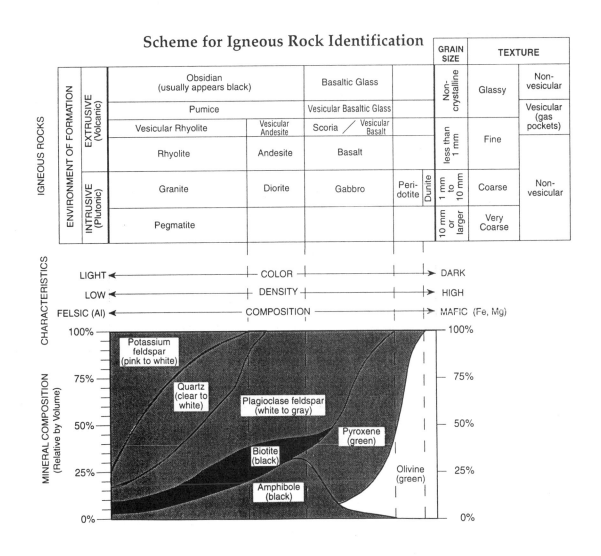

Scheme for Sedimentary Rock Identification

INORGANIC LAND-DERIVED SEDIMENTARY ROCKS

TEXTURE	GRAIN SIZE	COMPOSITION	COMMENTS	ROCK NAME	MAP SYMBOL
Clastic (fragmental)	Pebbles, cobbles, and/or boulders embedded in sand, silt, and/or clay	Mostly quartz, feldspar, and clay minerals; may contain fragments of other rocks and minerals	Rounded fragments	Conglomerate	
			Angular fragments	Breccia	
	Sand (0.2 to 0.006 cm)		Fine to coarse	Sandstone	
	Silt (0.006 to 0.0004 cm)		Very fine grain	Siltstone	
	Clay (less than 0.0004 cm)		Compact; may split easily	Shale	

CHEMICALLY AND/OR ORGANICALLY FORMED SEDIMENTARY ROCKS

TEXTURE	GRAIN SIZE	COMPOSITION	COMMENTS	ROCK NAME	MAP SYMBOL
Crystalline	Varied	Halite	Crystals from chemical precipitates and evaporites	Rock Salt	
	Varied	Gypsum		Rock Gypsum	
	Varied	Dolomite		Dolostone	
Bioclastic	Microscopic to coarse	Calcite	Cemented shell fragments or precipitates of biologic origin	Limestone	
	Varied	Carbon	From plant remains	Coal	

Scheme for Metamorphic Rock Identification

TEXTURE	GRAIN SIZE	COMPOSITION	TYPE OF METAMORPHISM	COMMENTS	ROCK NAME	MAP SYMBOL
FOLIATED — MINERAL ALIGNMENT	Fine	MICA QUARTZ FELDSPAR AMPHIBOLE GARNET PYROXENE	Regional (Heat and pressure increase with depth)	Low-grade metamorphism of shale	Slate	
	Fine to medium			Foliation surfaces shiny from microscopic mica crystals	Phyllite	
				Platy mica crystals visible from metamorphism of clay or feldspars	Schist	
FOLIATED — BANDING	Medium to coarse			High-grade metamorphism; some mica changed to feldspar; segregated by mineral type into bands	Gneiss	
NONFOLIATED	Fine	Variable	Contact (Heat)	Various rocks changed by heat from nearby magma/lava	Hornfels	
	Fine to coarse	Quartz	Regional or Contact	Metamorphism of quartz sandstone	Quartzite	
		Calcite and/or dolomite		Metamorphism of limestone or dolostone	Marble	
	Coarse	Various minerals in particles and matrix		Pebbles may be distorted or stretched	Metaconglomerate	

Earth Science Reference Tables — 2001 Edition

Reviewing Earth Science

Dewpoint Temperatures (°C)

Dry-Bulb Tempera-ture (°C)	Difference Between Wet-Bulb and Dry-Bulb Temperatures (C°)															
	0	1	2	3	4	5	6	7	8	9	10	11	12	13	14	15
−20	−20	−33														
−18	−18	−28														
−16	−16	−24														
−14	−14	−21	−36													
−12	−12	−18	−28													
−10	−10	−14	−22													
−8	−8	−12	−18	−29												
−6	−6	−10	−14	−22												
−4	−4	−7	−12	−17	−29											
−2	−2	−5	−8	−13	−20											
0	0	−3	−6	−9	−15	−24										
2	2	−1	−3	−6	−11	−17										
4	4	1	−1	−4	−7	−11	−19									
6	6	4	1	−1	−4	−7	−13	−21								
8	8	6	3	1	−2	−5	−9	−14								
10	10	8	6	4	1	−2	−5	−9	−14	−28						
12	12	10	8	6	4	1	−2	−5	−9	−16						
14	14	12	11	9	6	4	1	−2	−5	−10	−17					
16	16	14	13	11	9	7	4	1	−1	−6	−10	−17				
18	18	16	15	13	11	9·	7	4	2	−2	−5	−10	−19			
20	20	19	17	15	14	12	10	7	4	2	−2	−5	−10	−19		
22	22	21	19	17	16	14	12	10	8	5	3	−1	−5	−10	−19	
24	24	23	21	20	18	16	14	12	10	8	6	2	−1	−5	−10	−18
26	26	25	23	22	20	18	17	15	13	11	9	6	3	0	−4	−9
28	28	27	25	24	22	21	19	17	16	14	11	9	7	4	1	−3
30	30	29	27	26	24	23	21	19	18	16	14	12	10	8	5	1

Relative Humidity (%)

Dry-Bulb Tempera-ture (°C)	Difference Between Wet-Bulb and Dry-Bulb Temperatures (C°)															
	0	1	2	3	4	5	6	7	8	9	10	11	12	13	14	15
−20	100	28														
−18	100	40														
−16	100	48														
−14	100	55	11													
−12	100	61	23													
−10	100	66	33													
−8	100	71	41	13												
−6	100	73	48	20												
−4	100	77	54	32	11											
−2	100	79	58	37	20	1										
0	100	81	63	45	28	11										
2	100	83	67	51	36	20	6									
4	100	85	70	56	42	27	14									
6	100	86	72	59	46	35	22	10								
8	100	87	74	62	51	39	28	17	6							
10	100	88	76	65	54	43	33	24	13	4						
12	100	88	78	67	57	48	38	28	19	10	2					
14	100	89	79	69	60	50	41	33	25	16	8	1				
16	100	90	80	71	62	54	45	37	29	21	14	7	1			
18	100	91	81	72	64	56	48	40	33	26	19	12	6			
20	100	91	82	74	66	58	51	44	36	30	23	17	11	5		
22	100	92	83	75	68	60	53	46	40	33	27	21	15	10	4	
24	100	92	84	76	69	62	55	49	42	36	30	25	20	14	9	4
26	100	92	85	77	70	64	57	51	45	39	34	28	23	18	13	9
28	100	93	86	78	71	65	59	53	47	42	36	31	26	21	17	12
30	100	93	86	79	72	66	61	55	49	44	39	34	29	25	20	16

Earth Science Reference Tables — 2001 Edition

GEOLOGIC HISTO

(Fossils not drawn to scale)

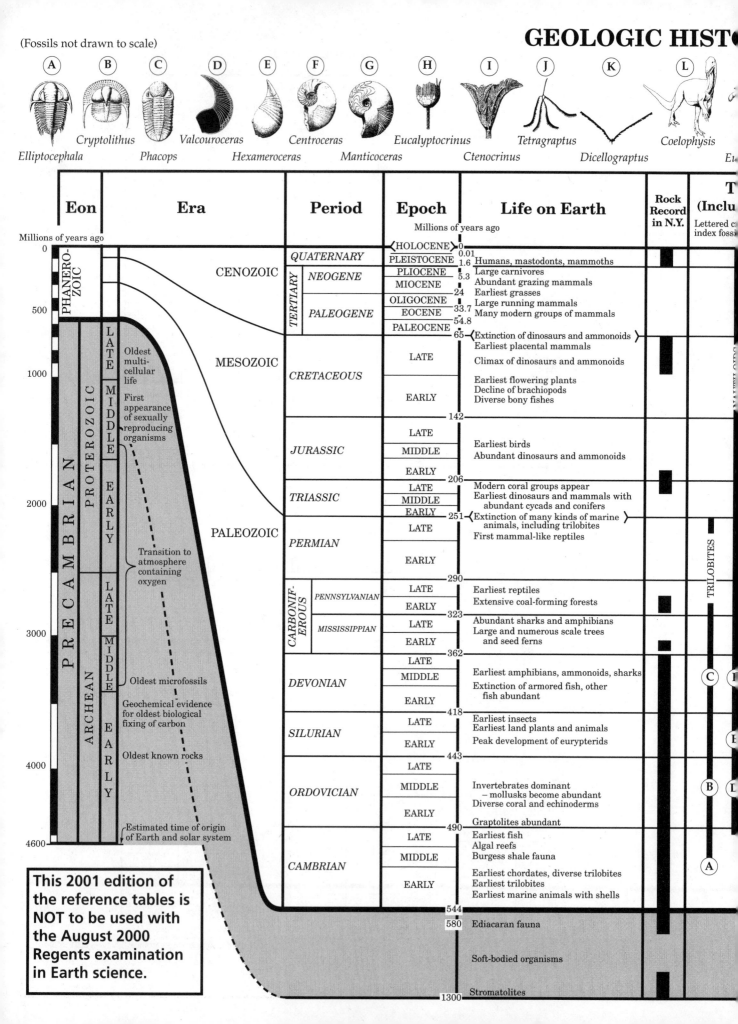

(A) Elliptocephala	(B) Cryptolithus	(C) Phacops	(D) Valcouroceras Hexameroceras	(E)	(F) Centroceras	(G) Manticoceras	(H) Eucalyptocrinus	(I) Ctenocrinus	(J) Tetragraptus	(K) Dicellograptus	(L) Coelophysis	Eu

Eon		Era	Period		Epoch	Life on Earth	Rock Record in N.Y.	T (Inclu
					Millions of years ago			Lettered c index fossi

Millions of years ago

0					HOLOCENE — 0.01			
			QUATERNARY		PLEISTOCENE — 1.6	Humans, mastodonts, mammoths		
		CENOZOIC	TERTIARY — NEOGENE		PLIOCENE — 5.3	Large carnivores		
					MIOCENE — 24	Abundant grazing mammals		
500	PHANEROZOIC				OLIGOCENE — 33.7	Earliest grasses / Large running mammals		
			PALEOGENE		EOCENE — 54.8	Many modern groups of mammals		
					PALEOCENE — 65	Extinction of dinosaurs and ammonoids		
						Earliest placental mammals		
		MESOZOIC	CRETACEOUS		LATE	Climax of dinosaurs and ammonoids		
1000					EARLY	Earliest flowering plants / Decline of brachiopods / Diverse bony fishes		
	PROTEROZOIC				— 142			
			JURASSIC		LATE			
					MIDDLE	Earliest birds / Abundant dinosaurs and ammonoids		
					EARLY — 206			
2000			TRIASSIC		LATE	Modern coral groups appear		
					MIDDLE	Earliest dinosaurs and mammals with abundant cycads and conifers		
					EARLY — 251	Extinction of many kinds of marine animals, including trilobites		
		PALEOZOIC	PERMIAN		LATE	First mammal-like reptiles		TRILOBITES
					EARLY			
					— 290			
	ARCHEAN		CARBONIFEROUS — PENNSYLVANIAN		LATE	Earliest reptiles		
3000					EARLY — 323	Extensive coal-forming forests		
			MISSISSIPPIAN		LATE	Abundant sharks and amphibians		
					EARLY — 362	Large and numerous scale trees and seed ferns		
			DEVONIAN		LATE			
					MIDDLE	Earliest amphibians, ammonoids, sharks		(C)
					EARLY	Extinction of armored fish, other fish abundant		
					— 418			
			SILURIAN		LATE	Earliest insects / Earliest land plants and animals		
4000					EARLY — 443	Peak development of eurypterids		
			ORDOVICIAN		LATE			(B)
					MIDDLE	Invertebrates dominant – mollusks become abundant / Diverse coral and echinoderms		
					EARLY — 490	Graptolites abundant		
			CAMBRIAN		LATE	Earliest fish / Algal reefs / Burgess shale fauna		(A)
4600					MIDDLE			
					EARLY	Earliest chordates, diverse trilobites / Earliest trilobites / Earliest marine animals with shells		
					— 544			

PRECAMBRIAN

PHANEROZOIC · PROTEROZOIC · ARCHEAN

LATE / MIDDLE / EARLY

Oldest multicellular life

First appearance of sexually reproducing organisms

Transition to atmosphere containing oxygen

Oldest microfossils

Geochemical evidence for oldest biological fixing of carbon

Oldest known rocks

Estimated time of origin of Earth and solar system

580 — Ediacaran fauna

Soft-bodied organisms

1300 — Stromatolites

This 2001 edition of the reference tables is NOT to be used with the August 2000 Regents examination in Earth science.

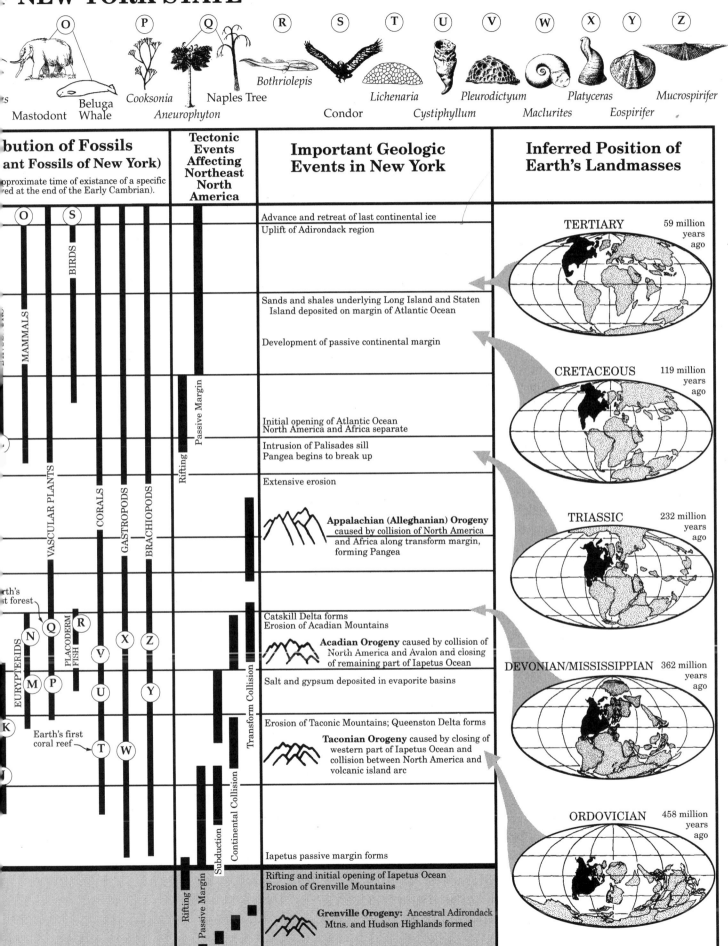

NEW YORK STATE

O — Mastodont
— Beluga Whale
P — Cooksonia
Q — Aneurophyton
— Naples Tree
— Bothriolepis
R — Condor
S —
T — Lichenaria
U — Cystiphyllum
V — Pleurodictyum
W — Maclurites
X — Platyceras
Y — Eospirifer
Z — Mucrospirifer

bution of Fossils (ant Fossils of New York)	Tectonic Events Affecting Northeast North America	Important Geologic Events in New York	Inferred Position of Earth's Landmasses

bution of Fossils
(ant Fossils of New York)

oproximate time of existence of a specific
red at the end of the Early Cambrian).

Important Geologic Events in New York

Advance and retreat of last continental ice
Uplift of Adirondack region

Sands and shales underlying Long Island and Staten Island deposited on margin of Atlantic Ocean

Development of passive continental margin

Initial opening of Atlantic Ocean
North America and Africa separate

Intrusion of Palisades sill
Pangea begins to break up

Extensive erosion

Appalachian (Alleghanian) Orogeny caused by collision of North America and Africa along transform margin, forming Pangea

Catskill Delta forms
Erosion of Acadian Mountains

Acadian Orogeny caused by collision of North America and Avalon and closing of remaining part of Iapetus Ocean

Salt and gypsum deposited in evaporite basins

Erosion of Taconic Mountains; Queenston Delta forms

Taconian Orogeny caused by closing of western part of Iapetus Ocean and collision between North America and volcanic island arc

Iapetus passive margin forms

Rifting and initial opening of Iapetus Ocean
Erosion of Grenville Mountains

Grenville Orogeny: Ancestral Adirondack Mtns. and Hudson Highlands formed

Tectonic Events Affecting Northeast North America:
Rifting — Passive Margin — Transform Collision — Subduction — Continental Collision — Rifting — Passive Margin

Fossils / Distribution:
MAMMALS — BIRDS — VASCULAR PLANTS — CORALS — GASTROPODS — BRACHIOPODS — PLACODERM FISH — EURYPTERIDS

O, S, N, Q, R, M, P, V, X, Z, U, Y, T, W, K

Earth's first forest
Earth's first coral reef

Inferred Position of Earth's Landmasses:

TERTIARY — 59 million years ago

CRETACEOUS — 119 million years ago

TRIASSIC — 232 million years ago

DEVONIAN/MISSISSIPPIAN — 362 million years ago

ORDOVICIAN — 458 million years ago

99-098 CDK(rev) 6/2000

Selected Properties of Earth's Atmosphere

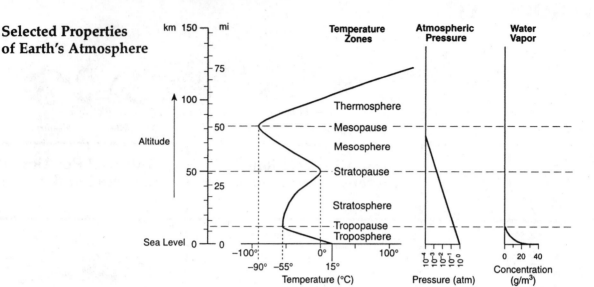

Electromagnetic Spectrum

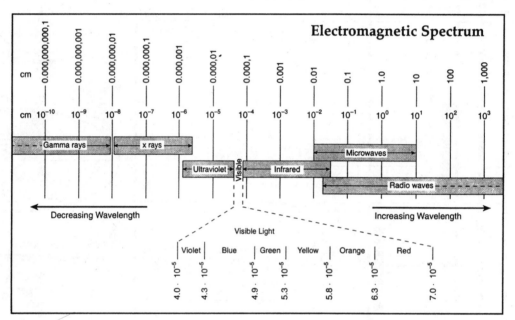

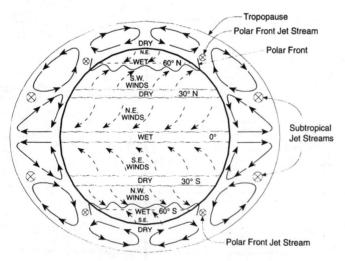

Planetary Wind and Moisture Belts in the Troposphere

The drawing to the left shows the locations of the belts near the time of an equinox. The locations shift somewhat with the changing latitude of the Sun's vertical ray. In the Northern Hemisphere, the belts shift northward in summer and southward in winter.

PHYSICAL CONSTANTS

Radioactive Decay Data

RADIOACTIVE ISOTOPE	DISINTEGRATION	HALF-LIFE (years)
Carbon-14	$C^{14} \rightarrow N^{14}$	$5.7 \cdot 10^3$
Potassium-40	$K^{40} \nearrow Ar^{40} \searrow Ca^{40}$	$1.3 \cdot 10^9$
Uranium-238	$U^{238} \rightarrow Pb^{206}$	$4.5 \cdot 10^9$
Rubidium-87	$Rb^{87} \rightarrow Sr^{87}$	$4.9 \cdot 10^{10}$

Specific Heats of Common Materials

MATERIAL		SPECIFIC HEAT (calories/gram • C°)
Water	solid	0.5
	liquid	1.0
	gas	0.5
Dry air		0.24
Basalt		0.20
Granite		0.19
Iron		0.11
Copper		0.09
Lead		0.03

Properties of Water

Energy gained during melting	80 calories/gram
Energy released during freezing	80 calories/gram
Energy gained during vaporization	540 calories/gram
Energy released during condensation	540 calories/gram
Density at 3.98°C	1.00 gram/milliliter

EQUATIONS

Percent deviation from accepted value

$$\text{deviation (\%)} = \frac{\text{difference from accepted value}}{\text{accepted value}} \cdot 100$$

Eccentricity of an ellipse

$$\text{eccentricity} = \frac{\text{distance between foci}}{\text{length of major axis}}$$

Gradient

$$\text{gradient} = \frac{\text{change in field value}}{\text{distance}}$$

Rate of change

$$\text{rate of change} = \frac{\text{change in field value}}{\text{time}}$$

Density of a substance

$$\text{density} = \frac{\text{mass}}{\text{volume}}$$

2001 EDITION

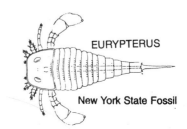

EURYPTERUS

New York State Fossil

Temperature

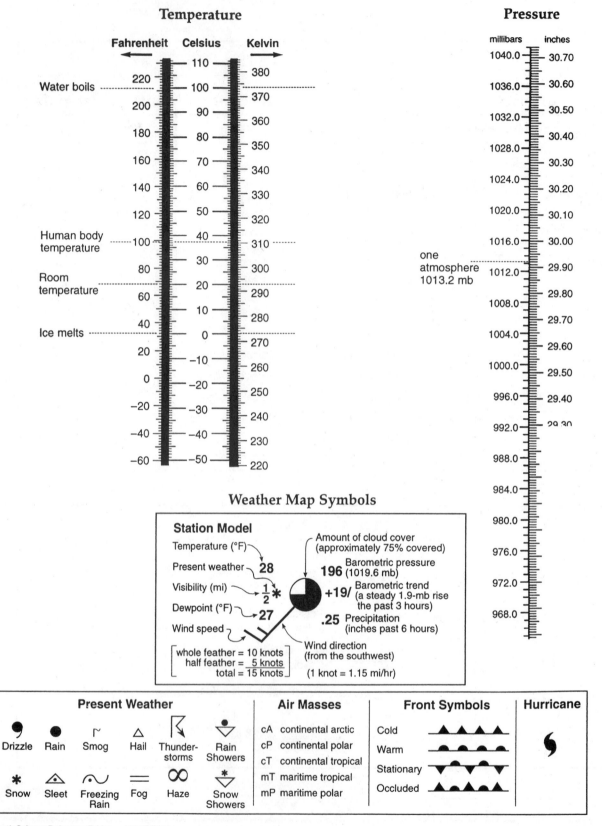

Fahrenheit   Celsius   Kelvin

Water boils 100 370

Human body
temperature 100 310

Room
temperature 20

Ice melts 0 270

Pressure

millibars   inches

one
atmosphere   1012.0   29.90
1013.2 mb

Weather Map Symbols

Station Model

Temperature (°F)
Present weather — **28**
Visibility (mi) — 1/2 ✳
Dewpoint (°F) — **27**
Wind speed

whole feather = 10 knots
half feather = 5 knots
total = 15 knots

Amount of cloud cover
(approximately 75% covered)

196 Barometric pressure
(1019.6 mb)

+19/ Barometric trend
(a steady 1.9-mb rise
the past 3 hours)

.25 Precipitation
(inches past 6 hours)

Wind direction
(from the southwest)

(1 knot = 1.15 mi/hr)

Present Weather						Air Masses	Front Symbols	Hurricane
Drizzle	Rain	Smog	Hail	Thunder-storms	Rain Showers	cA continental arctic	Cold	
Snow	Sleet	Freezing Rain	Fog	Haze	Snow Showers	cP continental polar	Warm	
						cT continental tropical	Stationary	
						mT maritime tropical	Occluded	
						mP maritime polar		

Earth Science Reference Tables — 2001 Edition

Luminosity and Temperature of Stars

(Name in italics refers to star shown by a ⊕)

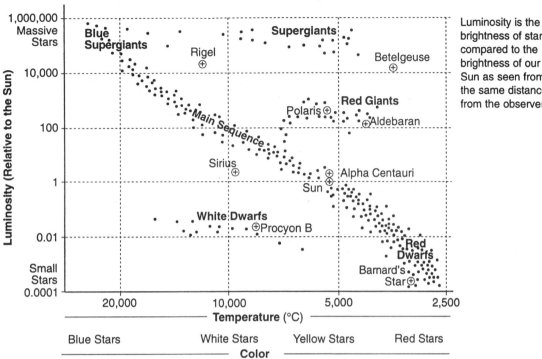

Luminosity is the brightness of stars compared to the brightness of our Sun as seen from the same distance from the observer.

Solar System Data

Object	Mean Distance from Sun (millions of km)	Period of Revolution	Period of Rotation	Eccentricity of Orbit	Equatorial Diameter (km)	Mass (Earth = 1)	Density (g/cm³)	Number of Moons
SUN	—	—	27 days	—	1,392,000	333,000.00	1.4	–
MERCURY	57.9	88 days	59 days	0.206	4,880	0.553	5.4	0
VENUS	108.2	224.7 days	243 days	0.007	12,104	0.815	5.2	0
EARTH	149.6	365.26 days	23 hr 56 min 4 sec	0.017	12,756	1.00	5.5	1
MARS	227.9	687 days	24 hr 37 min 23 sec	0.093	6,787	0.1074	3.9	2
JUPITER	778.3	11.86 years	9 hr 50 min 30 sec	0.048	142,800	317.896	1.3	16
SATURN	1,427	29.46 years	10 hr 14 min	0.056	120,000	95.185	0.7	18
URANUS	2,869	84.0 years	17 hr 14 min	0.047	51,800	14.537	1.2	21
NEPTUNE	4,496	164.8 years	16 hr	0.009	49,500	17.151	1.7	8
PLUTO	5,900	247.7 years	6 days 9 hr	0.250	2,300	0.0025	2.0	1
EARTH'S MOON	149.6 (0.386 from Earth)	27.3 days	27 days 8 hr	0.055	3,476	0.0123	3.3	—

Average Chemical Composition
of Earth's Crust, Hydrosphere, and Troposphere

ELEMENT (symbol)	CRUST		HYDROSPHERE	TROPOSPHERE
	Percent by Mass	Percent by Volume	Percent by Volume	Percent by Volume
Oxygen (O)	46.40	94.04	33.0	21.0
Silicon (Si)	28.15	0.88		
Aluminum (Al)	8.23	0.48		
Iron (Fe)	5.63	0.49		
Calcium (Ca)	4.15	1.18		
Sodium (Na)	2.36	1.11		
Magnesium (Mg)	2.33	0.33		
Potassium (K)	2.09	1.42		
Nitrogen (N)				78.0
Hydrogen (H)			66.0	
Other	0.66	0.07	1.0	1.0

Inferred Properties of Earth's Interior

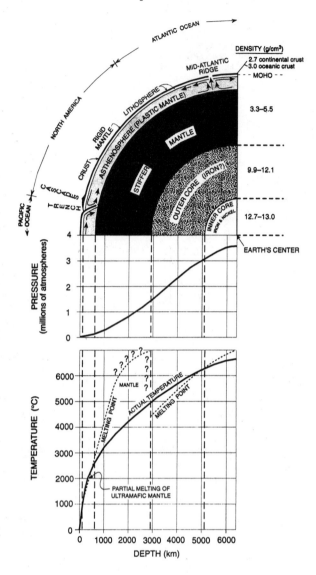

Earthquake P-wave and S-wave Travel Time

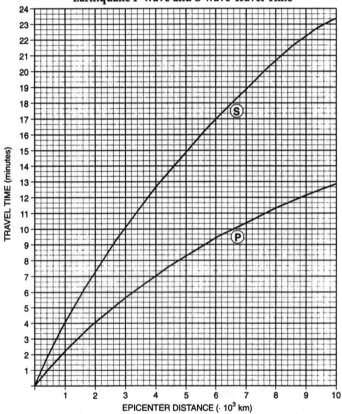

Properties of Common Minerals

LUSTER	HARD-NESS	CLEAVAGE	FRACTURE	COMMON COLORS	DISTINGUISHING CHARACTERISTICS	USE(S)	MINERAL NAME	COMPOSITION*
Metallic Luster	1–2	✔		silver to gray	black streak, greasy feel	pencil lead, lubricants	**Graphite**	C
	2.5	✔		metallic silver	very dense (7.6 g/cm³), gray-black streak	ore of lead	**Galena**	PbS
	5.5–6.5		✔	black to silver	attracted by magnet, black streak	ore of iron	**Magnetite**	Fe_3O_4
	6.5		✔	brassy yellow	green-black streak, cubic crystals	ore of sulfur	**Pyrite**	FeS_2
Either	1–6.5		✔	metallic silver or earthy red	red-brown streak	ore of iron	**Hematite**	Fe_2O_3
Nonmetallic Luster	1	✔		white to green	greasy feel	talcum powder, soapstone	**Talc**	$Mg_3Si_4O_{10}(OH)_2$
	2		✔	yellow to amber	easily melted, may smell	vulcanize rubber, sulfuric acid	**Sulfur**	S
	2	✔		white to pink or gray	easily scratched by fingernail	plaster of Paris and drywall	**Gypsum** (Selenite)	$CaSO_4 \cdot 2H_2O$
	2–2.5	✔		colorless to yellow	flexible in thin sheets	electrical insulator	**Muscovite Mica**	$KAl_3Si_3O_{10}(OH)_2$
	2.5	✔		colorless to white	cubic cleavage, salty taste	food additive, melts ice	**Halite**	NaCl
	2.5–3	✔		black to dark brown	flexible in thin sheets	electrical insulator	**Biotite Mica**	$K(Mg,Fe)_3$ $AlSi_3O_{10}(OH)_2$
	3	✔		colorless or variable	bubbles with acid	cement, polarizing prisms	**Calcite**	$CaCO_3$
	3.5	✔		colorless or variable	bubbles with acid when powdered	source of magnesium	**Dolomite**	$CaMg(CO_3)_2$
	4	✔		colorless or variable	cleaves in 4 directions	hydrofluoric acid	**Fluorite**	CaF_2
	5–6	✔		black to dark green	cleaves in 2 directions at 90°	mineral collections	**Pyroxene** (commonly Augite)	$(Ca,Na)(Mg,Fe,Al)$ $(Si,Al)_2O_6$
	5.5	✔		black to dark green	cleaves at 56° and 124°	mineral collections	**Amphiboles** (commonly Hornblende)	$CaNa(Mg,Fe)_4(Al,Fe,Ti)_3$ $Si_6O_{22}(O,OH)_2$
	6	✔		white to pink	cleaves in 2 directions at 90°	ceramics and glass	**Potassium Feldspar** (Orthoclase)	$KAlSi_3O_8$
	6	✔		white to gray	cleaves in 2 directions, striations visable	ceramics and glass	**Plagioclase Feldspar** (Na-Ca Feldspar)	$(Na,Ca)AlSi_3O_8$
	6.5		✔	green to gray or brown	commonly light green and granular	furnace bricks and jewelry	**Olivine**	$(Fe,Mg)_2SiO_4$
	7		✔	colorless or variable	glassy luster, may form hexagonal crystals	glass, jewelry, and electronics	**Quartz**	SiO_2
	7		✔	dark red to green	glassy luster, often seen as red grains in NYS metamorphic rocks	jewelry and abrasives	**Garnet** (commonly Almandine)	$Fe_3Al_2Si_3O_{12}$

*Chemical Symbols:

Al = aluminum	Cl = chlorine	H = hydrogen	Na = sodium	S = sulfur
C = carbon	F = fluorine	K = potassium	O = oxygen	Si = silicon
Ca = calcium	Fe = iron	Mg = magnesium	Pb = lead	Ti = titanium

✔ = dominant form of breakage

EARTH SCIENCE
JUNE 1997

PROGRAM MODIFICATION EDITION

Directions (1–40): For *each* statement or question, select the word or expression that, of those given, best completes the statement or answers the question. Record your answer on the separate answer paper in accordance with the directions on the front page of this booklet. Some questions may require the use of the *Earth Science Reference Tables*. [40]

1 A large earthquake occurred at 45° N 75° W on September 5, 1994. Which location in New York State was closest to the epicenter of the earthquake?

1 Buffalo
2 Massena
3 Albany
4 New York City

2 Isolines on the map below show elevations above sea level, measured in meters.

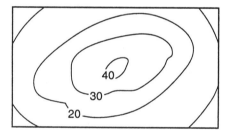

What is the highest possible elevation represented on this map?

(1) 39 m
(2) 41 m
(3) 49 m
(4) 51 m

3 A conglomerate contains pebbles of limestone, sandstone, and granite. Based on this information, which inference about the pebbles in the conglomerate is most accurate?

1 They had various origins.
2 They came from other conglomerates.
3 They are all the same age.
4 They were eroded quickly.

4 Which rock is usually composed of several different minerals?

1 rock gypsum
2 chemical limestone
3 quartzite
4 gneiss

5 Which statement about the formation of a rock is best supported by the rock cycle?

1 Magma must be weathered before it can change to metamorphic rock.
2 Sediment must be compacted and cemented before it can change to sedimentary rock.
3 Sedimentary rock must melt before it can change to metamorphic rock.
4 Metamorphic rock must melt before it can change to sedimentary rock.

6 Which granite sample most likely formed from magma that cooled and solidified at the slowest rate?

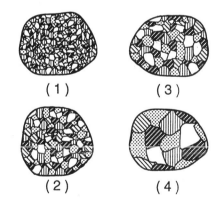

7 The interpretation that the Earth's outer core is liquid was made primarily from

1 deep-sea drilling data
2 magnetic data
3 seismic data
4 satellite data

8 What is the direction of crustal movement of the Australian plate?

1 northward
2 southward
3 northwestward
4 southeastward

9 The cartoon below presents a humorous view of Earth science.

The cartoon character on the right realizes that the sand castle will eventually be

1 compacted into solid bedrock
2 removed by agents of erosion
3 preserved as fossil evidence
4 deformed during metamorphic change

10 A deposit of rock particles that are scratched and unsorted has most likely been transported and deposited by

1 wind   3 running water
2 glacial ice   4 ocean waves

11 The diagram below shows a process called frost wedging.

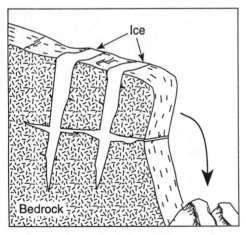

Frost wedging is an example of

1 weathering   3 metamorphism
2 cementing   4 deposition

12 The diagram below shows a soil profile formed in an area of granite bedrock. Four different soil horizons, A, B, C, and D, are shown.

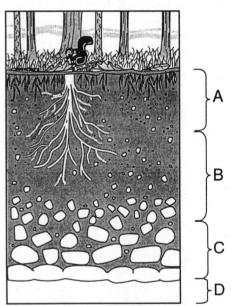

Which soil horizon contains the greatest amount of material formed by biological activity?

(1) A   (3) C
(2) B   (4) D

13 The map below shows the ancient location of evaporating seawater, which formed the Silurian-age deposits of rock salt and rock gypsum now found in some New York State crustal bedrock.

Within which two landscape regions are these large rock salt and rock gypsum deposits found?

1 Hudson Highlands and Taconic Mountains
2 Tug Hill Plateau and Adirondack Mountains
3 Erie-Ontario Lowlands and Allegheny Plateau
4 the Catskills and Hudson-Mohawk Lowlands

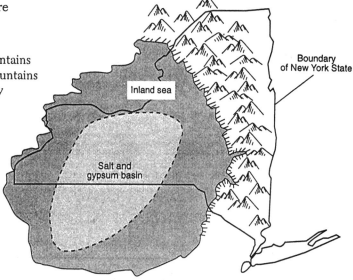

14 The diagrams below represent geologic cross sections from two widely separated regions.

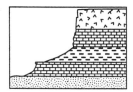 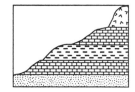

The layers of rock appear very similar, but the hillslopes and shapes are different. These differences are most likely the result of

1 volcanic eruptions   3 soil formation
2 earthquake activity   4 climate variations

15 Which statement correctly describes an age relationship in the geologic cross section below?

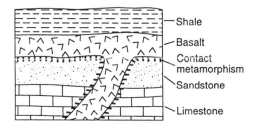

1 The sandstone is younger than the basalt.
2 The shale is younger than the basalt.
3 The limestone is younger than the shale.
4 The limestone is younger than the basalt.

16 Present-day corals live in warm, tropical ocean water. Which inference is best supported by the discovery of Ordovician-age corals in the surface bedrock of western New York State?

1 Western New York State was covered by a warm, shallow sea during Ordovician time.

2 Ordovician-age corals lived in the forests of western New York State.
3 Ordovician-age corals were transported to western New York State by cold, freshwater streams.
4 Western New York was covered by a continental ice sheet that created coral fossils of Ordovician time.

17 The diagram below represents the radioactive decay of uranium-238.

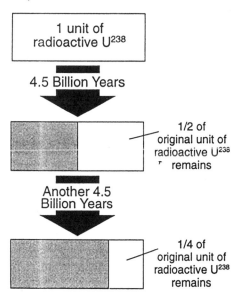

Shaded areas on the diagram represent the amount of

1 undecayed radioactive uranium-238 (U^{238})
2 undecayed radioactive rubidium-87 (Rb^{87})
3 stable carbon-14 (C^{14})
4 stable lead-206 (Pb^{206})

18 By which process does water vapor change into clouds?

1 condensation   3 convection
2 evaporation   4 precipitation

19 A geologist collected the fossils shown below from locations in New York State.

Which sequence correctly shows the fossils from oldest to youngest?

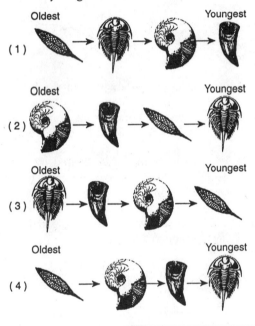

20 Which list shows atmospheric layers in the correct order upward from the Earth's surface?

1 thermosphere, mesosphere, stratosphere, troposphere
2 troposphere, stratosphere, mesosphere, thermosphere
3 stratosphere, mesosphere, troposphere, thermosphere
4 thermosphere, troposphere, mesosphere, stratosphere

21 Which statement best explains why precipitation occurs at frontal boundaries?

1 Cold fronts move slower than warm fronts.
2 Cold fronts move faster than warm fronts.
3 Warm, moist air sinks when it meets cold, dry air.
4 Warm, moist air rises when it meets cold, dry air.

Base your answers to questions 22 and 23 on the weather instrument shown in the diagram below.

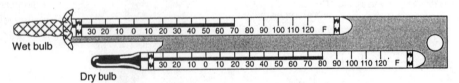

22 What are the equivalent Celsius temperature readings for the Fahrenheit readings shown?

1 wet 21°C, dry 27°C   3 wet 70°C, dry 80°C
2 wet 26°C, dry 37°C   4 wet 158°C, dry 176°C

23 Which weather variables are most easily determined by using this weather instrument?

1 air temperature and windspeed   3 relative humidity and dewpoint
2 visibility and wind direction   4 air pressure and cloud type

24 How do clouds affect the temperature at the Earth's surface?

1 Clouds block sunlight during the day and prevent heat from escaping at night.
2 Clouds block sunlight during the day and allow heat to escape at night.
3 Clouds allow sunlight to reach the Earth during the day and prevent heat from escaping at night.
4 Clouds allow sunlight to reach the Earth during the day and allow heat to escape at night.

25 A low-pressure system is shown on the weather map below.

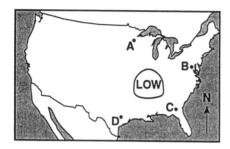

Toward which point will the low-pressure system move if it follows a normal storm track?

(1) *A*   (3) *C*
(2) *B*   (4) *D*

26 Compared to an inland location of the same elevation and latitude, a coastal location is likely to have

1 warmer summers and cooler winters
2 warmer summers and warmer winters
3 cooler summers and cooler winters
4 cooler summers and warmer winters

27 Which graph best represents the relationship between average yearly temperature and latitude?

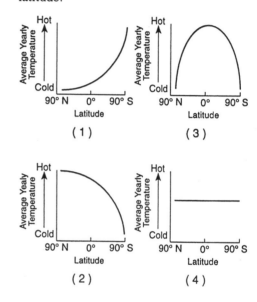

Base your answers to questions 28 through 30 on the *Earth Science Reference Tables* and the weather map below. The map shows a low-pressure system. Weather data is given for cities *A* through *D*.

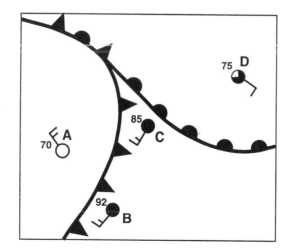

28 Which map correctly shows the locations of the continental polar (cP) and maritime tropical (mT) air masses?

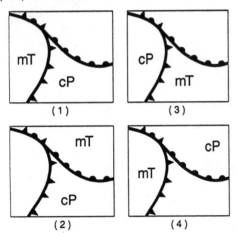

30 Which map correctly shows arrows indicating the probable surface wind pattern?

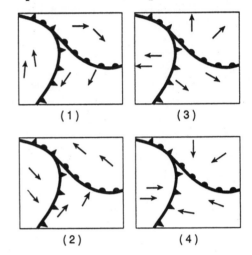

29 Which city is *least* likely to have precipitation starting in the next few hours?

(1) A   (3) C
(2) B   (4) D

Base your answers to questions 31 through 33 on the *Earth Science Reference Tables* and the map below. The map represents a view of the Earth looking down from above the North Pole, showing the Earth's 24 standard time zones. The Sun's rays are striking the Earth from the right. Points A, B, C, and D are locations on the Earth's surface.

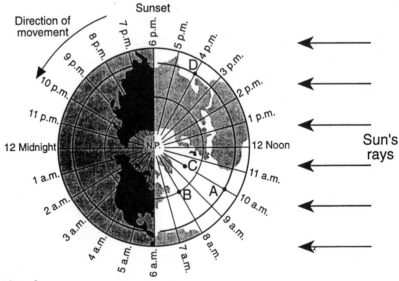

31 At which position would the altitude of the North Star (Polaris) be greatest?

(1) A   (3) C
(2) B   (4) D

32 Which date could this diagram represent?

1 January 21   3 June 21
2 March 21   4 August 21

33 Areas within a time zone generally keep the same standard clock time. In degrees of longitude, approximately how wide is one standard time zone?

(1) $7\frac{1}{2}°$ (3) $23\frac{1}{2}°$
(2) 15°   (4) 30°

34 Why do the locations of sunrise and sunset vary in a cyclical pattern throughout the year?

1 The Earth rotates on a tilted axis while revolving around the Sun.
2 The Sun rotates on a tilted axis while revolving around the Earth.
3 The Earth's orbit around the Sun is an ellipse.
4 The Sun's orbit around the Earth is an ellipse.

35 Compared to Jupiter and Saturn, Venus and Mars have greater

1 periods of revolution
2 orbital velocities
3 mean distances from the Sun
4 equatorial diameters

36 Billions of stars in the same region of the universe are called

1 solar systems
2 asteroid belts
3 constellations
4 galaxies

Base your answers to questions 37 and 38 on the diagram below, which represents the path of a planet in an elliptical orbit around a star. Points A, B, C, and D indicate four orbital positions of the planet.

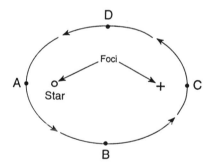

37 The eccentricity of the planet's orbit is approximately

(1) 0.18
(2) 0.65
(3) 1.55
(4) 5.64

38 Which graph best represents the gravitational attraction between the star and the planet?

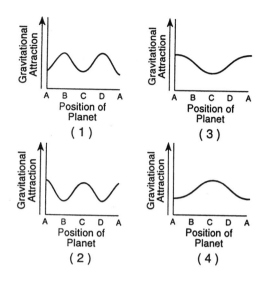

39 Which graph best represents the most common relationship between the amount of air pollution and the distance from an industrial city?

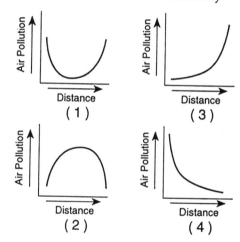

40 Which diagram best shows how air inside a greenhouse warms as a result of energy from the Sun?

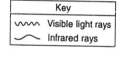

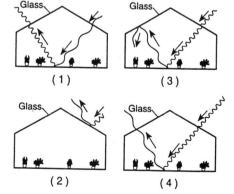

Part II

This part consists of six groups, each containing ten questions. Choose any one of these six groups. Be sure that you answer all ten questions in the single group chosen. Record the answers to these questions on the separate answer paper in accordance with the directions on the front cover of this booklet. Some questions may require the use of the *Earth Science Reference Tables.*   [10]

Group A — Rocks and Minerals

If you choose this group, be sure to answer questions 41–50.

Base your answers to questions 41 through 43 on the cross section below. The cross section shows the surface and subsurface rock formations near New York City.

Geologic Section Across the Hudson River

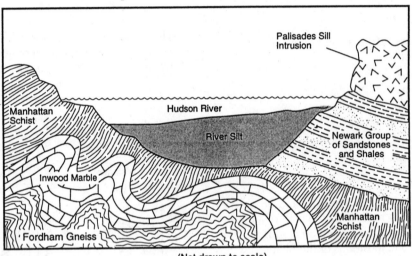

(Not drawn to scale)

41 The portion of the Palisades sill that contains large crystals of plagioclase feldspar and pyroxene is considered to be similar in texture and composition to

1 obsidian   3 basalt glass
2 granite   4 gabbro

42 Which rock formation was originally limestone?

1 Palisades sill
2 Fordham gneiss
3 Inwood marble
4 Manhattan schist

43 The rock types shown on the left side of this geologic cross section were mainly the result of

1 heat and pressure exerted on previously existing rock
2 melting and solidification of crustal rocks at great depths
3 tectonic plate boundaries diverging at the mid-ocean ridge
4 compaction and cementation of sediments under ocean waters

Base your answers to questions 44 and 45 on the diagram below, which represents a cross section of an area of the Earth's crust. Letters *A* through *F* represent rock units.

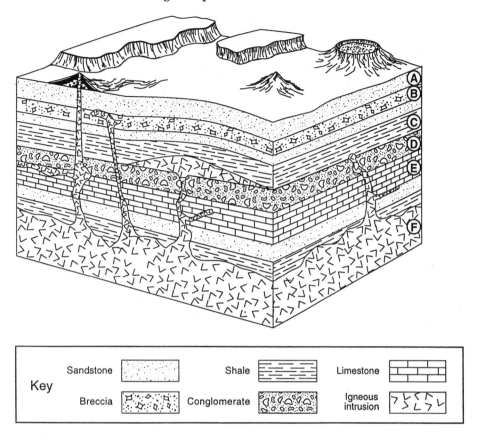

Key	Sandstone		Shale		Limestone	
	Breccia		Conglomerate		Igneous intrusion	

44 Which rock most likely had a chemical origin?

(1) *A*   (2) *E*   (3) *C*   (4) *F*

45 Which statement best describes how rock layers *B* and *D* are different from each other?

1 One is intrusive and the other is extrusive.
2 One is clastic and the other is nonclastic.
3 One is foliated and the other is nonfoliated.
4 One has angular fragments and the other has rounded fragments.

Base your answers to questions 46 through 48 on the table below, which gives the properties of four varieties of the mineral garnet.

Garnet				
Variety	Composition	Density (g/cm³)	Hardness	Typical Color
Pyrope	$Mg_3Al_2Si_3O_{12}$	3.6	7 to 7.5	Deep red to nearly black
Almandine	$Fe_3Al_2Si_3O_{12}$	4.3	7 to 7.5	Brownish red
Spessartine	$Mn_3Al_2Si_3O_{12}$	4.2	7 to 7.5	Orange red
Grossular	$Ca_3Al_2Si_3O_{12}$	3.6	6.5 to 7	Yellowish green

Chemical Symbols
Al — aluminum
Ca — calcium
Fe — iron
Mg — magnesium
Mn — manganese
O — oxygen
Si — silicon

46 Which variety is correctly described as a calcium garnet?

1 pyrope 3 spessartine
2 almandine 4 grossular

47 Garnets such as almandine are generally found in metamorphic rocks. In which metamorphic rocks are garnets most likely to be found?

1 schist and gneiss 3 quartzite and marble
2 gneiss and quartzite 4 marble and schist

48 In which New York State landscape region are garnets most likely to be found in surface bedrock?

1 Newark Lowlands
2 Adirondack Mountains
3 Erie-Ontario Lowlands
4 Allegheny Plateau

49 The cleavage or fracture of a mineral is normally determined by the mineral's

1 density
2 oxygen content
3 internal arrangement of atoms
4 position among surrounding minerals

50 Oxygen is the most abundant element by volume in the Earth's

1 inner core 3 hydrosphere
2 troposphere 4 crust

Group B — Plate Tectonics

If you choose this group, be sure to answer questions 51–60.

Base your answers to questions 51 and 52 on the diagrams below of geologic cross sections of the upper mantle and crust at four different Earth locations, A, B, C, and D. Movement of the crustal sections (plates) is indicated by arrows, and the locations of frequent earthquakes are indicated by ✱. Diagrams are not drawn to scale.

51 Which location best represents the boundary between the African plate and the South American plate?

(1) A (3) C
(2) B (4) D

52 Which diagram represents plate movement associated with transform faults such as those causing California earthquakes?

(1) A (3) C
(2) B (4) D

53 The diagram below represents a cross section of a portion of the Earth's crust.

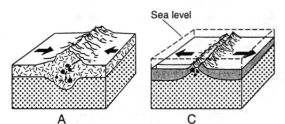

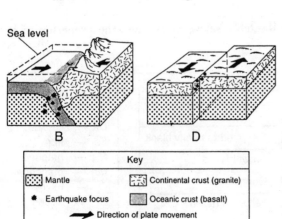

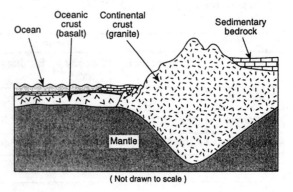

(Not drawn to scale)

Which statement about the Earth's crust is best supported by the diagram?

1 The oceanic crust is thicker than the mantle.
2 The continental crust is thicker than the oceanic crust.
3 The continental crust is composed primarily of sedimentary rock.
4 The crust is composed of denser rock than the mantle is.

54 At a depth of 2,000 kilometers, the temperature of the stiffer mantle is inferred to be

(1) 6,500°C   (3) 3,500°C
(2) 4,200°C   (4) 1,500°C

55 Hot springs on the ocean floor near the mid-ocean ridges provide evidence that

1 convection currents exist in the asthenosphere
2 meteor craters are found beneath the oceans
3 climate change has melted huge glaciers
4 marine fossils have been uplifted to high elevations

56 Which geologic event occurred most recently?

1 initial opening of the Atlantic Ocean
2 formation of the Hudson Highlands
3 formation of the Catskill delta
4 collision of North America and Africa

Base your answers to questions 57 through 60 on the four seismograms below. The seismograms show the arrival of P-waves and S-waves from the same earthquake at four different seismograph stations.

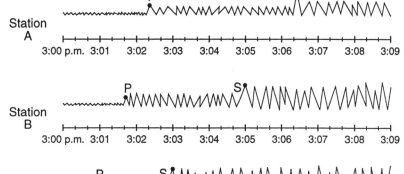

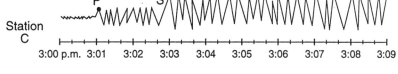

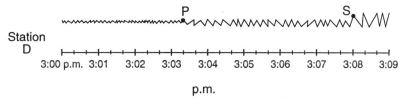

p.m.

57 Which station is farthest from the epicenter of the earthquake?

(1) A   (3) C
(2) B   (4) D

58 How many seismograms are needed to locate the epicenter of this earthquake?

1 Any one of the seismograms may be used.
2 Any two of the seismograms may be used.
3 Any three of the seismograms may be used.
4 All four seismograms must be used.

59 What is the distance between station A and the epicenter of the earthquake?

(1) 1,000 km   (3) 2,600 km
(2) 2,000 km   (4) 3,200 km

60 A fifth seismic station, located 5,600 kilometers from the earthquake epicenter, recorded the arrival of the P-wave at 3:06 p.m. What time did the earthquake occur?

(1) 2:05 p.m.   (3) 2:34 p.m.
(2) 2:13 p.m.   (4) 2:57 p.m.

Group C — Oceanography

If you choose this group, be sure to answer questions 61–70.

Base your answers to questions 61 and 62 on the diagram below. The diagram shows a coastal area with a mountain range and a portion of the ocean floor. A turbidity current through a submarine canyon has formed a fan-shaped sediment deposit on the ocean floor.

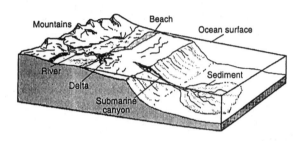

61 Which diagram best represents a cross section of the sediment in the fan-shaped deposit?

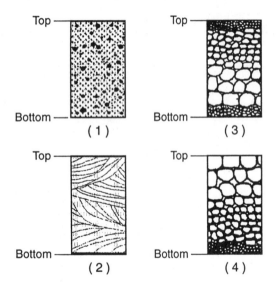

62 In which region of the ocean is the submarine canyon located?

  1 tidal zone
  2 continental margin
  3 deep ocean basin
  4 mid-ocean ridge

63 The scale below shows the age of rocks in relation to their distance from the Mid-Atlantic Ridge.

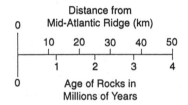

Some igneous rocks that originally formed at the Mid-Atlantic Ridge are now 37 kilometers from the ridge. Approximately how long ago did these rocks form?

  (1) 1.8 million years ago
  (2) 2.0 million years ago
  (3) 3.0 million years ago
  (4) 45.0 million years ago

64 The shaded areas of the map below indicate concentrations of pollutants along the coastlines of North America.

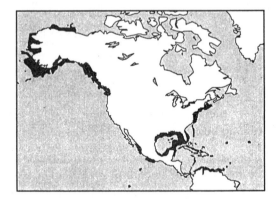

Polluting material may have been carried to the Alaska area by the

  1 California Current
  2 North Pacific Current
  3 Florida Current
  4 Labrador Current

Base your answers to questions 65 and 66 on the diagram below. The diagram represents a shoreline with waves approaching at an angle. The exposed bedrock of the wavecut cliff is granite. Arrow *A* shows the direction of the longshore current and arrow *B* shows the general path of wave travel.

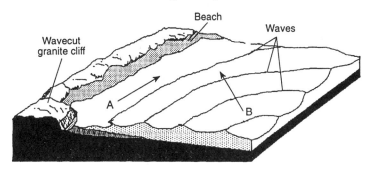

65 Which minerals are most likely to be found in the beach sand?

1 olivine and hornblende
2 pyroxene and plagioclase feldspar
3 plagioclase feldspar and olivine
4 quartz and potassium feldspar

66 A large storm with high winds that develops out at sea is most likely to result in

1 decreased erosion along the shoreline
2 increased deposition along the shoreline
3 increased wave height near the shore
4 unchanged shoreline features

Base your answers to questions 67 through 70 on the *Earth Science Reference Tables* and the graphs below. Graph I shows the yearly precipitation and evaporation at different latitudes, and graph II shows the salinity of the ocean at different latitudes. Salinity is a measure of the total amount of dissolved minerals in seawater, expressed as parts per thousand.

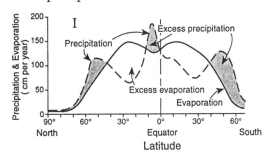
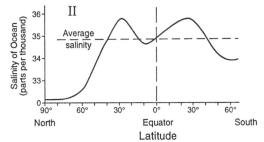

67 Compared to the amount of precipitation at the North Pole, the amount of precipitation at the Equator is

1 half as much   3 about the same
2 twice as much   4 more than ten times greater

68 At which latitude is ocean salinity *least*?

(1) 90° N   (3) 0°
(2) 30° N   (4) 60° S

69 The concentration of dissolved minerals in seawater would be increased by

1 rapid evaporation   3 melting glaciers
2 heavy rainfall   4 tsunamis

70 What is the source of most of the dissolved minerals that cause surface salinity?

1 ice sheets   3 continental erosion
2 industrial pollutants 4 tropical storms

Group D — Glacial Processes

If you choose this group, be sure to answer questions 71–80.

Base your answers to questions 71 through 74 on the diagrams below. Diagram I shows an imaginary present-day continent covered by an advancing glacial ice sheet. Isolines called isopachs are drawn, representing the thickness of the ice sheet in meters. Diagram II shows a cross section of the glacier with the land beneath it along reference line *XY*. Point *A* is a location on the glacier.

Diagram I

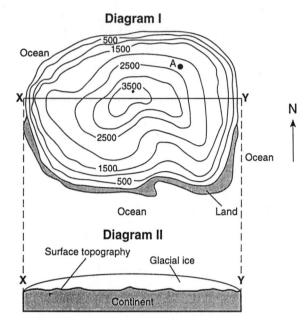

Diagram II

Surface topography

Glacial ice

Continent

71 Chemical analysis of an ice sample taken from the central core of the glacier would most likely be used to study

1 subsurface bedrock
2 past atmospheric conditions
3 the glacier's rate of movement
4 the exact location of the ice sheet

72 Which statement best describes the movement of this continental glacier?

1 The glacier is advancing from north to south, only.
2 The glacier is advancing from south to north, only.
3 The glacier is moving outward in all directions from the central zone of accumulation.
4 The glacier is moving inward from all directions toward the center of the continent.

73 What is the approximate thickness of the ice at location *A*?

(1) 1800 m   (3) 2800 m
(2) 2250 m   (4) 3400 m

74 Which statement best explains why the glacier originally formed on this continent?

1 The accumulation of yearly rainwater froze every winter.
2 The accumulation of snow during the cold season exceeded the melting of ice during the warm season.
3 Icebergs from the surrounding sea accumulated.
4 The continent has a low latitude and a low elevation.

Base your answers to questions 75 through 78 on the diagrams below. Diagram I shows melting ice lobes of a continental glacier during the Pleistocene Epoch. Diagram II represents the landscape features of the same region at present, after the retreat of the continental ice sheet. Letters *A* through *F* indicate surface features in this region.

Diagram I   **Diagram II**

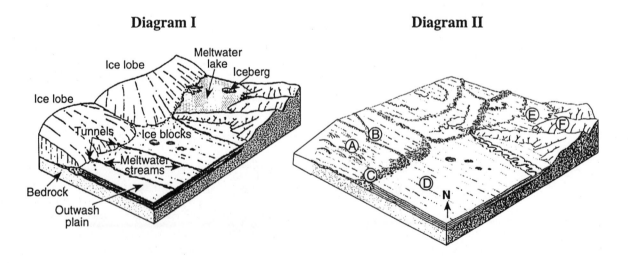

75 Which erosional feature most likely formed on the surface of the bedrock under the glacial ice?

1 sorted sands
2 sand dunes
3 parallel grooves
4 a V-shaped valley

76 Which features in diagram II are composed of till directly deposited by the glacial ice?

(1) A and C
(2) B and D
(3) C and E
(4) E and F

77 Which fossil has been found in glacial areas like those represented by D in diagram II?

1 placoderm fish
2 ammonoid
3 stromatolite
4 mastodont

Note that question 78 has only three choices.

78 In the interval between the time represented by diagram I and the time represented by diagram II, sea level most likely had

1 decreased
2 increased
3 remained the same

79 Which New York State landscape feature was formed primarily as a result of glacial deposition?

1 Adirondack Mountains
2 Hudson-Mohawk Lowlands
3 Tug Hill Plateau
4 Long Island

80 Glacial movement is caused primarily by

1 gravity
2 erosion
3 Earth's rotation
4 global winds

Group E — Atmospheric Energy

If you choose this group, be sure to answer questions 81–90.

81 Which source provides the most energy for atmospheric weather changes?

1 radiation from the Sun
2 radioactivity from the Earth's interior
3 heat stored in ocean water
4 heat stored in polar ice caps

82 Which form of electromagnetic energy has a wavelength of 0.0001 meter?

(1) ultraviolet
(2) infrared
(3) FM and TV
(4) shortwave and AM radio

83 Daily weather forecasts are based primarily on

1 ocean currents
2 seismic data
3 phases of the Moon
4 air-mass movements

84 The diagram below shows air rising from the Earth's surface to form a thunderstorm cloud.

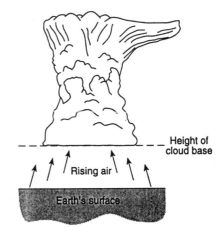

According to the Lapse Rate chart, what is the height of the base of the thunderstorm cloud when the air at the Earth's surface has a temperature of 20°C and a dewpoint of 12°C?

(1) 1.0 km
(2) 1.5 km
(3) 3.0 km
(4) 0.7 km

85 Which cross section best shows the normal movement of the air over Oswego, New York, on a very hot summer afternoon?

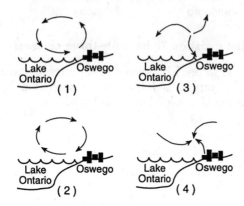

86 The diagram below represents an activity in which an eye dropper was used to place a drop of water on a spinning globe. Instead of flowing due south toward the target point, the drop appeared to follow a curved path and missed the target.

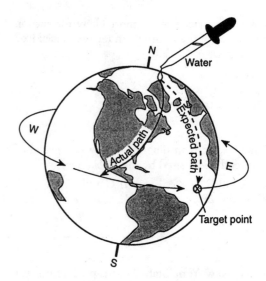

This curved-path phenomenon most directly affects the Earth's

1 tilt

2 Moon phases

3 wind belts

4 tectonic plates

Base your answers to questions 87 through 90 on the graph below. The graph shows the results of a laboratory activity in which a sample of ice at –50°C was heated at a uniform rate for 80 minutes. The ice has a mass of 200 grams.

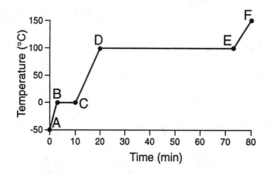

87 What was the temperature of the water 20 minutes after heating began?

(1) 70°C   (3) 110°C

(2) 100°C   (4) 150°C

88 Which change could shorten the time needed to melt the ice completely?

1 using colder ice

2 stirring the sample more slowly

3 reducing the initial sample to 100 grams of ice

4 reducing the number of temperature readings taken

89 What was the total amount of energy absorbed by the sample during the time between points B and C on the graph?

(1) 200 calories   (3) 10,800 calories

(2) 800 calories   (4) 16,000 calories

90 During which interval of the graph is a phase change occurring?

(1) A to B   (3) C to D

(2) E to F   (4) D to E

Group F — Astronomy

If you choose this group, be sure to answer questions 91–100.

91 Which graph best illustrates the average temperatures of the planets in the solar system?

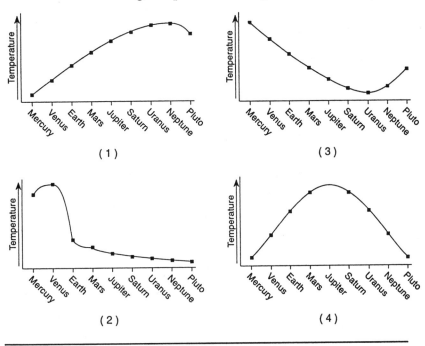

92 A belt of asteroids is located an average distance of 503 million kilometers from the Sun. Between which two planets is this belt located?

1 Mars and Jupiter   3 Jupiter and Saturn
2 Mars and Earth   4 Saturn and Uranus

93 Why are impact structures (craters) more common on the surface of Mars than on the surfaces of Venus, Earth, and Jupiter?

1 Mars has the greatest surface area and receives more impacts.
2 The tiny moons of Mars are breaking into pieces and showering its surface with rock fragments.
3 Mars has a strong magnetic field that attracts iron-containing rock fragments from space.
4 The thin atmosphere of Mars offers little protection against falling rock fragments from space.

94 The diagram below represents part of the night sky including the constellation Leo. The black circles represent stars. The open circles represent the changing positions of one celestial object over a period of a few weeks.

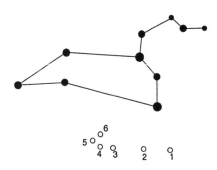

The celestial object represented by the open circles most likely is

1 a galaxy   3 Earth's Moon
2 a planet   4 another star

Base your answers to questions 95 and 96 on the graphs below. The graphs show the composition of the atmospheres of Venus, Earth, Mars, and Jupiter.

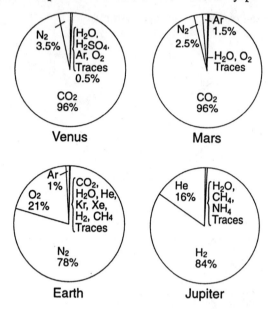

Venus Mars

Earth Jupiter

95 Which gas is present in the atmospheres of Venus, Earth, and Mars but is *not* present in the atmosphere of Jupiter?

1 argon (Ar) 3 hydrogen (H_2)
2 methane (CH_4) 4 water vapor (H_2O)

96 Which planet has an atmosphere composed primarily of CO_2 and a period of rotation greater than its period of revolution?

1 Venus 3 Earth
2 Mercury 4 Mars

97 In which type of model are the Sun, other stars, and the Moon in orbit around the Earth?

1 heliocentric model 3 concentric model
2 tetrahedral model 4 geocentric model

98 In 1851, the French physicist Jean Foucault constructed a large pendulum that always changed its direction of swing at the same rate in a clockwise direction. According to Foucault, this change in direction of swing was caused by the

1 Moon's rotation on its axis
2 Moon's revolution around the Earth
3 Earth's rotation on its axis
4 Earth's revolution around the Sun

99 Which planet has vast amounts of liquid water at its surface?

1 Venus 3 Jupiter
2 Mars 4 Earth

100 The diagram below represents a standard dark-line spectrum for an element.

The spectral lines of this element are observed in light from a distant galaxy. Which diagram represents these spectral lines?

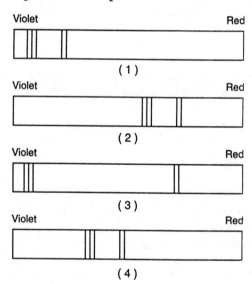

Part III

This part consists of questions 101 through 120. Be sure that you answer all questions in this part. Record your answers in the spaces provided on the separate answer paper. You may use pen or pencil. Some questions may require the use of the *Earth Science Reference Tables*. [25]

Base your answers to questions 101 and 102 on the temperature field map below. The map shows 25 measurements (in °C) that were made in a temperature field and recorded as shown. The dots represent the exact locations of the measurements. *A* and *B* are locations within the field.

Temperature Field Map (°C)

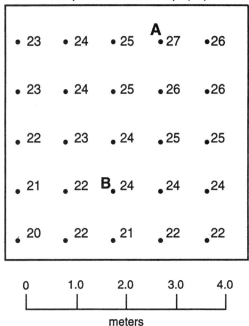

101 On the temperature field map provided *on your answer paper,* draw three isotherms: the 23°C isotherm, the 24°C isotherm, and the 25°C isotherm. [2]

102 In the space provided *on your answer paper,* calculate the temperature gradient between locations *A* and *B* on the temperature field map, following the directions below.

    a Write the equation for gradient.   [1]
    b Substitute data from the map into the equation.   [1]
    c Calculate the gradient and label it with the proper units.   [1]

Base your answers to questions 103 through 105 on the diagram below. The diagram represents the supercontinent Pangaea, which began to break up approximately 220 million years ago.

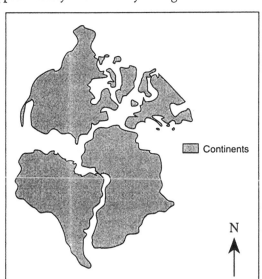

103 During which geologic period within the Mesozoic Era did the supercontinent Pangaea begin to break apart?   [1]

104 State one form of evidence that supports the inference that Pangaea existed.   [1]

105 State the compass direction toward which North America has moved since Pangaea began to break apart.   [1]

Base your answers to questions 106 through 108 on the information below.

    A mountain is a landform with steeply sloping sides whose peak is usually thousands of feet higher than its base. Mountains often contain a great deal of nonsedimentary rock and have distorted rock structures caused by faulting and folding of the crust.

    A plateau is a broad, level area at a high elevation. It usually has an undistorted, horizontal rock structure. A plateau may have steep slopes as a result of erosion.

106 State why marine fossils are *not* usually found in the bedrock of the Adirondack Mountains. [1]

107 State the agent of erosion that is most likely responsible for shaping the Catskill Plateau so that it physically resembles a mountainous region.   [1]

108 State the approximate age of the surface bedrock of the Catskills.   [1]

Base your answers to questions 109 through 112 on the diagram and the stream data table below.

The diagram represents a stream flowing into a lake. Arrows show the direction of flow. Point P is a location in the stream. Line XY is a reference line across the stream. Points X and Y are locations on the banks. The data table gives the depth of water in the stream along line XY.

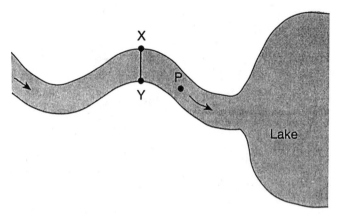

Stream Data Table

	Location X							Location Y
Distance from X (meters)	0	5	10	15	20	25	30	35
Depth of Water (meters)	0	5.0	5.5	4.5	3.5	2.0	0.5	0

Directions (109–110): Use the information in the data table to construct a profile of the depth of water. Use the grid provided *on your answer paper*, following the directions below.

109 On the vertical axis, mark an appropriate scale for the depth of water. Note that the zero (0) at the top of the axis represents the water surface.   [1]

110 Plot the data for the depth of water in the stream along line XY and connect the points. (Distance is measured from point X.)   [2]

Example:

111 State why the depth of water near the bank at point X is different from the depth of water near the bank at point Y.   [1]

112 At point P, the water velocity is 100 centimeters per second. State the name of the largest sediment that can be transported by the stream at point P.   [1]

Base your answers to questions 113 through 115 on the weather maps below. The weather maps show the positions of a tropical storm at 10 a.m. on July 2 and on July 3.

July 2

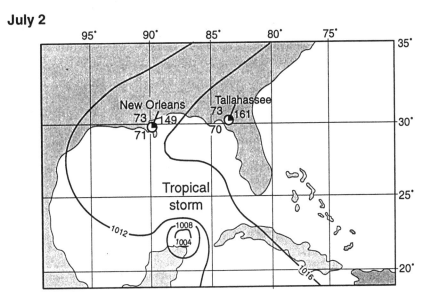

July 3

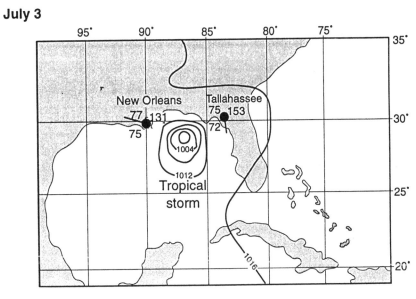

113 State the dewpoint temperature in Tallahassee on July 2.   [1]

114 Windspeed has been omitted from the station models. In one or more sentences, state how an increase in the storm's windspeed from July 2 to July 3 could be inferred from the maps.   [2]

115 The storm formed over warm tropical water. State what will most likely happen to the windspeed when the storm moves over land.   [1]

Base your answers to questions 116 through 118 on the diagrams below. Diagram I represents the Moon orbiting the Earth as viewed from space above the North Pole. The Moon is shown at 8 different positions in its orbit. Diagram II represents phases of the Moon as seen from the Earth when the Moon is at position 2 and at position 4.

Diagram I

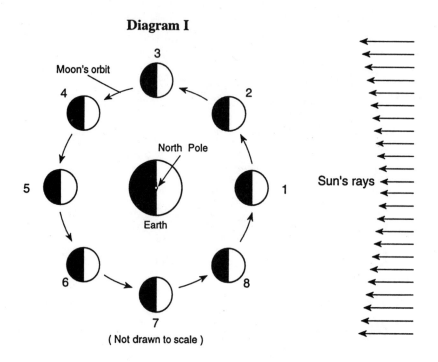

(Not drawn to scale)

Diagram II

Phase of the Moon as seen from the Earth

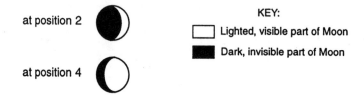

at position 2

at position 4

KEY:
☐ Lighted, visible part of Moon
■ Dark, invisible part of Moon

116 Shade the circle provided *on your answer paper* to illustrate the Moon's phase as seen from the Earth when the Moon is at position 7.   [1]

117 State the two positions of the Moon at which an eclipse could occur.   [1]

118 State the approximate length of time required for one complete revolution of the Moon around the Earth.   [1]

Base your answers to questions 119 and 120 on the graph below. The graph shows the average water temperature and the dissolved oxygen levels of water in a stream over a 12-month period. The level of dissolved oxygen is measured in parts per million (ppm).

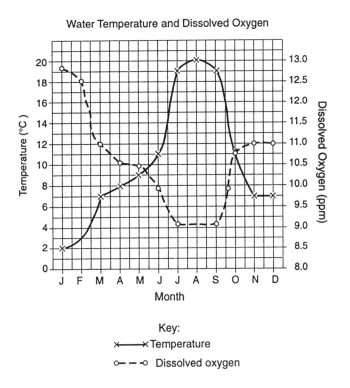

Water Temperature and Dissolved Oxygen

Key:
×——×Temperature
o- - -o Dissolved oxygen

119 State the difference in average water temperature, in degrees Celsius, between January and August.   [1]

120 State the relationship between the temperature of the water and the level of dissolved oxygen in the water.   [1]

EARTH SCIENCE
PROGRAM MODIFICATION EDITION
JUNE 1997

ANSWER PAPER

Part I Credits . . . .

Part II Credits . . . .

Part III Credits . . . .

Performance Test Credits. . . . .

Local Project Credits . . . .

Total (Official Regents)
    Examination Mark . . . .

Reviewer's Initials: _____

Student . . . .

Teacher . . . . School . . . .

Grade   (circle one)   8   9   10   11   12

Record all of your answers on this answer paper in accordance with the instructions on the front cover of the test booklet.

Part I (40 credits)

1	1 2 3 4	15	1 2 3 4	29	1 2 3 4
2	1 2 3 4	16	1 2 3 4	30	1 2 3 4
3	1 2 3 4	17	1 2 3 4	31	1 2 3 4
4	1 2 3 4	18	1 2 3 4	32	1 2 3 4
5	1 2 3 4	19	1 2 3 4	33	1 2 3 4
6	1 2 3 4	20	1 2 3 4	34	1 2 3 4
7	1 2 3 4	21	1 2 3 4	35	1 2 3 4
8	1 2 3 4	22	1 2 3 4	36	1 2 3 4
9	1 2 3 4	23	1 2 3 4	37	1 2 3 4
10	1 2 3 4	24	1 2 3 4	38	1 2 3 4
11	1 2 3 4	25	1 2 3 4	39	1 2 3 4
12	1 2 3 4	26	1 2 3 4	40	1 2 3 4
13	1 2 3 4	27	1 2 3 4		
14	1 2 3 4	28	1 2 3 4		

Part II (10 credits)

Answer the questions in only one of the six groups in this part. Be sure to mark the answers to the group you choose in accordance with the instructions on the front cover of the test booklet. Leave blank the spaces for the five groups of questions you do not choose to answer.

Group A
Rocks and Minerals

41 1 2 3 4
42 1 2 3 4
43 1 2 3 4
44 1 2 3 4
45 1 2 3 4
46 1 2 3 4
47 1 2 3 4
48 1 2 3 4
49 1 2 3 4
50 1 2 3 4

Group B
Plate Tectonics

51 1 2 3 4
52 1 2 3 4
53 1 2 3 4
54 1 2 3 4
55 1 2 3 4
56 1 2 3 4
57 1 2 3 4
58 1 2 3 4
59 1 2 3 4
60 1 2 3 4

Group C
Oceanography

61 1 2 3 4
62 1 2 3 4
63 1 2 3 4
64 1 2 3 4
65 1 2 3 4
66 1 2 3 4
67 1 2 3 4
68 1 2 3 4
69 1 2 3 4
70 1 2 3 4

Group D
Glacial Processes

71 1 2 3 4
72 1 2 3 4
73 1 2 3 4
74 1 2 3 4
75 1 2 3 4
76 1 2 3 4
77 1 2 3 4
78 1 2 3
79 1 2 3 4
80 1 2 3 4

Group E
Atmospheric Energy

81 1 2 3 4
82 1 2 3 4
83 1 2 3 4
84 1 2 3 4
85 1 2 3 4
86 1 2 3 4
87 1 2 3 4
88 1 2 3 4
89 1 2 3 4
90 1 2 3 4

Group F
Astronomy

91   1 2 3 4
92   1 2 3 4
93   1 2 3 4
94   1 2 3 4
95   1 2 3 4
96   1 2 3 4
97   1 2 3 4
98   1 2 3 4
99   1 2 3 4
100 1 2 3 4

101

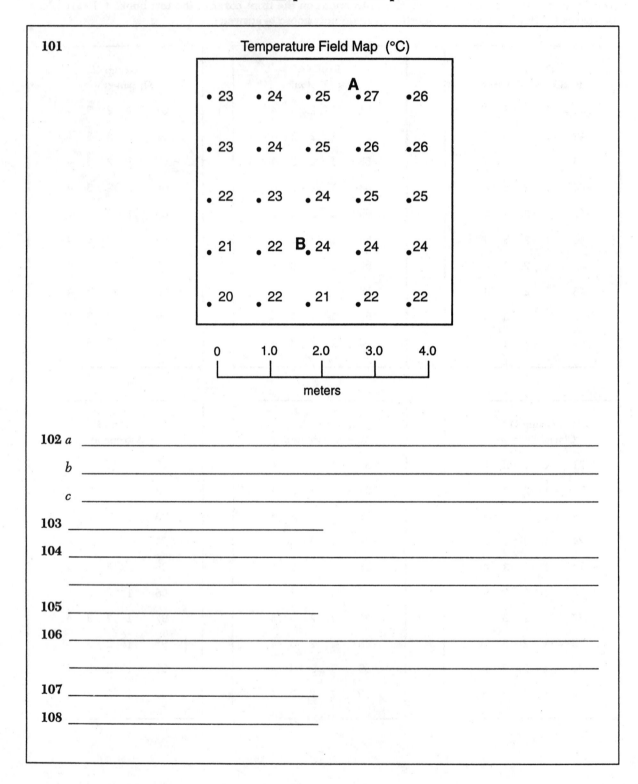

Temperature Field Map (°C)

102 *a* _____

b _____

c _____

103 _____

104 _____

_____

105 _____

106 _____

_____

107 _____

108 _____

Stream Profile Graph

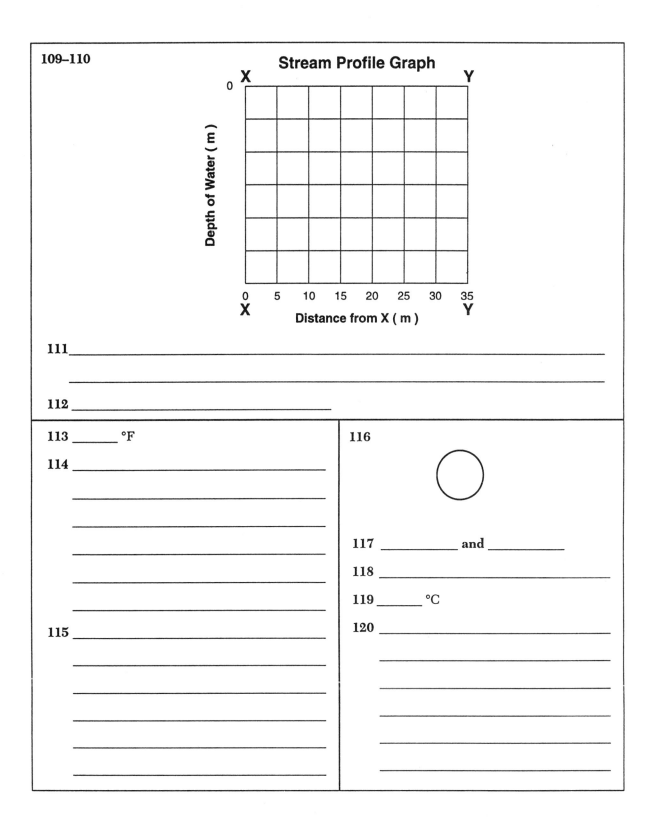

X   Y

Depth of Water (m)

0

0   5   10   15   20   25   30   35

X   Y

Distance from X (m)

111 _____

_____

112 _____

113 _____ °F

114 _____

_____

_____

_____

_____

_____

115 _____

_____

_____

_____

_____

116

117 _____ and _____

118 _____

119 _____ °C

120 _____

_____

_____

_____

_____

EARTH SCIENCE
JUNE 1998

Part I

Answer all 40 questions in this part.

Directions (1–40): For *each* statement or question, select the word or expression that, of those given, best completes the statement or answers the question. Record your answer on the separate answer paper in accordance with the directions on the front page of this booklet. Some questions may require the use of the *Earth Science Reference Tables*.   [40]

Base your answers to questions 1 through 3 on the contour map below. Elevations are expressed in feet. The ▲ indicates the exact elevation of the top of Basket Dome.

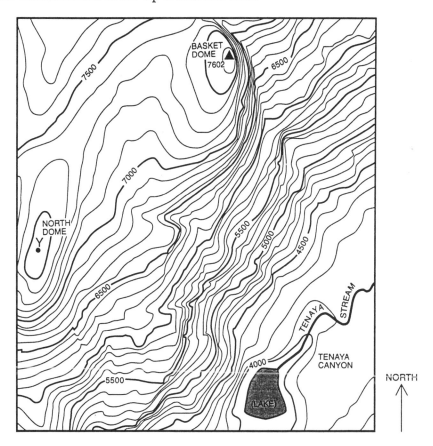

1 What is the highest possible elevation of point Y on North Dome?

   (1) 7,500 ft   (3) 7,599 ft
   (2) 7,590 ft   (4) 7,601 ft

2 Forty years ago, the highest elevation of Basket Dome was 7,600 feet. What is the rate of crustal uplift for Basket Dome?

   (1) 0.05 ft/yr   (3) 0.5 ft/yr
   (2) 2 ft/yr   (4) 20 ft/yr

3 In which general direction does Tenaya Stream flow?

   1 southeast to northwest
   2 northwest to southeast
   3 southwest to northeast
   4 northeast to southwest

4 Each series below, labeled A through D, represents a sequence of events over the passage of time.

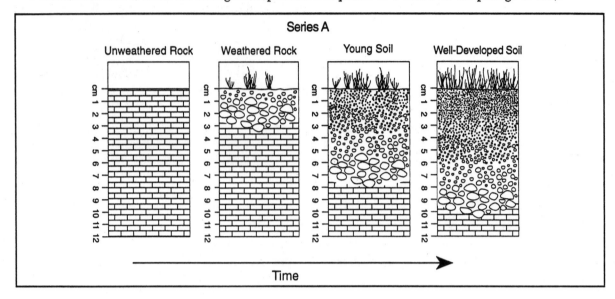

Series A

Series B

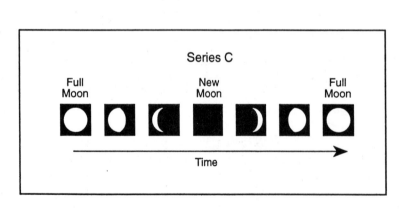

Series C

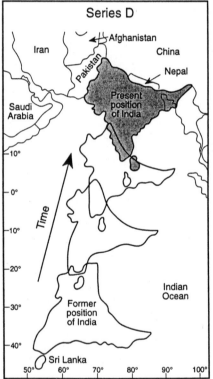

Series D

Which series would take the *least* amount of time to complete?

(1) A

(2) B

(3) C

(4) D

5 Which New York State landscape region is located at 42° N 75° W?

1 Erie-Ontario Lowlands
2 the Catskills
3 Hudson-Mohawk Lowlands
4 Tug Hill Plateau

6 The diagrams below represent photographs of a large sailboat taken through telescopes over time as the boat sailed away from shore out to sea. The number above each diagram shows the magnification of the telescope lens.

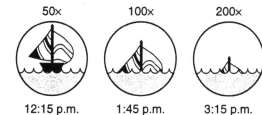

Which statement best explains the apparent sinking of this sailboat?

1 The sailboat is moving around the curved surface of Earth.
2 The sailboat appears smaller as it moves farther away.
3 The change in density of the atmosphere is causing refraction of light rays.
4 The tide is causing an increase in the depth of the ocean.

7 Which rocks usually have the mineral quartz as part of their composition?

1 conglomerate, gabbro, rock salt, and schist
2 breccia, fossil limestone, bituminous coal, and siltstone
3 shale, scoria, gneiss, and marble
4 granite, rhyolite, sandstone, and hornfels

8 Which sedimentary rock may have both a chemical origin and an organic origin?

1 limestone   3 rock salt
2 rock gypsum   4 shale

9 The diagrams below represent four different mineral samples.

Which mineral property is best represented by the samples?

1 density   3 hardness
2 cleavage   4 streak

10 The photograph below represents a mountainous area in the Pacific Northwest.

Scientists believe that sedimentary rocks like these represent evidence of crustal change because these rocks were

1 formed by igneous intrusion
2 faulted during deposition
3 originally deposited in horizontal layers
4 changed from metamorphic rocks

11 Which feature is commonly formed at a plate boundary where oceanic crust converges with continental crust?

1 a mid-ocean ridge   3 a transform fault
2 an ocean trench   4 new oceanic crust

Base your answers to questions 12 and 13 on the map below, which shows a portion of California along the San Andreas Fault zone. The map gives the probability (percentage chance) that an earthquake strong enough to damage buildings and other structures will occur between the present time and the year 2024.

Earthquake Damage Probability

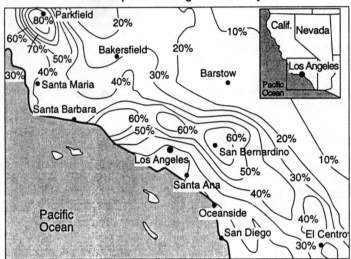

12 Which map represents the most likely location of the San Andreas Fault line?

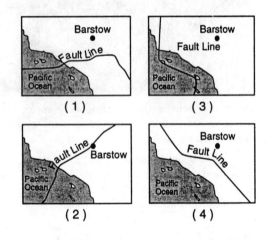

13 Which city has the greatest danger of damage from an earthquake?

1 Parkfield   3 Santa Barbara
2 San Diego   4 San Bernardino

14 The diagram below is a map view of a stream flowing through an area of loose sediments. Arrows show the location of the strongest current.

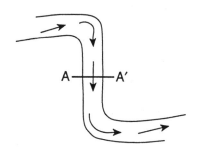

Which stream profile best represents the cross section from *A* to *A'*?

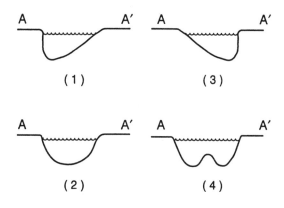

15 The diagram below represents a landscape area.

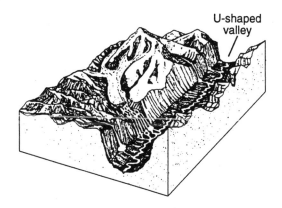

The main valley in this landscape area resulted mostly from

1 chemical weathering   3 glacial erosion
2 volcanic activity   4 stream erosion

16 Which New York State landscape region is composed mostly of intensely metamorphosed surface bedrock?

1 Hudson Highlands
2 Allegheny Plateau
3 Atlantic Coastal Plain
4 Erie-Ontario Lowlands

17 A geologic cross section is shown below.

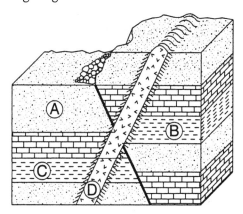

Key

Sandstone	Shale
Limestone	Igneous rock
Contact metamorphism	

The most recently formed rock unit is at location

(1) *A*   (3) *C*
(2) *B*   (4) *D*

18 Based on studies of fossils found in subsurface rocks near Buffalo, New York, scientists have inferred that the climate of this area during the Ordovician Period was much warmer than the present climate. Which statement best explains this change in climate?

1 The Sun emitted less sunlight during the Ordovician Period.
2 Earth was farther from the Sun during the Ordovician Period.
3 The North American Continent was nearer to the Equator during the Ordovician Period.
4 Many huge volcanic eruptions occurred during the Ordovician Period.

Base your answers to questions 19 and 20 on the diagram and data table for the laboratory activity described below. Diagrams are not drawn to scale.

Laboratory Activity

Different combinations of the particles shown in the data table were placed in a tube filled with a thick liquid and allowed to fall to the bottom. The tube was then stoppered and quickly turned upside down, allowing the particles to settle.

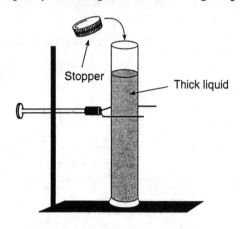

Data Table Particles Used in Activities		
	Diameter	Density
	15 mm Al (aluminum)	2.7 g/cm³
	15 mm Fe (iron)	7.9 g/cm³
	15 mm Pb (lead)	11.4 g/cm³

19 Which diagram represents the sorting that most likely occurred when the tube was turned upside down and the particles of the three different metals were allowed to settle?

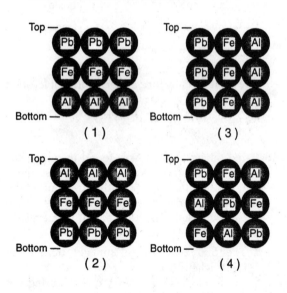

20 In another activity, round, oval, and flat aluminum particles with identical masses were dropped individually into the tube. Which table shows the most likely average settling times of the different-shaped particles?

Particle Shape	Average Settling Time
Round	5.1 sec
Oval	5.1 sec
Flat	5.1 sec

(1)

Particle Shape	Average Settling Time
Round	6.7 sec
Oval	5.1 sec
Flat	3.2 sec

(3)

Particle Shape	Average Settling Time
Round	5.1 sec
Oval	3.2 sec
Flat	6.7 sec

(2)

Particle Shape	Average Settling Time
Round	3.2 sec
Oval	5.1 sec
Flat	6.7 sec

(4)

21 The diagrams below represent the rock layers and fossils found at four widely separated rock outcrops.

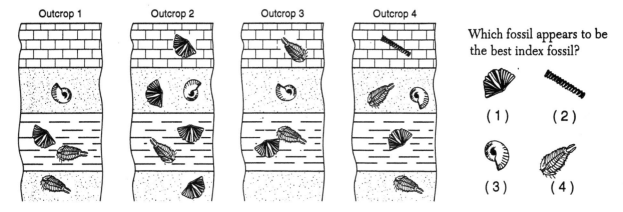

Which fossil appears to be the best index fossil?

22 Which column best represents the relative lengths of time of the major intervals of geologic history?

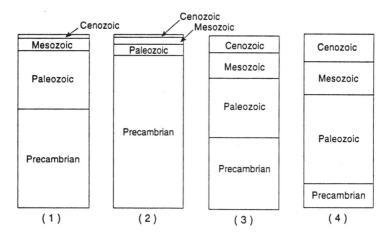

Note that question 23 has only three choices.

23 The map below represents a satellite image of Hurricane Gilbert in the Gulf of Mexico. Each **X** represents the position of the center of the storm on the date indicated.

Compared to its strength on September 16, the strength of Hurricane Gilbert on September 18 was

1 less
2 greater
3 the same

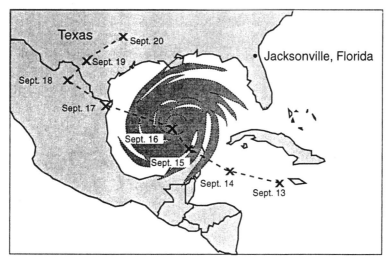

24 Which graph best represents the radioactive decay of uranium-238 into lead-206?

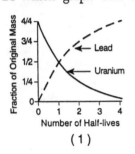
(1)

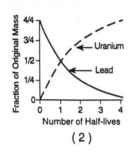
(2)

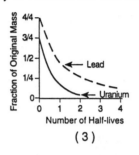
(3)

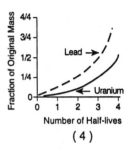
(4)

25 Winds are blowing from high-pressure to low-pressure systems over identical ocean surfaces. Which diagram represents the area of greatest windspeed? [Arrows represent wind direction.]

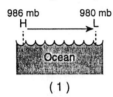
(1)

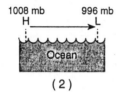
(2)

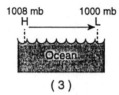
(3)

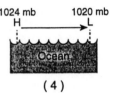
(4)

Base your answers to questions 26 through 29 on the weather map below. The map shows a weather system that is affecting part of the United States.

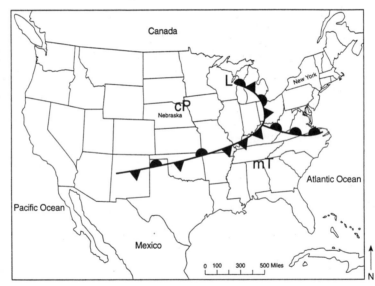

26 Which diagram shows the surface air movements most likely associated with the low-pressure system?

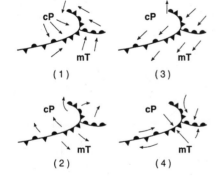

27 What is the total number of different kinds of weather fronts shown on this weather map?

(1) 1   (3) 3
(2) 2   (4) 4

28 The air mass influencing the weather of Nebraska most likely originated in

1 the northern Pacific Ocean
2 the northern Atlantic Ocean
3 central Canada
4 central Mexico

29 Which map shows the area where precipitation is most likely occurring? [Shaded areas represent precipitation.]

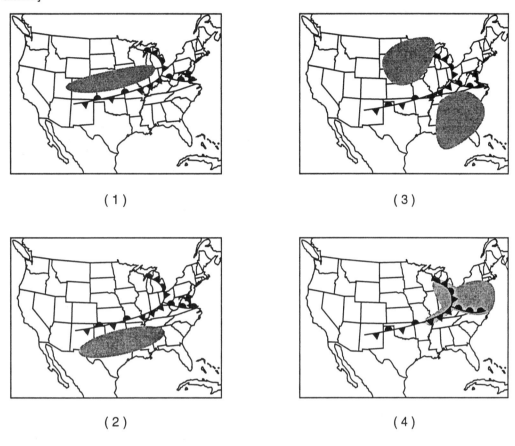

(1)

(3)

(2)

(4)

---

30 Locations in New York State are warmer in summer than in winter because in summer

  1 the solar radiation reaching Earth's surface is more intense, and the number of daylight hours is fewer

  2 the solar radiation reaching Earth's surface is more intense, and the number of daylight hours is greater

  3 the solar radiation reaching Earth's surface is less intense, and the number of daylight hours is fewer

  4 the solar radiation reaching Earth's surface is less intense, and the number of daylight hours is greater

31 A parcel of air has a dry-bulb temperature of 16°C and a wet-bulb temperature of 10°C. What are the dewpoint and relative humidity readings of the air?

  (1) –10°C dewpoint and 14% relative humidity
  (2) –10°C dewpoint and 45% relative humidity
  (3) 4°C dewpoint and 14% relative humidity
  (4) 4°C dewpoint and 45% relative humidity

Base your answers to questions 32 and 33 on the diagrams below. Diagram I shows a house located in New York State. Diagram II shows a solar collector that the homeowner is using to help heat the house.

Diagram I

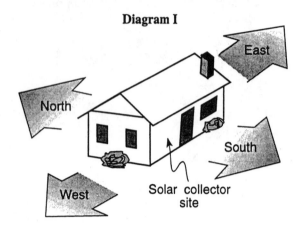

Diagram II
Solar Collector

32 Which side view shows the correct placement of the solar collector on the side of this house to collect the maximum amount of sunlight?

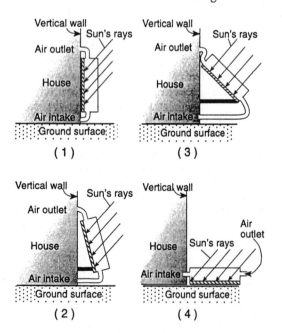

33 Which diagram best represents both the wavelength of visible light entering this house through a window and the wavelength of infrared rays being given off by a chair?

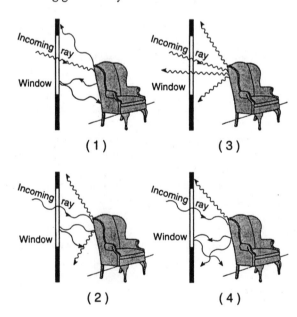

34 Which fact provides the best evidence that Earth's axis is tilted?

1 Locations on Earth's Equator receive 12 hours of daylight every day.
2 The apparent diameter of the Sun shows predictable changes in size.
3 Planetary winds are deflected to the right in the Northern Hemisphere and to the left in the Southern Hemisphere.
4 Winter occurs in the Southern Hemisphere at the same time that summer occurs in the Northern Hemisphere.

35 The diagram below represents a planet revolving in an elliptical orbit around a star.

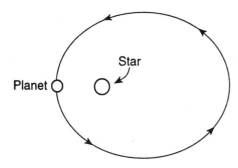

As the planet makes one complete revolution around the star, starting at the position shown, the gravitational attraction between the star and the planet will

1 decrease, then increase
2 increase, then decrease
3 continually decrease
4 remain the same

36 A student in New York State observed that the altitude of the Sun at noon is decreasing each day. During which month could the student have made these observations?

1 January   3 May
2 March   4 October

37 Which member of the solar system has a diameter of 3.48×10^3 kilometers?

1 Pluto   3 Earth's Moon
2 Earth   4 the Sun

38 The diagram below represents a portion of the solar system.

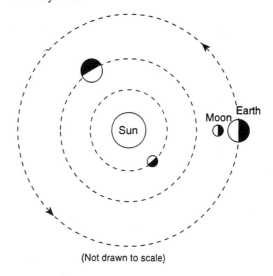

(Not drawn to scale)

In addition to Earth, which planets are represented by the diagram?

1 Saturn and Pluto
2 Mercury and Venus
3 Uranus and Neptune
4 Jupiter and Mars

39 Tropical rain forests remove carbon dioxide gas from Earth's atmosphere. The destruction of the rain forests could affect Earth's overall average temperature because

1 more of Earth's reradiation would be absorbed by the atmosphere
2 more sunlight would be reflected back to space by Earth's atmosphere
3 more visible light would be absorbed by Earth's atmosphere
4 more ultraviolet light would be transmitted through Earth's atmosphere

40 The maps below show changes occurring around a small New York State lake over a 30-year period.

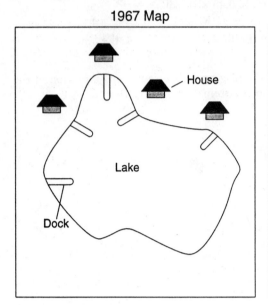

1967 Map

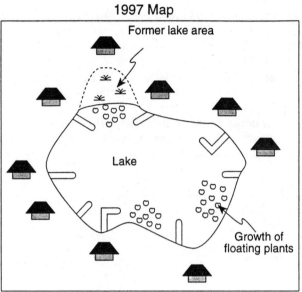

1997 Map

Which graph shows the probable changes in the quality of ground water and lake water in this region from 1967 to 1997? [Ground water is water that has infiltrated beneath Earth's surface.]

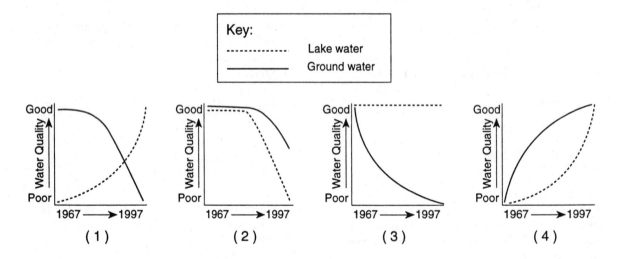

Part II

This part consists of six groups, each containing five questions. Choose any *two* of these six groups. Be sure that you answer all five questions in each of the two groups chosen. Record the answers to these questions on the separate answer paper in accordance with the directions on the front cover of this booklet. Some questions may require the use of the *Earth Science Reference Tables.* [10]

Group A — Rocks and Minerals

If you choose this group, be sure to answer questions 41–45.

41 Slate is formed by the

1 deposition of chlorite and mica
2 foliation of schist
3 metamorphism of shale
4 folding and faulting of gneiss

42 Which property of a mineral most directly results from the internal arrangement of its atoms?

1 volume   3 crystal shape
2 color   4 streak

43 The diagram below shows a cross section through a portion of Earth's crust.

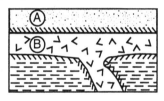

Key

[▢]	Sandstone
[▣]	Shale
[▨]	Granite
[◿]	Contact metamorphism

Rock found in the zone between *A* and *B* is non-foliated and fine grained. This rock is most likely

1 metaconglomerate   3 marble
2 gneiss   4 quartzite

44 The graph below represents the percentage of each mineral found in a sample of igneous rock. Which mineral is represented by the letter *X* in the graph?

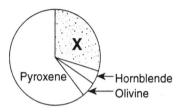

1 potassium feldspar   3 quartz
2 plagioclase feldspar 4 biotite

45 The diagram below represents top and side views of models of the silicate tetrahedron.

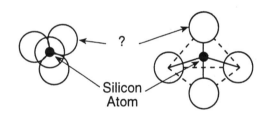

Which element combines with silicon to form the tetrahedron?

1 oxygen   3 potassium
2 nitrogen   4 hydrogen

Group B — Plate Tectonics

If you choose this group, be sure to answer questions 46–50.

46 Which cross-sectional diagram of Earth correctly shows the paths of seismic waves from an earthquake traveling through Earth's interior?

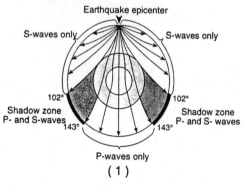

(1)

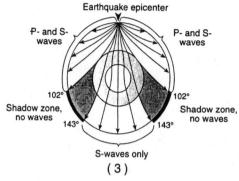

(3)

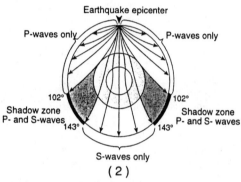

(2)

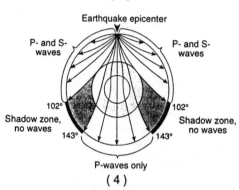

(4)

47 The actual temperature at the boundary between the stiffer mantle and the outer core is estimated to be approximately

(1) 1.5°C   (3) 3000°C
(2) 250°C   (4) 5000°C

48 How far from an earthquake epicenter is a city where the difference between the P-wave and S-wave arrival times is 6 minutes and 20 seconds?

(1) 1.7×10^3 km   (3) 3.5×10^3 km
(2) 9.9×10^3 km   (4) 4.7×10^3 km

49 Compared to oceanic crust, continental crust is generally

1 older and thinner
2 older and thicker
3 younger and thinner
4 younger and thicker

50 Which map best represents the general pattern of magnetism in the oceanic bedrock near the mid-Atlantic Ridge?

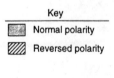

Key
Normal polarity
Reversed polarity

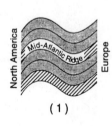

(1)

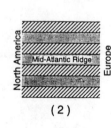

(2)

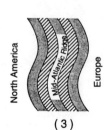

(3)

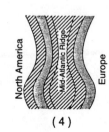

(4)

Group C — Oceanography

If you choose this group, be sure to answer questions 51–55.

51 The cartoon below presents a humorous look at ocean wave action.

"Here comes another big one, Roy, and here — we — gooooooowheeeeeeeoooo!"

The ocean waves that are providing enjoyment for Roy's companion are the result of the

1 interaction of the hydrosphere with the moving atmosphere
2 interaction of the lithosphere with the moving troposphere
3 absorption of short-wave radiation in the stratosphere
4 absorption of energy in the asthenosphere

52 What is the main source of dissolved salts in the ocean?

1 human activities
2 minerals carried from the land by rivers
3 precipitation from storm fronts
4 weathered basalts at mid-ocean ridges

53 Diagrams *A*, *B*, *C*, and *D* below represent a sequence of events that occurred in the deep ocean and that resulted in a tsunami. Diagram *A* represents the first event of the sequence, and diagram *D* represents the fourth event.

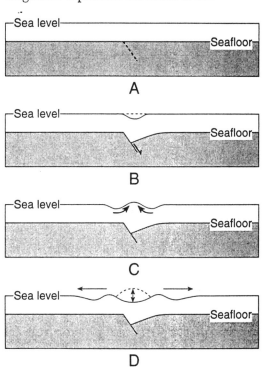

The surface waves shown in diagram *D* were most likely caused by

1 a submarine landslide
2 folding of the ocean floor
3 displacement by a fault
4 strong winds from a hurricane

Base your answers to questions 54 and 55 on the table below, which lists the four main classes of ocean-floor sediments and shows the origin and an example of each sediment.

Ocean-Floor Sediments

Classification	Origin	Examples
Lithogenic	Land-derived	Muds and clays
Biogenic	Shells of microscopic organisms	Oozes
Turbigenic	Turbidity currents	Graded beds in the deep ocean
Authigenic	Ocean water by chemical precipitation directly on the ocean floor	Manganese nodules

54 Which statement best explains why turbigenic sediments are found in graded beds?

1 The Moon's gravitational force causes the cyclic pattern of sediment deposition.
2 Ocean-floor organisms sort fresh sediments into layers of similar sizes.
3 During cementation, smaller particles rise to the top, leaving larger particles at the bottom of each layer.
4 During deposition, larger particles usually settle to the bottom faster than smaller particles do.

55 Icebergs carry material that has been eroded from the land by a moving glacier. When this material is deposited in the ocean by a melting iceberg, it is classified as

1 lithogenic   3 authigenic
2 biogenic   4 turbigenic

Group D — Glacial Processes

If you choose this group, be sure to answer questions 56–60.

56 At the end of the last period of glaciation, the natural environment of New York State probably looked like the present environment in

1 Alaska   3 Texas
2 North Carolina   4 Ohio

57 Which geological resource in New York State resulted from glaciation?

1 coal and oil deposits
2 sand and gravel deposits
3 iron and zinc ores
4 garnet and quartz crystals

58 Evidence that several periods of glaciation occurred in the geologic past is provided by

1 glacial erratics in New York State
2 glacial erosion in the high regions of the Adirondack Mountains
3 layers of glacial till deposited on top of each other
4 discovery of mastodont fossils in the surface bedrock of the Adirondack Mountains

59 The cross section below represents the transport of sediments by an advancing glacier. The arrow shows the direction of movement.

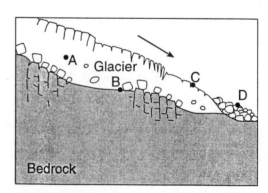

At which location are striations and glacial grooves most likely being carved?

(1) A   (3) C
(2) B   (4) D

60 On which New York State map does the arrow indicate the most likely direction of advance of the last continental ice sheet?

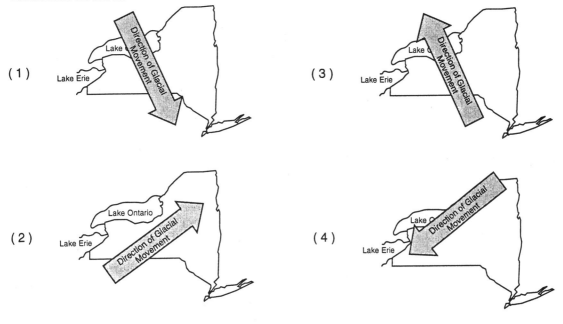

Group E — Atmospheric Energy

If you choose this group, be sure to answer questions 61–65.

61 At 1 p.m. at a location in New York State, the surface air temperature was 20°C and the dew-point temperature was 10°C. At 3 p.m. at the same location, the altitude of the cloud base was 1.2 kilometers. Compared to the altitude of the cloud base at 1 p.m., the altitude of the cloud base at 3 p.m. was

(1) 0.5 km lower
(2) 2.0 km lower
(3) 0.5 km higher
(4) nearly the same

62 On a very hot summer afternoon, the air over Long Island is warmer than the air over the nearby ocean. As a result, the air over Long Island tends to

1 sink and cool, causing clouds to form
2 sink and warm, causing clouds to disappear
3 rise and cool, causing clouds to form
4 rise and warm, causing clouds to disappear

63 Why have weather predictions become more accurate and reliable in recent years?

1 Weather conditions now change more slowly than they did in the past.
2 More people today watch televised weather reports.
3 Scientists have developed better methods of controlling the weather.
4 Scientists have developed better technology to observe weather conditions.

Base your answers to questions 64 and 65 on the diagrams below. Beaker *A* contains 100 milliliters of boiling water. Beaker *B* contains 225 milliliters of boiling water. The hot plates are adding equal amounts of heat to each beaker each minute.

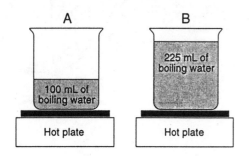

64 What is the total number of calories that must be added to completely change the 100 milliliters of boiling water (mass = 100 grams) in beaker *A* into water vapor?

(1) 54,000 cal   (3) 640 cal
(2) 8,000 cal   (4) 5.4 cal

Note that question 65 has only three choices.

65 Thermometers are placed in both beakers and allowed to adjust as the water boils. The thermometers will show that, compared to the temperature of the water in beaker *A*, the temperature of the water in beaker *B* is

1 lower
2 higher
3 the same

Group F — Astronomy

If you choose this group, be sure to answer questions 66–70.

66 Which diagram best represents the heliocentric model of a portion of the solar system? [*S* = Sun, *E* = Earth, and *M* = Moon. The diagrams are not drawn to scale.]

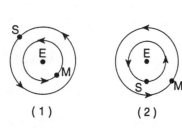 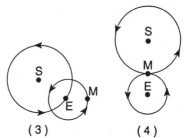

67 The planets known as "gas giants" include Jupiter, Uranus, and

1 Pluto   3 Mars
2 Saturn   4 Earth

68 A comparison of the age of Earth obtained from radioactive dating and the age of the universe based on galactic Doppler shifts suggests that

1 Earth is about the same age as the universe
2 the universe is much younger than Earth
3 the solar system and Earth formed billions of years after the universe began
4 the two dating methods contradict one another

69 The Moon has more surface craters than Earth does because the Moon has

1 no significant atmosphere
2 a surface more sensitive to impacts
3 a smaller diameter than Earth
4 a stronger gravitational force

70 With respect to one another, galaxies have been found to be

1 moving closer together
2 moving farther apart
3 moving in random directions
4 stationary

Part III

This part consists of questions 71 through 88. Be sure that you answer *all* questions in this part. Record your answers in the spaces provided on the separate answer paper. You may use pen or pencil. Some questions may require the use of the *Earth Science Reference Tables*. [25]

71 A total solar eclipse was visible to observers in the southeastern United States on February 26, 1998. The diagram below shows the Sun and Earth as they were viewed from space on that date. The same diagram appears on your answer paper.

(Not drawn to scale)

On the diagram provided *on your answer paper*, draw the Moon (◯), showing its position at the time of the solar eclipse. [1]

Base your answers to questions 72 through 74 on the diagram below, which shows the Sun's apparent path as viewed by an observer in New York State on March 21.

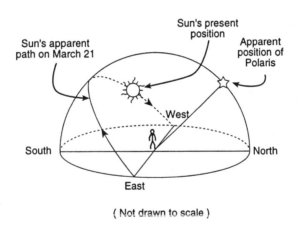

(Not drawn to scale)

72 State how the apparent position of Polaris is related to the latitude of the observer. [1]

73 At approximately what hour of the day would the Sun be at the position shown in the diagram? [1]

74 On the diagram provided *on your answer paper*, draw the Sun's apparent path as viewed by the observer on December 21. [1]

Base your answers to questions 75 through 77 on the map below. The star symbol represents a volcano located on the mid-Atlantic Ridge in Iceland. The isolines represent the thickness, in centimeters, of volcanic ash deposited from an eruption of this volcano. Points *A* and *B* represent locations in the area.

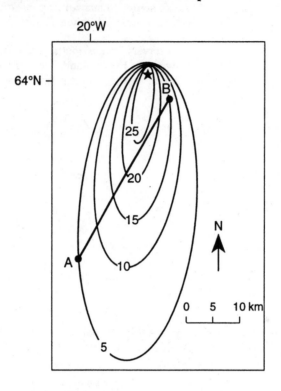

75 On the grid provided *on your answer paper*, construct a profile of the ash thickness between point *A* and point *B*, following the directions below.

   a Plot the thickness of the volcanic ash along line *AB* by marking with a dot each point where an isoline is crossed by line *AB*.   [2]

   b Connect the dots to complete the profile of the thickness of the volcanic ash.   [1]

76 State one factor that could have produced this pattern of deposition of the ash.   [1]

77 State why volcanic eruptions are likely to occur in Iceland.   [1]

Base your answers to questions 78 through 81 on the diagrams below. Columns *A* and *B* represent two widely separated outcrops of rocks. The symbols show the rock types and the locations of fossils found in the rock layers. The rock layers have not been overturned.

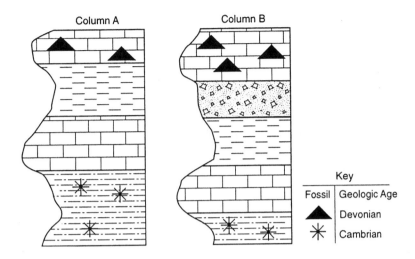

78 State one method used to correlate rock layers found in the outcrop represented by column *A* with rock layers found in the outcrop represented by column *B*.   [1]

79 An unconformity (buried erosional surface) exists between two layers in the outcrop represented by column *A*. Identify the location of the unconformity by drawing a thick wavy line (∿∿∿) at the correct position on column *A* *on your answer paper*.   [1]

80 *In one or more sentences*, state the evidence that limestone is the most resistant layer in these outcrops.   [2]

81 State the oldest possible age, in millions of years, for the fossils in the siltstone layer.   [1]

Base your answers to questions 82 and 83 on the meteorological conditions shown in the table and partial station model below, as reported by the weather bureau in the city of Oswego, New York. The diagram of the station model also appears on your answer paper.

Air temperature: 65°F
Wind direction: from the southeast
Windspeed: 20 knots
Barometeric pressure: 1017.5 mb
Dewpoint: 53°F

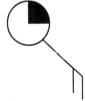

82 Using the meteorological conditions given, complete the station model provided *on your answer paper* by recording the air temperature, dewpoint, and barometric pressure in the proper format.   [2]

83 State the sky conditions or amount of cloud cover over Oswego as shown by the station model.   [1]

Base your answers to questions 84 through 87 on the information and data table below.

The snowline is the lowest elevation at which snow remains on the ground all year. The data table below shows the elevation of the snowline at different latitudes in the Northern Hemisphere.

Latitude (°N)	Elevation of Snowline (m)
0	5400
10	4900
25	3800
35	3100
50	1600
65	500
80	100
90	0

84 On the grid provided *on your answer paper*, plot the latitude and elevation of the snowline for the locations in the data table. Use a dot for each point and connect the dots with a line.   [2]

85 Mt. Mitchell, in North Carolina, is located at 36° N and has a peak elevation of 2037 meters. Plot the latitude and elevation of Mt. Mitchell on your graph. Use a plus sign (+) to mark this point.   [1]

86 Using your graph, determine, to the *nearest whole degree*, the lowest latitude at which a peak with the same elevation as Mt. Mitchell would have permanent snow.   [1]

87 State the relationship between latitude and elevation of the snowline.   [1]

88 The diagram below represents the elliptical orbit of a spacecraft around the Sun.

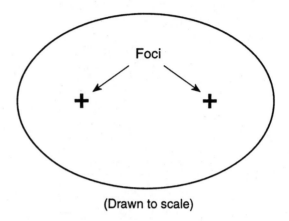

(Drawn to scale)

In the space provided *on your answer paper*, calculate the eccentricity of the spacecraft's orbit following the directions below:

a Write the equation for eccentricity.   [1]

b Substitute measurements of the diagram into the equation.   [1]

c Calculate the eccentricity and record your answer in decimal form.   [1]

EARTH SCIENCE
JUNE 1998

ANSWER PAPER

Student . . . .   Sex: ☐ Male ☐ Female

Teacher . . . . School . . . .

Grade   (circle one)   8   9   10   11   12

Record all of your answers on this answer paper in accordance with the instructions on the front cover of the test booklet.

Part I (40 credits)

1	1 2 3 4	15	1 2 3 4	29	1 2 3 4
2	1 2 3 4	16	1 2 3 4	30	1 2 3 4
3	1 2 3 4	17	1 2 3 4	31	1 2 3 4
4	1 2 3 4	18	1 2 3 4	32	1 2 3 4
5	1 2 3 4	19	1 2 3 4	33	1 2 3 4
6	1 2 3 4	20	1 2 3 4	34	1 2 3 4
7	1 2 3 4	21	1 2 3 4	35	1 2 3 4
8	1 2 3 4	22	1 2 3 4	36	1 2 3 4
9	1 2 3 4	23	1 2 3	37	1 2 3 4
10	1 2 3 4	24	1 2 3 4	38	1 2 3 4
11	1 2 3 4	25	1 2 3 4	39	1 2 3 4
12	1 2 3 4	26	1 2 3 4	40	1 2 3 4
13	1 2 3 4	27	1 2 3 4		
14	1 2 3 4	28	1 2 3 4		

Part II (10 credits)

Answer the questions in two of the six groups in this part. Be sure to mark the answers to the groups you choose in accordance with the instructions on the front cover of the test booklet. Leave blank the spaces for the four groups of questions you do not choose to answer.

Group A Rocks and Minerals				
41	1	2	3	4
42	1	2	3	4
43	1	2	3	4
44	1	2	3	4
45	1	2	3	4

Group B Plate Tectonics				
46	1	2	3	4
47	1	2	3	4
48	1	2	3	4
49	1	2	3	4
50	1	2	3	4

Group C Oceanography				
51	1	2	3	4
52	1	2	3	4
53	1	2	3	4
54	1	2	3	4
55	1	2	3	4

Group D Glacial Processes				
56	1	2	3	4
57	1	2	3	4
58	1	2	3	4
59	1	2	3	4
60	1	2	3	4

Group E Atmospheric Energy				
61	1	2	3	4
62	1	2	3	4
63	1	2	3	4
64	1	2	3	4
65	1	2	3	

Group F Astronomy				
66	1	2	3	4
67	1	2	3	4
68	1	2	3	4
69	1	2	3	4
70	1	2	3	4

Part III (25 credits)

Answer *all* questions in this part.

71

Sun

Earth

(Not drawn to scale)

72 _____

_____

_____

_____

73 _____ p.m.

74

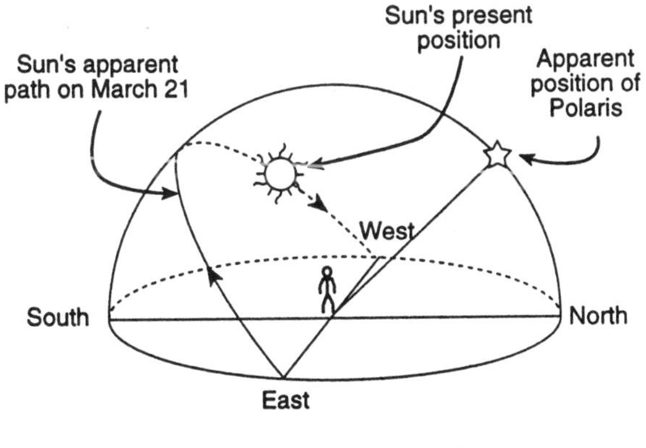

Sun's present position

Sun's apparent path on March 21

Apparent position of Polaris

West

South

North

East

(Not drawn to scale)

75 *a–b*

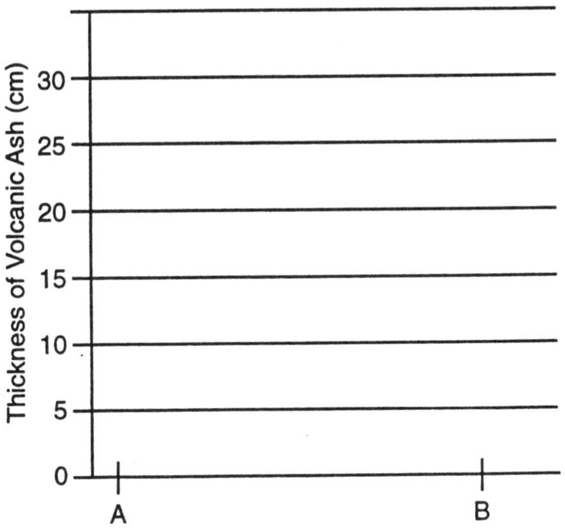

Thickness of Volcanic Ash (cm)

30

25

20

15

10

5

0

A

B

76 _____

_____

77 _____

_____

_____

78 _____

_____

_____

79

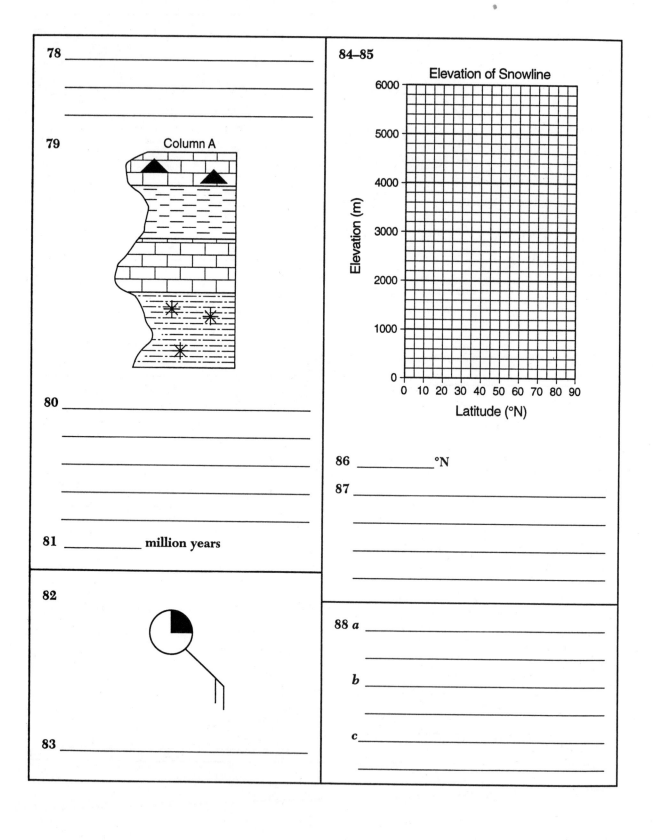

Column A

80 _____

_____

_____

_____

_____

81 _____ million years

82

83 _____

84–85

Elevation of Snowline

Elevation (m)

Latitude (°N)

86 _____ °N

87 _____

_____

_____

_____

88 a _____

_____

b _____

_____

c _____

_____

EARTH SCIENCE
JUNE 1999

Part I

Answer all 40 questions in this part.

Directions (1–40): For *each* statement or question, select the word or expression that, of those given, best completes the statement or answers the question. Record your answer on the separate answer paper in accordance with the directions on the front page of this booklet. Some questions may require the use of the *Earth Science Reference Tables.* [40]

1 The diagram below is a three-dimensional model of a landscape region.

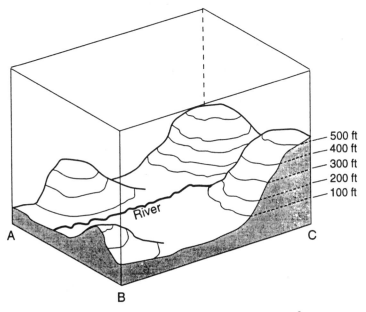

Which map view best represents the topography of this region?

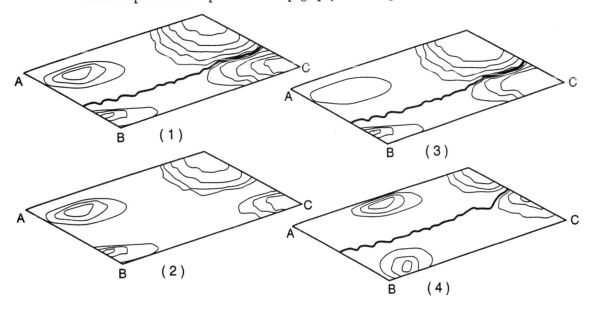

2 The map below shows the location and diameter, in kilometers, of four meteorite impact craters, *A, B, C,* and *D,* found in the United States.

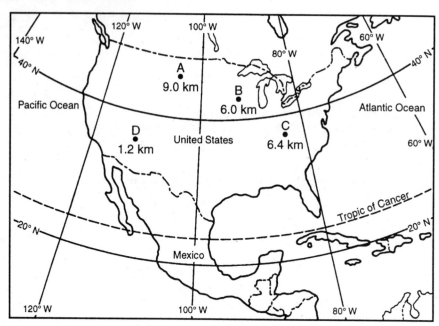

What is the approximate latitude and longitude of the largest crater?

(1) 35° N 111° W   (3) 44° N 90° W

(2) 39° N 83° W   (4) 47° N 104° W

---

3 Which diagram best shows the altitude of Polaris observed near Buffalo, New York?

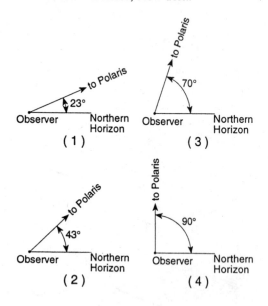

4 Although more than 2,000 minerals have been identified, 90% of Earth's lithosphere is composed of the 12 minerals listed below.

Rock-Forming Minerals	
feldspar	augite
quartz	garnet
mica	magnetite
calcite	olivine
hornblende	pyrite
kaolinite	talc

The best explanation for this fact is that most rocks

1 are monomineralic

2 are composed only of recrystallized minerals

3 have a number of minerals in common

4 have a 10% nonmineral composition

Base your answers to questions 5 through 8 on the diagram below, which represents a scheme for classifying rocks. The letters *A, B, C* and *X, Y, Z* represent missing labels.

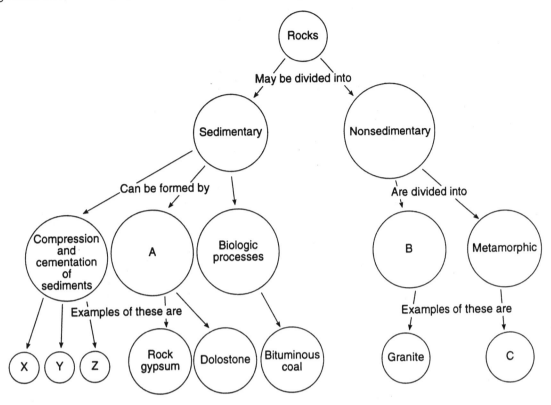

5 The classification of rocks into sedimentary or nonsedimentary groups is based primarily on the rocks'

1 origin   3 color
2 density   4 age

6 Which processes would form the type of rock that is represented by circle *B*?

1 deposition and compaction
2 weathering and erosion
3 melting and solidification
4 faulting and folding

7 If the rock in circle *C* formed from limestone, it would be called

1 schist   3 marble
2 anthracite coal   4 slate

8 Which rocks could be represented by circles *X, Y,* and *Z*?

1 shale, slate, and schist
2 sandstone, shale, and siltstone
3 anthracite coal, metaconglomerate, and rock salt
4 breccia, gneiss, and rhyolite

9 What is the largest particle that can generally be transported by a stream that is moving at 200 centimeters per second?

1 sand   3 cobble
2 pebble   4 boulder

10 Which agent of erosion formed the long U-shaped valleys now occupied by the Finger Lakes in central New York State?

1 running water   3 wind
2 ocean currents   4 glacial ice

11 The diagram below shows two landscapes, A and B.

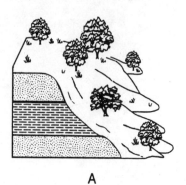
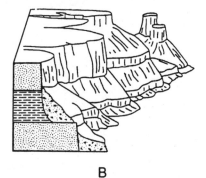

A   B

The difference in appearance of these two landscapes was caused mainly by a difference in the

1 climate   3 rock type
2 amount of uplift   4 rock structure

---

12 The diagram below shows a cross section of a portion of Earth's crust.

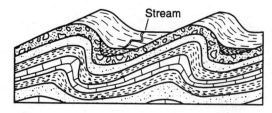

Stream

The hills of this area were formed primarily by

1 bedrock folding   3 stream erosion
2 bedrock faulting   4 volcanic activity

13 Which type of climate has the greatest amount of rock weathering caused by frost action?

1 a wet climate in which temperatures remain below freezing
2 a wet climate in which temperatures alternate from below freezing to above freezing
3 a dry climate in which temperatures remain below freezing
4 a dry climate in which temperatures alternate from below freezing to above freezing

14 The *Generalized Bedrock Geology Map of New York State* provides evidence that water flows from Lake Erie into Lake Ontario by showing that Lake Ontario

1 is north of Lake Erie
2 is deeper than Lake Erie
3 has a larger surface area than Lake Erie
4 has a lower surface elevation than Lake Erie

15 Quartz particles of varying sizes are dropped at the same time into deep, calm water. Which cross section best represents the settling pattern of these particles?

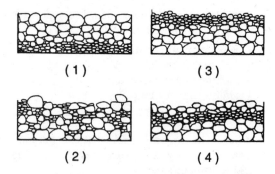

(1)   (3)

(2)   (4)

16 The diagrams below show the stages, A through D, in the formation of an oxbow lake over a period of time. [The arrows indicate the direction of streamflow.]

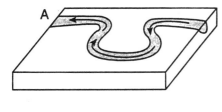

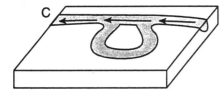

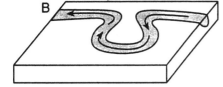

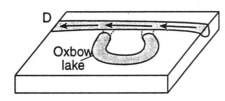

Oxbow lakes are generally formed by

1 erosion, resulting in a sudden increase in the stream's gradient
2 deposition, resulting in a sudden increase in the stream's gradient
3 erosion along the outside banks of the curve in a meandering stream
4 deposition along the outside banks of the curve in a meandering stream

17 Trilobite fossils were recently discovered in Himalayan Mountain bedrock. During which geologic period could these organisms have lived?

1 Tertiary   3 Triassic
2 Cretaceous   4 Cambrian

18 A graph of the radioactive decay of carbon-14 is shown below.

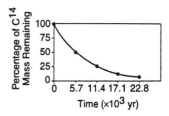

Which graph correctly shows the accumulation of nitrogen-14, the decay product of carbon-14, over the same period?

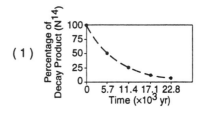

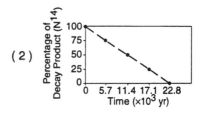

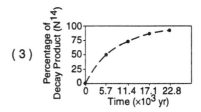

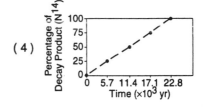

19 What is the geologic age of the surface bedrock of most of the Allegheny Plateau landscape region in New York State?

1 Cambrian   3 Silurian
2 Devonian   4 Ordovician

20 The dots on the map below show the present locations of living coral reefs. Site X indicates an area of fossil coral reefs preserved in rocks formed during the Jurassic Period.

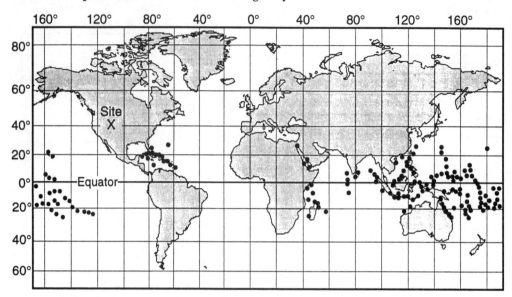

Which inference is best supported by this map?

1 The climate at site X during the Jurassic Period was colder than the present climate at site X.

2 Site X was covered by warm ocean water during the Jurassic Period.

3 Site X has drifted southward since the Jurassic Period.

4 The coral at site X evolved from ocean-dwelling animals into land-dwelling animals after the Jurassic Period.

21 The diagrams below show the sequence of events that formed sedimentary rock layers A, B, C, and D.

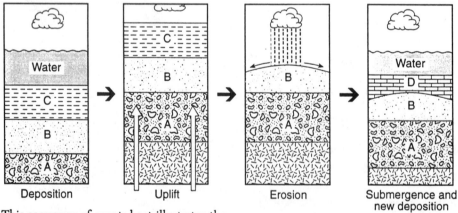

This sequence of events best illustrates the

1 formation of a buried erosional surface (unconformity)

2 movement of rock layers along a fault between layers B and D

3 overturning of rock layers

4 metamorphism of sandstone (layer B) into quartzite

22 The table below shows characteristics of three landscape regions, X, Y, and Z.

Landscape Region	Relief	Bedrock
X	Great relief, high peaks, deep valleys	Many types, including igneous and metamorphic rocks, nonhorizontal structure
Y	Moderate to high relief	Flat layers of sedimentary rock or lava flows
Z	Very little relief, low elevations	Many types and structures

Which terms, when substituted for X, Y, and Z, best complete the table?

(1) X = mountains, Y = plains, Z = plateaus
(2) X = plateaus, Y = mountains, Z = plains
(3) X = plains, Y = plateaus, Z = mountains
(4) X = mountains, Y = plateaus, Z = plains

Base your answers to questions 23 through 25 on the weather map below, which shows weather systems over the central and eastern United States and weather data for several cities.

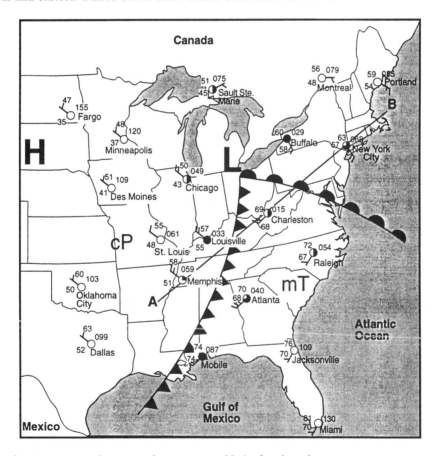

23 The cP air mass shown on the map most likely developed over

1 central Canada
2 central Mexico
3 the Gulf of Mexico
4 the North Atlantic

24 Which map correctly shows the movement of surface air associated with the high-pressure and low-pressure systems?

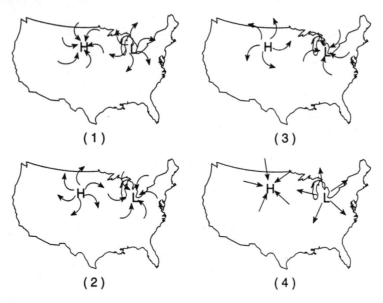

(1)   (3)

(2)   (4)

25 Which cross-sectional diagram of the lower atmosphere along line *AB* best represents the movement of the fronts and air masses?

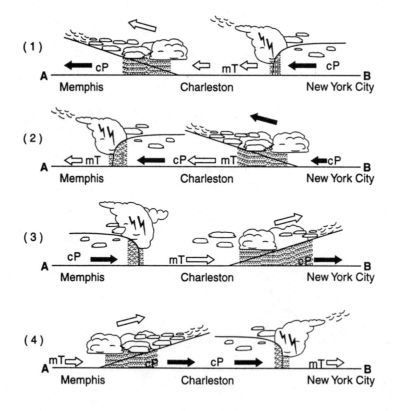

Base your answers to questions 26 through 28 on the map below. The map shows a portion of the eastern United States with New York State shaded. The isolines on the map indicate the average yearly total snowfall, in inches, recorded over a 20-year period. Points A, B, and C are locations on Earth's surface. Latitude and longitude coordinates are shown along the border of the map.

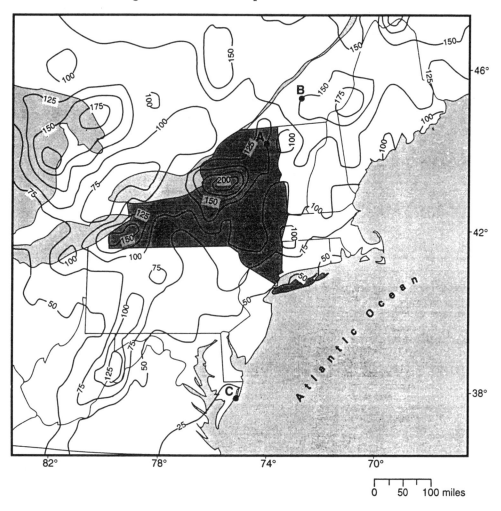

26 Location C has a lower average yearly snowfall than location A primarily because location C has a

1 lower latitude
2 higher longitude
3 higher elevation
4 different prevailing wind direction

27 What is the approximate average yearly total snowfall gradient between locations A and B?

(1) 0.25 in/mi   (3) 0.40 in/mi
(2) 2.50 in/mi   (4) 4.00 in/mi

28 The diagram below shows the location of five cities in New York State.

Which graph best represents the total average annual snowfall for each of the five cities?

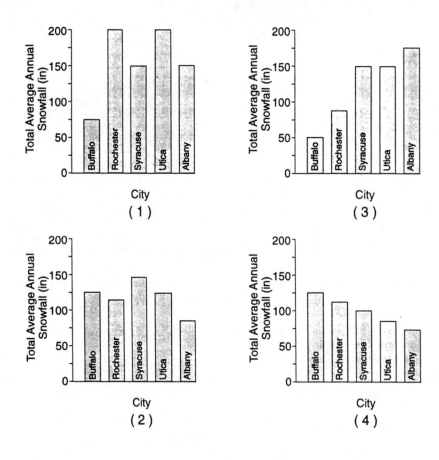

29 The shaded portion of the map below indicates areas of night and the unshaded portion indicates areas of daylight.

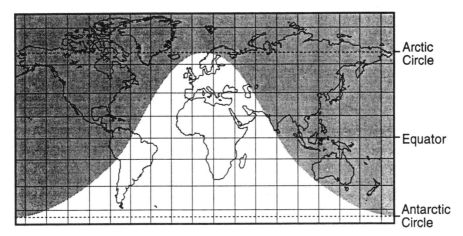

What day of the year is best represented by the map?

1 March 21   3 September 21
2 June 21   4 December 21

---

30 The graph below shows the air pressure recorded at the same time at several locations between Niagara Falls and Albany.

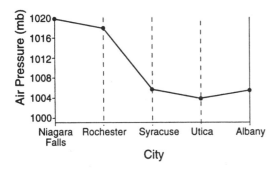

Based on the information in this graph, the wind velocity is probably greatest between which two cities?

1 Niagara Falls and Rochester
2 Rochester and Syracuse
3 Syracuse and Utica
4 Utica and Albany

31 Which current is a cool ocean current that flows completely around Earth?

1 West Wind Drift
2 Gulf Stream
3 North Equatorial Current
4 California Current

32 During how many days of a calendar year is the Sun directly overhead at noon in New York State?

(1) only 1 day   (3) 365 days
(2) only 2 days   (4) 0 days

33 Ozone is important to life on Earth because ozone

1 cools refrigerators and air-conditioners
2 absorbs energy that is reradiated by Earth
3 absorbs harmful ultraviolet radiation
4 destroys excess atmospheric carbon dioxide

Base your answers to questions 34 and 35 on the diagram below, which shows the Moon in four different positions, A, B, C, and D, as it orbits Earth.

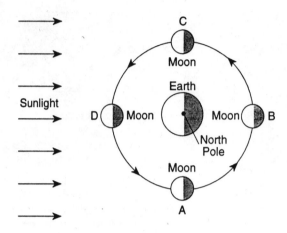

34 How does the Moon appear to an observer in New York State when the Moon is located at position A?

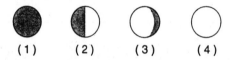

35 The cartoon below shows a comical view of an eclipse as viewed from Earth.

The type of eclipse represented in the cartoon might occur when the Moon is located at position

(1) A
(2) B
(3) C
(4) D

36 The diagram below represents the construction of a model of an elliptical orbit of a planet traveling around a star. The focal point and the center of the star represent the foci of the orbit.

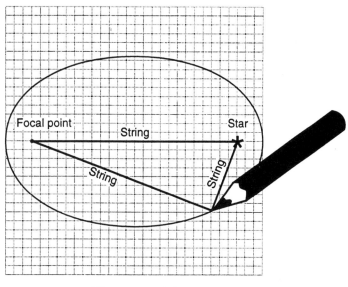

(Drawn to scale)

The eccentricity of this orbit is approximately

(1) 1.3   (3) 0.5
(2) 0.8   (4) 0.3

Base your answers to questions 37 and 38 on the diagram below. The diagram shows twelve constellations that are visible in the night sky to an observer in New York State, over the course of a year. Different positions of Earth are represented by letters *A* through *D*. The arrows represent the direction of Earth's motion around the Sun.

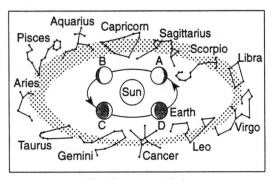

(Not drawn to scale)

37 Which constellations are both visible at midnight to an observer in New York State when Earth is located at position *D*?

  1 Aries and Taurus
  2 Pisces and Libra
  3 Leo and Virgo
  4 Aquarius and Scorpio

38 The constellations observed from New York State when Earth is at position *A* are different from the constellations observed when Earth is at position *C* because

  1 Earth moves in its orbit
  2 Earth is tilted on its axis
  3 the lengths of day and night are different
  4 the stars move around Earth as shown by star trails

39 The diagram below represents Earth.

Which diagram best represents Mars, drawn to the same scale?

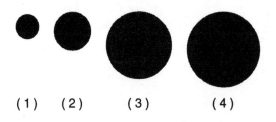

  (1)   (2)   (3)   (4)

40 Which graph shows the most probable effect of environmental pollution on the chances of human survival?

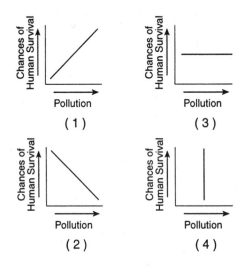

Part II

This part consists of six groups, each containing five questions. Choose any *two* of these six groups. Be sure that you answer all five questions in each of the two groups chosen. Record the answers to these questions on the separate answer paper in accordance with the directions on the front cover of this booklet. Some questions may require the use of the *Earth Science Reference Tables.* [10]

Group A — Rocks and Minerals

If you choose this group, be sure to answer questions 41–45.

Base your answers to questions 41 and 42 on the rock sample shown below.

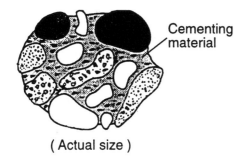

Cementing material

(Actual size)

41 The rounded pebbles of this rock have been cemented together to form

1 granite, an igneous rock
2 conglomerate, a sedimentary rock
3 siltstone, a sedimentary rock
4 gneiss, a metamorphic rock

42 The average size of the pebbles in the sample is approximately

(1) 1.2 cm
(2) 0.2 cm
(3) 6.4 cm
(4) 13.2 cm

43 Different arrangements of tetrahedra in the silicate group of minerals result in differences in the minerals'

1 age, density, and smoothness
2 cleavage, color, and abundance
3 hardness, cleavage, and crystal shape
4 chemical composition, size, and origin

44 Some Moon rock samples have coarse intergrown crystals composed of plagioclase feldspar, hornblende, and olivine. These Moon rock samples are most similar to Earth rock samples of

1 gabbro
2 marble
3 breccia
4 pumice

45 Which common mineral fizzes when dilute hydrochloric acid (HCl) is placed on it?

1 calcite
2 feldspar
3 quartz
4 talc

Group B — Plate Tectonics

If you choose this group, be sure to answer questions 46–50.

Base your answers to questions 46 and 47 on the map below. The map shows epicenters of some of the earthquakes that occurred in North America during a 2-week period. Five epicenters are labeled A through E. Denver and New York City are also indicated.

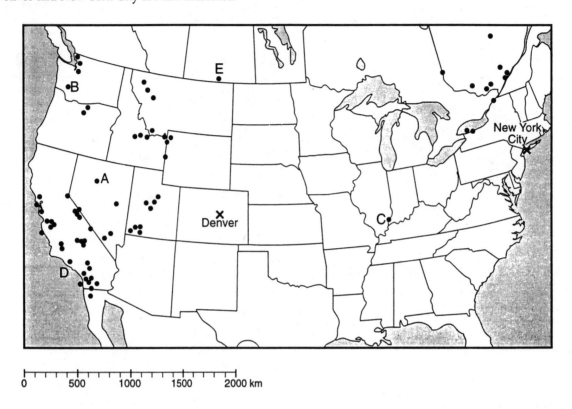

46 A seismograph station at Denver recorded the arrival of P-waves at 8:00 a.m. and the arrival of S-waves at 8:02 a.m. Which epicenter is located above the source of this earthquake?

(1) A   (3) C
(2) B   (4) D

47 The distance from epicenter E to New York City is 3,000 kilometers. What was the approximate travel time for the P-waves from this epicenter to New York City?

(1) 1 min 20 sec   (3) 7 min 30 sec
(2) 5 min 40 sec   (4) 10 min 00 sec

48 The cutaway diagram below shows the paths of earthquake waves generated at point *X*.

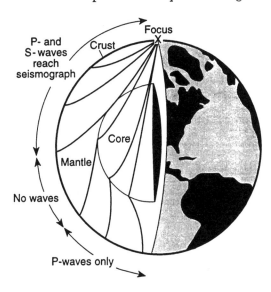

Only *P*-waves reach the side of Earth that is opposite the focus because *P*-waves

1 are stronger than *S*-waves
2 travel faster than *S*-waves
3 bend more than *S*-waves
4 can travel through liquids and *S*-waves cannot

49 Magnetic readings taken across mid-ocean ridges provide evidence that

1 the seafloor is spreading
2 the ocean basins are older than the continents
3 the mid-ocean ridges are higher than the nearby plains
4 Earth's rate of rotation has changed

50 Compared to Earth's oceanic crust, Earth's continental crust is

1 thinner and composed of granite
2 thinner and composed of basalt
3 thicker and composed of granite
4 thicker and composed of basalt

Group C — Oceanography

If you choose this group, be sure to answer questions 51–55.

51 The cross section below shows the ocean floor between two continents. Points *A* through *D* represent locations on the ocean floor where samples of oceanic crust were collected.

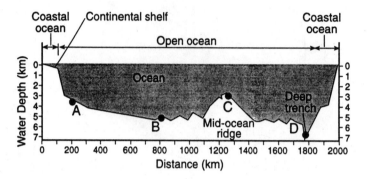

The youngest rock sample most likely was collected from location

(1) *A*

(2) *B*

(3) *C*

(4) *D*

---

52 Waste produced by people in New York State has been dumped into the Atlantic Ocean, where it is distributed by surface ocean currents. Which coastal area is most likely to become polluted by this waste?

1 western coast of Europe

2 southern coast of South America

3 western coast of Mexico

4 eastern coast of Africa

53 Tsunamis are caused by

1 Earth's rotation

2 dynamic equilibrium

3 hurricane winds

4 earthquakes

Base your answers to questions 54 and 55 on the map below, which shows Rockaway Peninsula, part of Long Island's south shore.

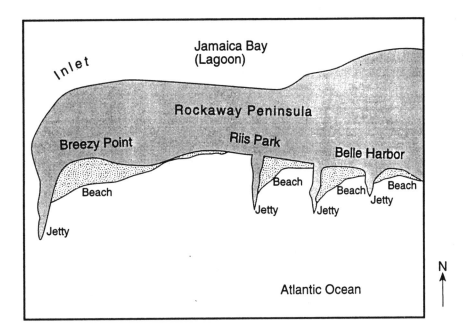

54 Students compared recent photographs of the beaches with photographs taken three years ago and discovered that parts of the shoreline have changed. Which characteristic of the shoreline probably has changed most?

1 composition of the beach sand
2 size of the beaches
3 positions of the jetties
4 length of the peninsula

55 Toward which direction is sand being transported along the shoreline within the zone of breaking waves?

1 northeast   3 southeast
2 south   4 west

Group D — Glacial Processes

If you choose this group, be sure to answer questions 56–60.

Base your answers to questions 56 and 57 on the three maps below, which show the ice movement and changes at the ice front of an alpine glacier from the years 1874 to 1882. Points A, B, C, D, and E represent the positions of large markers placed on the glacial ice and left there for a period of eight years.

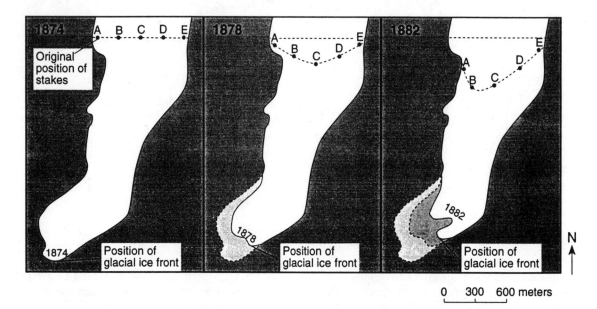

56 The changing positions of markers A, B, C, D, and E show that the glacial ice is

1 slowly becoming thicker
2 forming smaller crystals
3 gradually shifting northward
4 moving fastest near the middle

57 Which statement best describes the changes happening to this glacier between 1874 and 1882?

1 The ice front was advancing, and the ice within the glacier was advancing.
2 The ice front was advancing, and the ice within the glacier was retreating.
3 The ice front was retreating, and the ice within the glacier was advancing.
4 The ice front was retreating, and the ice within the glacier was retreating.

58 As a result of glaciation, New York State has

1 few lakes
2 many V-shaped valleys
3 many sand and gravel deposits
4 thick soils formed "in place" from underlying bedrock

Base your answers to questions 59 and 60 on the chart below, which shows the changing climatic conditions that led to alternating glacial and interglacial periods.

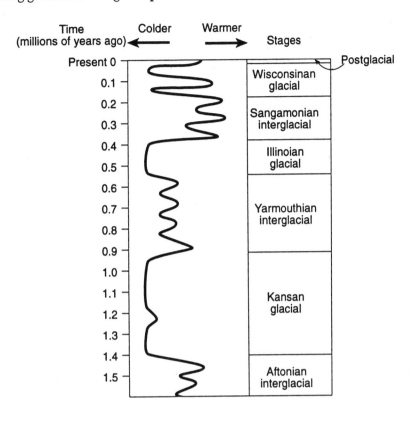

59 The interglacial stages were most likely caused by
 1 a drop in worldwide sea levels
 2 an increase in average worldwide temperature
 3 crustal plate movement
 4 a large increase in the amount of snowfall

60 The chart represents climatic conditions that occurred mostly during which geological time period?
 1 Triassic Period   3 Quaternary Period
 2 Ordovician Period   4 Cretaceous Period

Group E — Atmospheric Energy

If you choose this group, be sure to answer questions 61–65.

61 At which latitudes do currents of dry, sinking air cause the dry conditions of Earth's major deserts?

(1) 0° and 30° N   (3) 30° N and 30° S
(2) 60° N and 60° S   (4) 60° S and 90° S

62 At what approximate altitude would clouds begin to form when the surface air temperature is 30°C and the dewpoint is 14°C?

(1) 1.1 km   (3) 2.5 km
(2) 2.0 km   (4) 3.7 km

63 A large amount of latent heat is absorbed by water during

1 evaporation   3 condensation
2 freezing   4 precipitation

64 When would the water in a New York State pond evaporate fastest?

1 in January, when the pond is frozen
2 in March, when the pond ice is melting
3 in May on a calm, sunny day
4 in July on a hot, windy day

Note that question 65 has only three choices.

65 Compared to the accuracy of the 24-hour weather forecasts of the 1930's, the 24-hour weather forecasts of the 1990's are usually

1 less accurate
2 more accurate
3 equally accurate

Group F — Astronomy

If you choose this group, be sure to answer questions 66–70.

66 Which diagram represents a geocentric model? [Key: E = Earth, P = Planet, S = Sun]

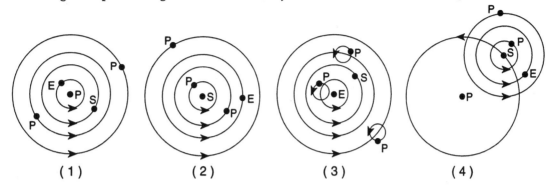

(1)   (2)   (3)   (4)

67 According to the big bang theory, the universe began as an explosion and is still expanding. This theory is supported by observations that the stellar spectra of distant galaxies show a

1 concentration in the yellow portion of the spectrum

2 concentration in the green portion of the spectrum

3 shift toward the blue end of the spectrum

4 shift toward the red end of the spectrum

68 Major ocean and air currents appear to curve to the right in the Northern Hemisphere because

1 Earth has seasons

2 Earth's axis is tilted

3 Earth rotates on its axis

4 Earth revolves around the Sun

69 Why are impact structures more obvious on the Moon than on Earth?

1 The Moon's gravity is stronger than Earth's gravity.

2 The Moon has little or no atmosphere.

3 The rocks on the Moon are weaker than those on Earth.

4 The Moon rotates at a slower rate than Earth does.

70 If the amount of greenhouse gases were to increase for a very long time, the atmosphere on Earth would become most like the atmosphere of

1 Mercury   3 Jupiter

2 Venus   4 Saturn

Part III

This part consists of questions 71 through 88. Be sure that you answer *all* questions in this part. Record your answers in the spaces provided on the separate answer paper. You may use pen or pencil. Some questions may require the use of the *Earth Science Reference Tables.*   [25]

Base your answers to questions 71 and 72 on the data table and profile below. The data table gives the average annual precipitation for locations *A* and *B*. The profile represents a mountain in the western United States. Points *A* and *B* are locations on different sides of the mountain.

Data Table

Location	Average Annual Precipitation (cm)
A	120
B	35

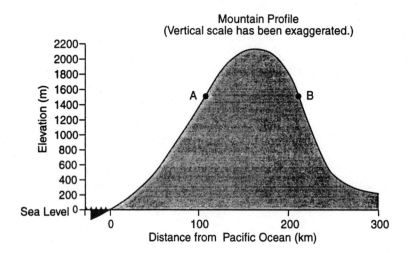

Mountain Profile
(Vertical scale has been exaggerated.)

71   State the elevation of location *A*.   [1]

72   State one probable reason for the difference in average annual precipitation between location *A* and location *B*.   [1]

73 State one way in which a hurricane differs from a tornado.   [1]

Base your answers to questions 74 through 76 on the geologic cross section below. The cross section shows an outcrop in which the layers have not been overturned. Rock units are labeled *A* through *E*.

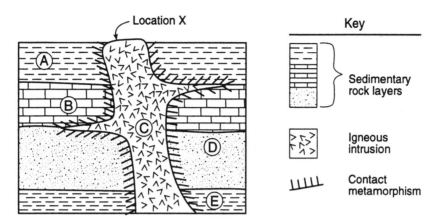

74 Using letters *A* through *E*, list the rock units in order from oldest to youngest. [2]

75 State the name of the sediment that was compacted to form rock unit *A*. [1]

76 State one observation about the crystals at location *X* that would provide evidence that igneous rock unit *C* was formed by very slow cooling of magma. [1]

77 A parcel of air has a dry-bulb temperature of 18°C and a wet-bulb temperature of 10°C. State the relative humidity of this parcel of air. [1]

Base your answers to questions 78 through 80 on the weather map below. The map shows temperature readings at weather stations in the continental United States.

78 On the weather map provided *on your answer paper,* draw three isotherms: the 40°F isotherm, the 50°F isotherm, and the 60°F isotherm.   [2]

79 In Richmond, Virginia, the wind direction is from the east at a speed of 20 knots. On the station model provided *on your answer paper,* draw the correct symbols for wind direction and windspeed.   [2]

80 In addition to temperature, one other weather variable for each weather station is shown on the map. State the other weather variable.   [1]

Base your answers to questions 81 and 82 on the information and map below.

The eruption of Mt. St. Helens in 1980 resulted in the movement of volcanic ash across the northwestern United States. The movement of the ash at 1.5 kilometers above sea level is shown as a shaded path on the map. The times marked on the path indicate the length of time the leading edge of the ash cloud took to travel from Mt. St. Helens to each location.

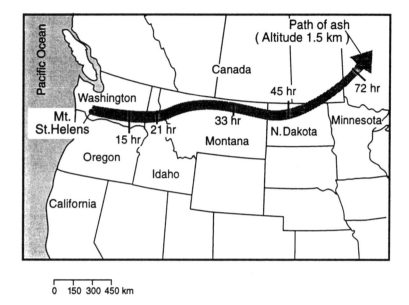

0 150 300 450 km

81 Calculate the average *rate* of movement of the volcanic ash for the first 15 hours, following the directions below.

    a Write the equation used to determine the average rate of the volcanic ash movement. [1]

    b Substitute values into the equation. [1]

    c Solve the equation and label the answer with the correct units. [2]

82 The movement of the ash occurred at an altitude of 1.5 kilometers. State the name of the layer of Earth's atmosphere in which the ash cloud traveled. [1]

Base your answers to questions 83 through 85 on the cross section of a portion of Earth's interior below. The cross section shows the focal depth of some earthquakes that occurred west of the Tonga Trench. Data were collected along the 22° S parallel of latitude.

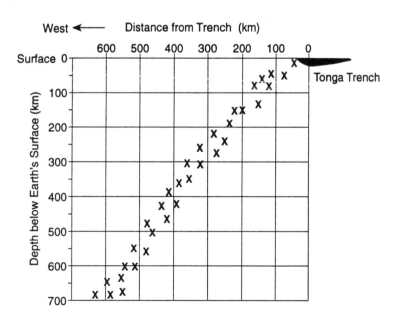

83 State the relationship between the depth of an earthquake's focus and the earthquake's distance from the Tonga Trench.   [1]

84 The Tonga Trench is the crustal surface boundary between two tectonic plates. State the names of the two plates.   [1]

85 The focal depth pattern shown on the cross section represents the location of the sub-surface boundary between the two tectonic plates. Describe the relative motion of the plates along this boundary.   [1]

Base your answers to questions 86 through 88 on the tables below. Table 1 shows the average distance from the Sun in astronomical units (AU) and the average orbital speed in kilometers per second (km/s) of the nine planets in our solar system. Table 2 lists five large asteroids and their average distances from the Sun.

Table 1

Planet	Average Distance from Sun (AU)	Average Orbital Speed (km/s)
Mercury	0.4	48.0
Venus	0.7	35.0
Earth	1.0	30.0
Mars	1.5	24.0
Jupiter	5.2	13.0
Saturn	9.6	10.0
Uranus	19.0	7.0
Neptune	30.0	5.1
Pluto	39.0	4.7

Table 2

Asteroid	Average Distance from Sun (AU)
Ceres	2.8
Pallas	2.8
Vesta	2.4
Hygiea	3.2
Juno	2.7

86 On the grid provided *on your answer paper,* plot the average distance from the Sun and the average orbital speed for each of the nine planets listed in table 1. Connect the nine points with a line.   [2]

87 State the relationship between a planet's average distance from the Sun and the planet's average orbital speed.   [1]

88 The orbits of the asteroids listed in table 2 are located between two adjacent planetary orbits. State the names of the two planets.   [1]

EARTH SCIENCE
JUNE 1999

PROGRAM MODIFICATION EDITION

Part I Credits	. . . .	. . . .
Part II Credits	. . . .	. . . .
Part III Credits	. . . .	. . . .
Performance Test Credits	. . . .	. . . .
Local Project Credits	. . . .	. . . .
Total (Official Regents) Examination Mark	. . . .	. . . .
Reviewer's Initials:		_____

ANSWER PAPER

Student . . . .   Sex: ☐ Male ☐ Female

Teacher . . . . School . . . .

Grade   (circle one)   8   9   10   11   12

Record all of your answers on this answer paper in accordance with the instructions on the front cover of the test booklet.

Part I (40 credits)

1	1 2 3 4	15	1 2 3 4	29	1 2 3 4
2	1 2 3 4	16	1 2 3 4	30	1 2 3 4
3	1 2 3 4	17	1 2 3 4	31	1 2 3 4
4	1 2 3 4	18	1 2 3 4	32	1 2 3 4
5	1 2 3 4	19	1 2 3 4	33	1 2 3 4
6	1 2 3 4	20	1 2 3 4	34	1 2 3 4
7	1 2 3 4	21	1 2 3 4	35	1 2 3 4
8	1 2 3 4	22	1 2 3 4	36	1 2 3 4
9	1 2 3 4	23	1 2 3 4	37	1 2 3 4
10	1 2 3 4	24	1 2 3 4	38	1 2 3 4
11	1 2 3 4	25	1 2 3 4	39	1 2 3 4
12	1 2 3 4	26	1 2 3 4	40	1 2 3 4
13	1 2 3 4	27	1 2 3 4		
14	1 2 3 4	28	1 2 3 4		

Part II (10 credits)

Answer the questions in two of the six groups in this part. Be sure to mark the answers to the groups you choose in accordance with the instructions on the front cover of the test booklet. Leave blank the spaces for the four groups of questions you do not choose to answer.

Group A Rocks and Minerals		
41 1 2 3 4		
42 1 2 3 4		
43 1 2 3 4		
44 1 2 3 4		
45 1 2 3 4		

Group B Plate Tectonics		
46 1 2 3 4		
47 1 2 3 4		
48 1 2 3 4		
49 1 2 3 4		
50 1 2 3 4		

Group C Oceanography		
51 1 2 3 4		
52 1 2 3 4		
53 1 2 3 4		
54 1 2 3 4		
55 1 2 3 4		

Group D Glacial Processes		
56 1 2 3 4		
57 1 2 3 4		
58 1 2 3 4		
59 1 2 3 4		
60 1 2 3 4		

Group E Atmospheric Energy		
61 1 2 3 4		
62 1 2 3 4		
63 1 2 3 4		
64 1 2 3 4		
65 1 2 3		

Group F Astronomy		
66 1 2 3 4		
67 1 2 3 4		
68 1 2 3 4		
69 1 2 3 4		
70 1 2 3 4		

Part III (25 credits)

Answer *all* questions in this part.

71 _____ meters

72 _____

_____

_____

_____

73 _____

_____

_____

_____

74

Oldest   Youngest

75 _____

76 _____

_____

_____

77_____ %

78

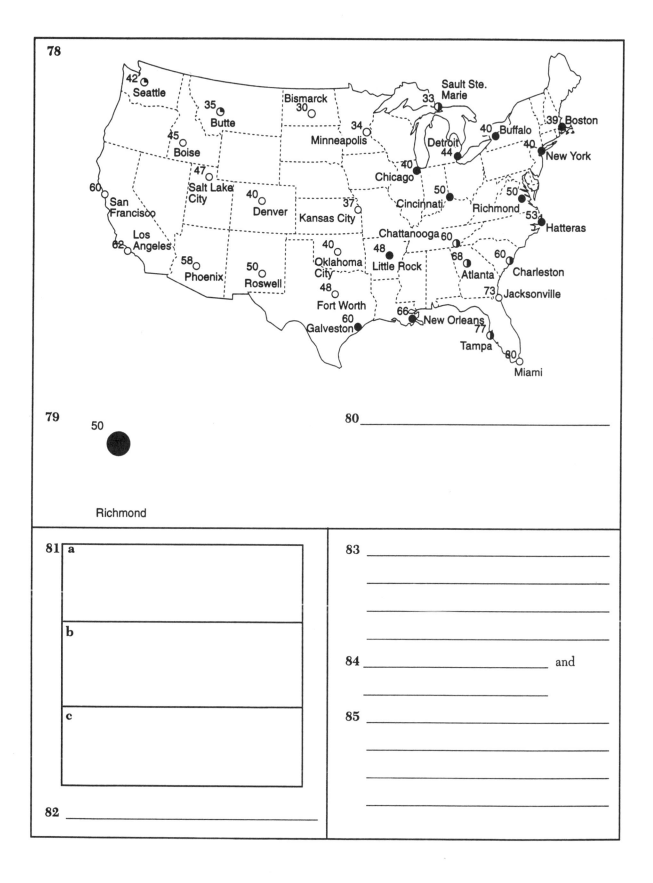

42 Seattle			
35 Butte		Bismarck 30	
45 Boise		34 Minneapolis	Sault Ste. Marie 33
	47 Salt Lake City		40 Detroit 44 Buffalo 40 39 Boston
60 San Francisco	40 Denver	40 Chicago	New York
		37 Kansas City	50 Cincinnati 50 Richmond
62 Los Angeles		Chattanooga 60	53 Hatteras
58 Phoenix	50 Roswell	40 Oklahoma City	48 Little Rock 68 Atlanta 60 Charleston
		48 Fort Worth	73 Jacksonville
		60 Galveston	66 New Orleans 77 Tampa 80 Miami

79   50 ⬤

Richmond

80 _____

81 **a**

b

c

82 _____

83 _____
_____
_____
_____

84 _____ and
_____

85 _____
_____
_____
_____
_____

86

Planets' Average Orbital Speed vs. Average Distance from Sun

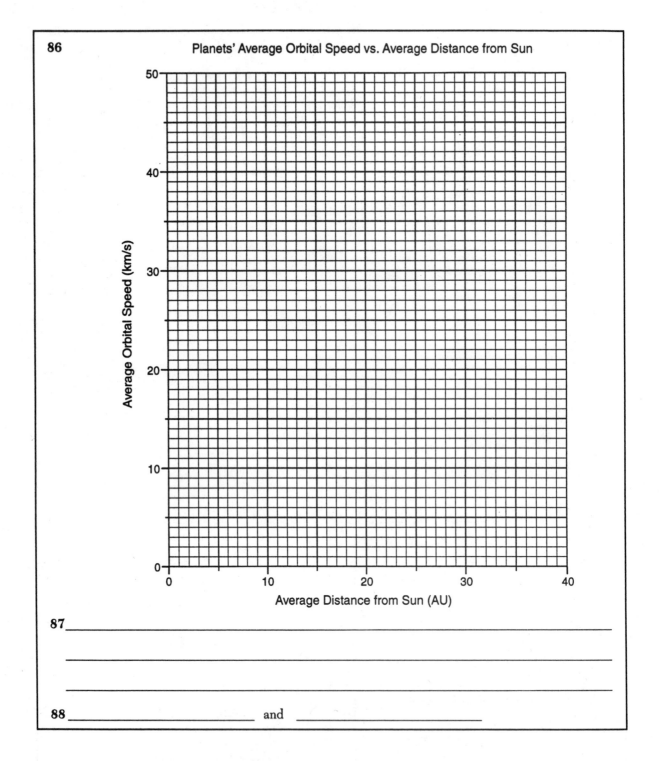

87 _____

_____

_____

88 _____ and _____

EARTH SCIENCE
JUNE 2000
PROGRAM MODIFICATION EDITION

Part I

Answer all 40 questions in this part.

Directions (1–40): For *each* statement or question, select the word or expression that, of those given, best completes the statement or answers the question. Record your answer on the separate answer paper in accordance with the directions on the front page of this booklet. Some questions may require the use of the *Earth Science Reference Tables.* [40]

1 Measurements of gravity are greater at the poles than at the Equator. This evidence best supports the inference that Earth has a

1 perfectly spherical shape
2 slightly oblate shape
3 very elliptical orbit
4 slightly elliptical orbit

2 A contour map is shown below. Elevations are shown in feet.

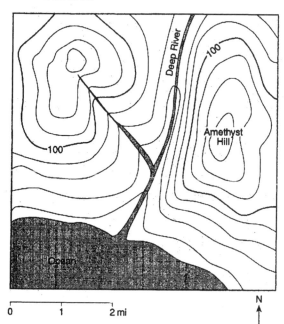

Which side of Amethyst Hill has the steepest slope?

1 north   3 east
2 south   4 west

3 The diagram below represents a rock sample containing fossilized *Coelophysis* footprints. The sample was found in New York State.

According to current knowledge of New York State fossils, during which geologic time period were these footprints most probably made?

1 Cambrian   3 Tertiary
2 Devonian   4 Triassic

4 The diagram below represents a side view of the Milky Way Galaxy.

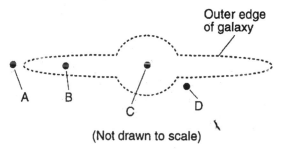

(Not drawn to scale)

At approximately which position is Earth's solar system located?

(1) *A*   (3) *C*
(2) *B*   (4) *D*

5 The geologic cross section below shows variations of mineral composition that can be observed in the Palisades Sill in southeastern New York State. The Palisades Sill is an intrusive igneous rock called diabase.

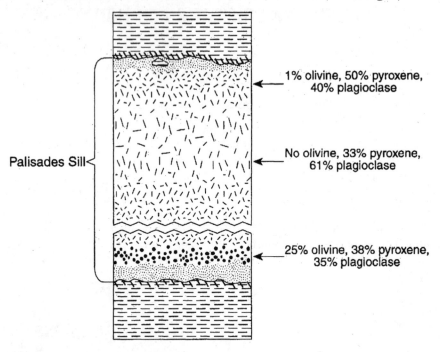

Palisades Sill

1% olivine, 50% pyroxene, 40% plagioclase

No olivine, 33% pyroxene, 61% plagioclase

25% olivine, 38% pyroxene, 35% plagioclase

Which other igneous rock is closest to diabase in mineral composition?

1 andesite
2 granite
3 rhyolite
4 gabbro

6 What is the direct cause of most earthquakes?

1 movement of bedrock along a fault line
2 gravitational pull on bedrock by the Moon
3 deposition of sediment in lakes and oceans
4 heat exchange between the crust and the atmosphere

7 Adding automobile exhaust gases to the atmosphere has had the greatest impact on landscape development by

1 changing the position of crustal plates
2 changing Earth's prevailing wind patterns
3 increasing the rate of chemical weathering
4 increasing the amount of ozone in ground water

8 Which map symbol is used in the *Earth Science Reference Tables* to represent an organically formed sedimentary rock composed mostly of carbon?

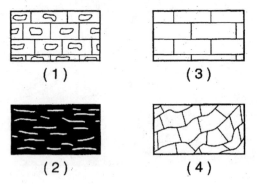

(1)

(3)

(2)

(4)

Base your answers to questions 9 through 11 on the diagram and field map below. The diagram shows an underground gasoline storage tank at a service station that is leaking gasoline into the soil. Ground-water monitoring wells were drilled to show the pattern of the leakage. The concentration of gasoline, in parts per million, at each well is indicated on the field map.

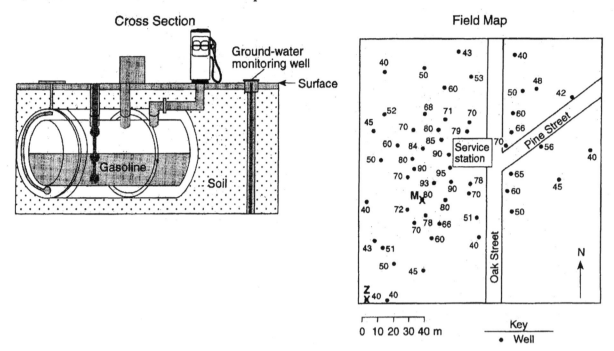

9 Which expression shows the approximate gradient (rate of change in gasoline concentration per meter) from point M to point Z?

1 gradient = $\dfrac{(80\ \text{ppm} - 40\ \text{ppm})}{70\ \text{meters}}$

2 gradient = $\dfrac{70\ \text{meters}}{(80\ \text{ppm} - 40\ \text{ppm})}$

3 gradient = $\dfrac{(80\ \text{ppm} - 70\ \text{ppm})}{40\ \text{meters}}$

4 gradient = $\dfrac{40\ \text{meters}}{(80\ \text{ppm} - 70\ \text{ppm})}$

10 Which isoline map best represents the pattern of gasoline concentration as measured in the wells?

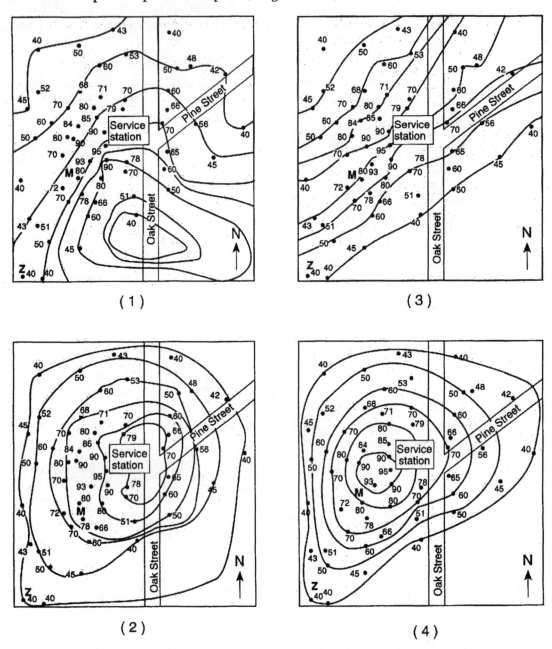

(1)   (3)

(2)   (4)

11 Which statement best describes the pollution field's size and concentration measurement if the gasoline continues to leak out of the tank?

 1 The size of the pollution field will decrease, and the concentration measurement will decrease.
 2 The size of the pollution field will decrease, and the concentration measurement will increase.
 3 The size of the pollution field will increase, and the concentration measurement will decrease.
 4 The size of the pollution field will increase, and the concentration measurement will increase.

12 Letters *A* through *D* shown on the map below are locations on Earth's surface.

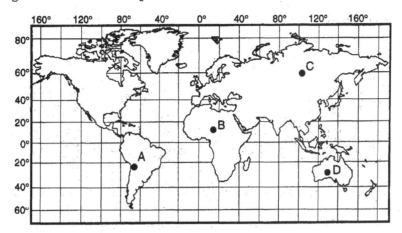

Which location is closest to a major zone of frequent earthquakes and volcanic activities?

(1) *A*   (3) *C*
(2) *B*   (4) *D*

---

13 Which diagram best shows the type of plate boundary found between the China Plate and the Philippine Plate?

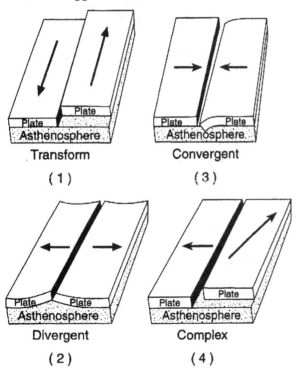

14 In a region that is being uplifted faster than it is being eroded, hills usually have

1 steep slopes and slow-moving streams
2 steep slopes and fast-moving streams
3 gentle slopes and slow-moving streams
4 gentle slopes and fast-moving streams

15 The four objects below are made of the same material and have the same mass. Which object will settle fastest in calm water?

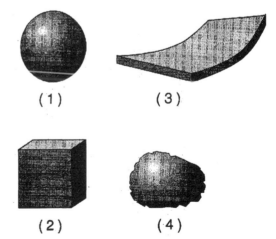

16 The diagram below shows two landscape regions with similar bedrock type and structure.

Landscape A

Landscape B

Which statement best explains why these two landscape regions are different in appearance?

1 Landscape A formed in a dry region, and landscape B formed in a humid region.
2 Landscape A formed in a dry region, and landscape B formed in a glaciated region.
3 Landscape A formed in a humid region, and landscape B formed in a dry region.
4 Landscape A formed in a humid region, and landscape B formed in a glaciated region.

17 The demonstration shown in the diagram below indicates that powdered limestone reacts faster than a single large piece of limestone of equal mass when both are placed in acid.

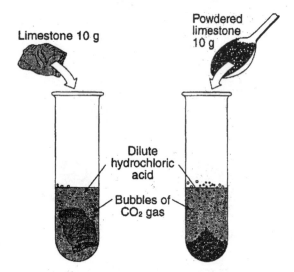

Limestone 10 g

Powdered limestone 10 g

Dilute hydrochloric acid

Bubbles of CO_2 gas

The most likely reason powdered limestone reacts faster is that it has

1 less total volume
2 more chemical bonds
3 more total surface area
4 lower density

18 Which process could be indicated by the expression below?

$$U^{238} \rightarrow Pb^{206}$$

1 crystallization of minerals in basalt
2 chemical weathering of marble
3 radioactive decay in granite
4 ozone depletion in the atmosphere

19 Which major mountain-building episode is most recent?

1 Grenville orogeny
2 Taconian orogeny
3 Acadian orogeny
4 Appalachian orogeny

20 The map below shows the surface bedrock in an area of the southwestern United States that formed from sediments deposited in a shallow sea that formerly existed in that area. These sediments were transported by a river that flowed into the sea.

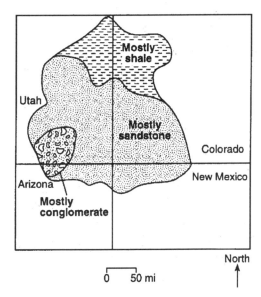

In which diagram does the arrow best show the direction of flow of the river that deposited these sediments and the point at which the river emptied into the sea?

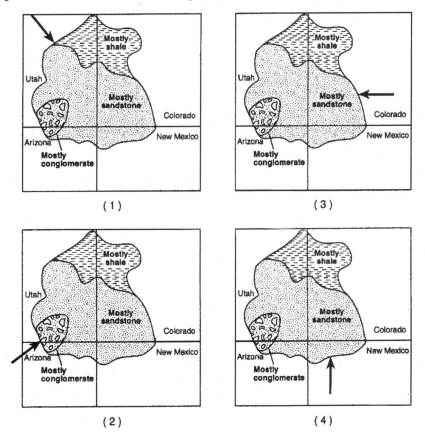

21 The time line below represents the geologic history of Earth. Letters *A*, *B*, *C*, and *D* represent specific times in Earth's history.

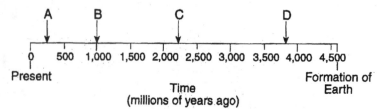

Which letter best indicates when trilobites became extinct?

(1) *A*   (3) *C*
(2) *B*   (4) *D*

Base your answers to questions 22 and 23 on the graph below, which shows the average yearly temperature and average yearly precipitation for Earth locations *A* through *E*.

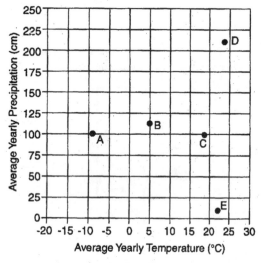

22 The climate indicated at location *E* on the graph would most likely be classified as

1 cold and dry
2 cold and humid
3 warm and dry
4 warm and humid

23 Which location has the climatic conditions necessary for the greatest amount of chemical weathering to occur?

(1) *A*   (3) *C*
(2) *B*   (4) *D*

24 Which type of air mass would most likely have low humidity and high air temperature?

(1) cT   (3) mT
(2) cP   (4) mP

25 In the diagram below, arrows represent air movement near an ocean coastline on a summer afternoon.

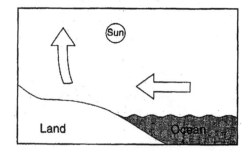

Compared to the air over the ocean, the air over the land has a

1 lower temperature and lower barometric pressure
2 lower temperature and higher barometric pressure
3 higher temperature and lower barometric pressure
4 higher temperature and higher barometric pressure

26 Which ocean current cools the climate of some locations along the western coastline of North America?

1 Florida Current   3 Canaries Current
2 California Current   4 Alaska Current

Base your answers to questions 27 through 29 on the weather map of North America below. A grid system of letters and numbers is provided along the edges of the map to assist in finding locations. Isobars are labeled in millibars. Letter X represents the center of a second low-pressure system.

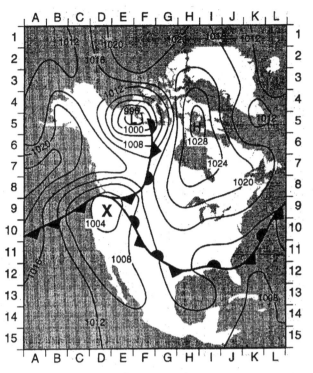

27 On which map do the arrows correctly show the surface wind pattern for the high- and low-pressure centers shown on the northern part of the weather map of North America?

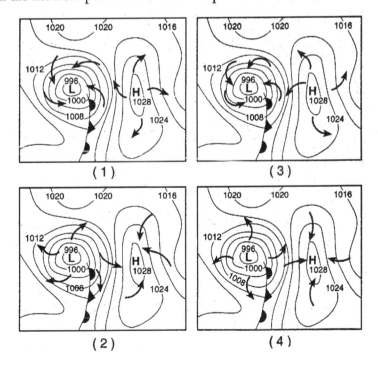

28 If the low-pressure center labeled X follows a typical storm track from its present location, the low-pressure center will move generally toward the

1 north   3 east
2 south   4 west

29 Which type of front is shown at grid coordinates A–10?

1 occluded   3 cold
2 stationary   4 warm

30 A student in New York State observed that the noon Sun increased in altitude each day during the first part of a certain month and then decreased in altitude each day later in the month. During which month were these observations made?

1 February   3 September
2 June   4 November

31 The data table below compares the percentage of sunlight reflected from various types of Earth surfaces.

Surface	Percent of Sunlight Reflected
Fresh snow	80–85
Old snow	50–60
Sand	20–30
Grass	20–25
Dry soil	15–25
Wet soil	10
Forest	5–10
Water (Sun at sunset)	50–80
Water (Sun overhead)	3–5
Thick cloud	70–80
Thin cloud	25–50

Which statement is best supported by the table?

1 Light-colored surfaces reflect more sunlight than dark-colored surfaces.
2 Rough surfaces reflect more sunlight than smooth surfaces.
3 Soil surfaces reflect more sunlight than cloud surfaces.
4 Vegetative surfaces reflect more sunlight than ice surfaces.

32 One reason Massena, New York, has a colder climate than Binghamton, New York, is that Massena

1 absorbs more rays of incoming solar radiation
2 is usually closer to the source of solar radiation
3 receives shorter wavelengths from the source of solar radiation
4 receives lower angle rays of incoming solar radiation

33 The diagram below shows a model of the Moon's orbit around Earth. Letters A, B, C, and D represent four positions in the Moon's orbit.

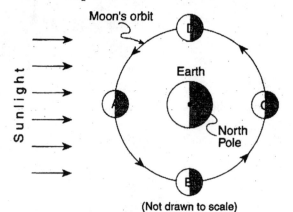

(Not drawn to scale)

What is the approximate length of time the Moon takes to travel from position A to position C?

(1) 1 day   (3) 30 days
(2) 15 days   (4) 365 days

34 The map below shows the average number of thunderstorms each year in the continental United States.

Average Number of Thunderstorms Each Year

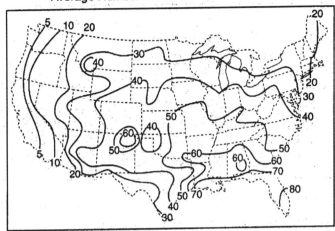

The average number of thunderstorms that occur each year in Albany, New York, is approximately

(1) 15

(2) 25

(3) 35

(4) 45

35 The graph below represents the average yearly concentration of carbon dioxide (CO_2) in Earth's atmosphere from 1972 to 1993.

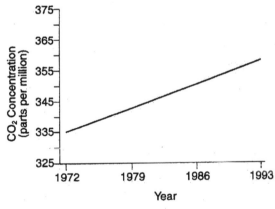

This change in CO_2 concentration most likely caused

1 a decrease in the average wavelength of solar radiation

2 a decrease in the thickness of Earth's atmosphere

3 an increase in the absorption of long-wave heat radiation by Earth's atmosphere

4 an increase in the thickness of Earth's glaciers

36 The diagram below shows a cross section of a cold front.

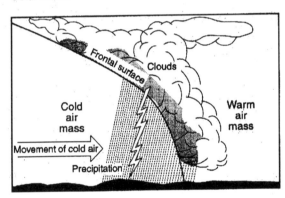

The cloud formation and precipitation shown in the cross section are caused by the

1 rising of cold, moist air

2 sinking of cold, moist air

3 rising of warm, moist air

4 sinking of warm, moist air

37 The diagram below shows the average yearly precipitation, in centimeters, at locations *A* through *E* across the State of Washington. Arrows indicate the direction of prevailing winds.

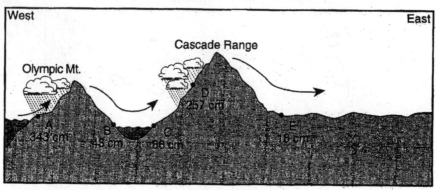

(Not drawn to scale)

Which statement best explains why location *B* and location *E* receive relatively low average yearly precipitation?

1 These locations are on the leeward side of mountain ranges.
2 These locations are on the windward side of mountain ranges.
3 These locations receive more insolation than the other locations.
4 These locations receive less insolation than the other locations.

38 The diagram below shows a view of Earth as seen from space at a certain time of the year.

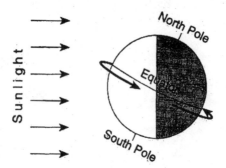

Compared to observers at 35° S latitude, observers at 35° N latitude are generally experiencing

1 fewer hours of daylight and warmer temperatures
2 fewer hours of daylight and cooler temperatures
3 more hours of daylight and warmer temperatures
4 more hours of daylight and cooler temperatures

39 Which photograph of star trails was taken by an observer facing directly north in New York State?

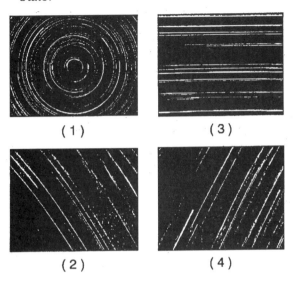

(1)   (3)

(2)   (4)

40 The cartoon characters below are watching the Sun set.

Toward which general direction are the characters looking?

1 north   3 east
2 south   4 west

Part II

This part consists of six groups, each containing five questions. Choose any *two* of these six groups. Be sure that you answer all five questions in each of the two groups chosen. Record the answers to these questions on the separate answer paper in accordance with the directions on the front cover of this booklet. Some questions may require the use of the *Earth Science Reference Tables.* [10]

Group A — Rocks and Minerals

If you choose this group, be sure to answer questions 41–45.

41 The diagram below represents the fossils found in a bedrock formation located in central New York State.

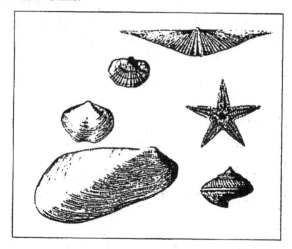

In which type of rock were the fossils most likely found?

1 sedimentary rock that formed in an ocean environment
2 sedimentary rock that formed in a land environment
3 igneous rock that formed in an ocean environment
4 igneous rock that formed in a land environment

42 How do the metamorphic rocks schist and quartzite differ?

1 Quartzite contains the mineral quartz and schist does not.
2 Quartzite forms from regional metamorphism and schist does not.
3 Schist is organically formed and quartzite is not.
4 Schist is foliated and quartzite is not.

43 The elements contained in four minerals are given in the table below. The basic structural unit of one of the minerals is also shown. The atom of element 1 is surrounded by four atoms of element 2.

Mineral	Element 1	Element 2
Fluorite	calcium	fluorine
Halite	sodium	chlorine
Quartz	silicon	oxygen
Galena	lead	sulfur

Basic Structural Unit

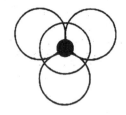

KEY
● Element 1   ○ Element 2

In which mineral are the atoms arranged as shown in the basic structural unit?

1 fluorite   3 quartz
2 halite   4 galena

44 Which natural resource is a source of fuel and plastic?

1 water   3 coal
2 petroleum   4 uranium

45 A mineral's crystal shape and cleavage are a direct result of the mineral's

1 hardness
2 abundance in nature
3 arrangement of atoms
4 exposure to the hydrosphere and atmosphere

Group B — Plate Tectonics

If you choose this group, be sure to answer questions 46–50.

46 Why is Earth's outer core inferred to be a liquid?

(1) *P*-waves can pass through the outer core.
(2) *P*-waves cannot pass through the outer core.
(3) *S*-waves can pass through the outer core.
(4) *S*-waves cannot pass through the outer core.

47 The cross section below shows the location of earthquakes near a plate boundary.

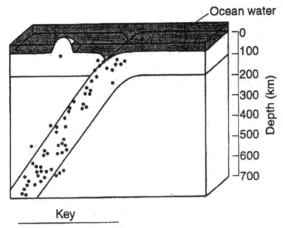

Key

• Earthquake focus

This distribution of earthquakes near the plate boundary is most likely caused by

1 a transform fault
2 a mantle hot spot
3 subduction of a crustal plate
4 divergence of crustal plates

48 Geologists have used information about the composition of meteorites to make inferences about Earth's

1 core properties
2 atmospheric structure
3 asthenosphere location
4 continental-crust thickness

49 The epicenter of an earthquake is located 2,800 kilometers from a seismic station. Approximately how long did the *S*-wave take to travel from the epicenter to the station?

(1) 11 min 15 sec   (3) 5 min 20 sec
(2) 9 min 35 sec   (4) 4 min 20 sec

50 The same earthquake was recorded by seismic stations in Eureka, California; Elko, Nevada; and Las Vegas, Nevada. The distance to the earthquake epicenter for each station is shown below.

Seismic Station Location	Distance to Epicenter
Eureka, CA	485 km
Elko, NV	705 km
Las Vegas, NV	622 km

On which map do the circles correctly show the epicenter distance from each of the seismic stations?

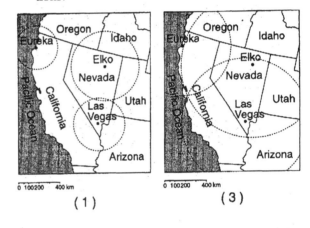

(1)

(3)

(2)

(4)

Group C — Oceanography
If you choose this group, be sure to answer questions 51–55.

51 What usually causes tsunamis?

1 hurricanes
2 high-pressure weather systems
3 undersea earthquakes
4 the collision of ocean currents

52 The diagrams below represent landscape features found along the seacoast. The arrows show ocean-wave direction. Which shoreline has been shaped more by deposition than by erosion?

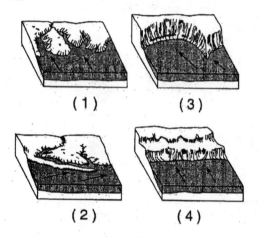

53 Which evidence causes most scientists to believe that seafloor spreading occurs at the mid-Atlantic Ridge?

1 Oceanic crust is oldest at the ridge.
2 Large sedimentary folds exist in the mantle near the ridge.
3 Oceanic crust on both sides of the ridge is less dense than continental crust.
4 Oceanic crust on both sides of the ridge shows matching patterns of reversed and normal magnetic polarity.

54 The curvature to the right by major ocean currents in the Northern Hemisphere is primarily due to

1 surface variations in ocean water salinity
2 differences in ocean water temperatures
3 the gravitational attraction of the Moon
4 the rotation of Earth

55 Which graph best shows the relationship between windspeed and the average height of ocean waves formed by the wind?

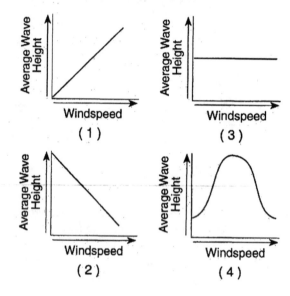

Group D — Glacial Processes

If you choose this group, be sure to answer questions 56–60.

56 Shaded areas on the diagrams below show the part of New York State that was covered by glacial ice during the last ice age.

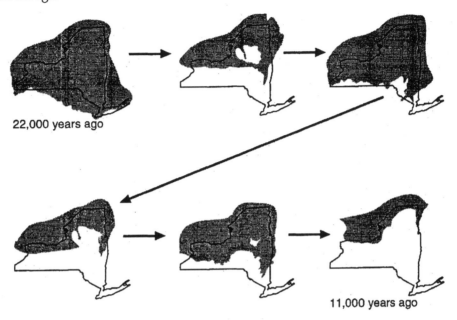

22,000 years ago

11,000 years ago

The best inference that can be made from these diagrams is that this glacial ice

1 was about 1 mile thick at New York City
2 advanced and retreated more than once
3 moved more slowly than the glaciers of earlier ice ages
4 changed the shape of Lake Ontario

57 What is the best evidence that a glacial erratic has been transported?

1 It is located at a high elevation in a mountainous area.
2 It is less than 25 centimeters in diameter.
3 Its composition is different from that of the bedrock under it.
4 It appears to have been intensely metamorphosed.

58 Which New York State resources are a direct result of the glaciers that once covered most of the State?

1 sand and gravel
2 halite and gypsum
3 magnetite and calcite
4 limestone and marble

59 Which condition causes glaciers to retreat?

1 They encounter the ocean.
2 The crust beneath them is uplifted.
3 Earth's average temperature decreases.
4 Their rate of melting exceeds their rate of advancing.

60 Which statement provides the best evidence that New York State's Finger Lakes formed as a result of continental glaciation?

1 The lake surfaces are above sea level.
2 The lakes fill long, narrow U-shaped valleys.
3 The lakes are partially filled with sorted beds of sediment.
4 The lakes are surrounded by sharp, jagged peaks and ridges.

Group E — Atmospheric Energy
If you choose this group, be sure to answer questions 61–65.

Base your answers to questions 61 and 62 on the diagram below, which shows temperature changes within a parcel of air on a summer day.

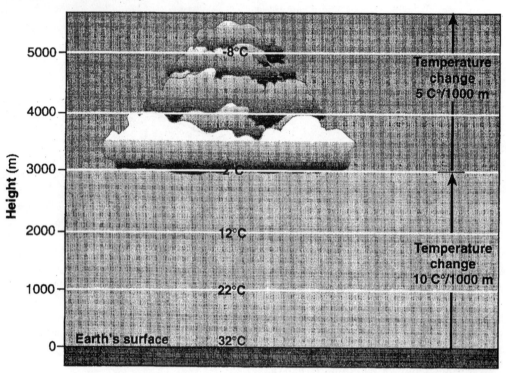

61 At 4,000 meters above Earth's surface, the temperature within the cloud is approximately

(1) –12°C   (3) 3°C
(2) –3°C   (4) 0°C

62 Which process slows the rate of cooling above 3,000 meters and results in cloud formation?

1 condensation   3 convection
2 evaporation   4 radiation

63 What is the latent heat of vaporization of water?

(1) 1.0 cal/g•C°   (3) 80.0 cal/g
(2) 0.5 cal/g•C°   (4) 540.0 cal/g

64 Which weather instrument has most improved the accuracy of weather forecasts over the past 40 years?

1 thermometer   3 weather satellite
2 sling psychrometer   4 weather balloon

65 Which form of electromagnetic radiation has a wavelength of 10^{-7} meter?

1 gamma rays   3 infrared
2 ultraviolet   4 radio waves

Group F — Astronomy

If you choose this group, be sure to answer questions 66–70.

Base your answers to questions 66 and 67 on the four graphs below, which represent trends for four characteristics of the planets in Earth's solar system. The planets are indicated in order of increasing distance from the Sun.

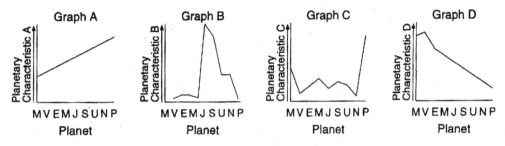

66 Which graph best illustrates the surface temperatures of the planets?

(1) A   (3) C

(2) B   (4) D

67 Which graph best represents the amount of time it takes each planet to orbit the Sun once?

(1) A   (3) C

(2) B   (4) D

---

68 The diagram below shows one model of a portion of the universe.

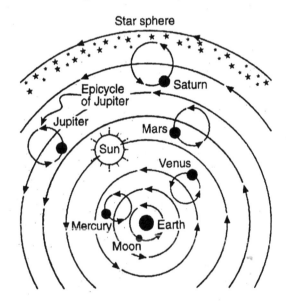

What type of model does the diagram best demonstrate?

1 a heliocentric model, in which celestial objects orbit Earth
2 a heliocentric model, in which celestial objects orbit the Sun
3 a geocentric model, in which celestial objects orbit Earth
4 a geocentric model, in which celestial objects orbit the Sun

69 The apparent change in direction of a Foucault pendulum is caused by

 1 star motions
 2 Earth's rotation
 3 the Moon's gravitational attraction
 4 density differences within the mantle

70 Based on the red-shift data on galaxies, most astronomers infer that the universe is currently

 1 expanding   3 moving randomly
 2 contracting   4 fixed and stationary

Part III

This part consists of questions 71 through 88. Be sure that you answer *all* questions in this part. Record your answers in the spaces provided on the separate answer paper. You may use pen or pencil. Some questions may require the use of the *Earth Science Reference Tables*. [25]

Base your answers to questions 71 and 72 on the data table below, which shows the percent and uses of different types of salt in the United States.

Uses of Salt in the United States

Salt Usage	Percent	How Used
Water softening	9	Sodium ions from salt replace calcium and magnesium ions in water.
Highways	69	Salt keeps highways free of ice in the winter.
Agriculture	6	Salt is provided for livestock and poultry to balance their diet.
Foods	5	Humans use salt in their diet.
Industry	11	Many industrial processes, such as paper-making, use salt.

71 On the pie graph provided *on your answer paper*, complete the graph to show the percent of *each* salt usage. (The percent of salt used in industry has been drawn and labeled.) Label *each* section of the pie graph to indicate the salt usage. [2]

72 Shaded areas on the map below represent some counties in New York State where salt is mined.

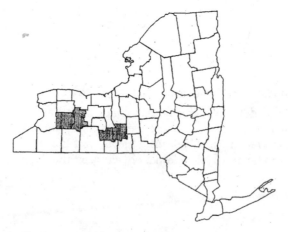

State the name of *one* New York State landscape region in which all or part of these counties are located. [1]

Base your answers to questions 73 through 75 on the information and data table below.

In August 1992, Hurricane Andrew, the most costly natural disaster in United States history, hit southern Florida. The data table below shows the location and classification of Hurricane Andrew on 7 days in August 1992.

Data Table

Day	Latitude	Longitude	Storm Classification
August 18	13° N	46° W	Tropical storm
August 20	19° N	59° W	Tropical storm
August 22	25° N	66° W	Hurricane
August 24	25° N	78° W	Hurricane
August 26	28° N	90° W	Hurricane
August 27	32° N	91° W	Tropical storm
August 28	34° N	86° W	Tropical storm

73 On the hurricane tracking map provided *on your answer paper*, plot the locations of Hurricane Andrew given in the data table, following the directions below.

   a Use an **X** to mark *each* location on the grid.   [1]

   b Label *each* **X** with the appropriate date. The data for August 18 has been plotted on your answer paper as an example.   [1]

   c Connect the **X**'s with a line to show the hurricane's path.   [1]

74 As Hurricane Andrew approached Miami, Florida, cloudiness and precipitation increased dramatically. State how the air pressure at Miami was changing at this time.   [1]

75 By August 27, Hurricane Andrew was downgraded from a hurricane to a tropical storm because its windspeed decreased. State *one* reason why Hurricane Andrew's windspeed decreased at this time.   [1]

76 The chart below shows the different rock families and their subdivisions. The circled letters, A, B, and C, indicate parts of the chart that have not been completed.

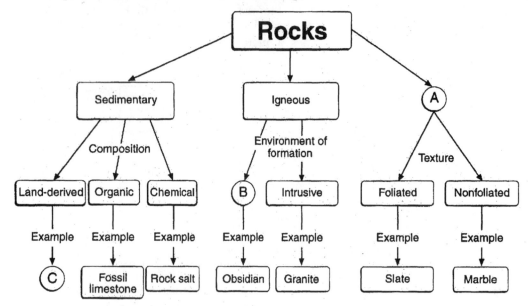

Complete the chart by writing the missing terms in the spaces labeled A, B, and C *on your answer paper.* [3]

Base your answers to questions 77 and 78 on the weather station model shown below.

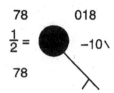

77 State the condition represented by the symbol for "present weather." [1]

78 State the relative humidity. [1]

---

79 The group of stars known as the Big Dipper can be used to locate the North Star (Polaris) in the night sky. On the diagram of the Big Dipper provided *on your answer paper,* draw a straight arrow passing through *two* stars to indicate the direction to Polaris. [1]

Base your answers to questions 80 through 82 on the diagram below. The diagram is a model of the sky (celestial sphere) for an observer at 50° N latitude. The Sun's apparent path on June 21 is shown.

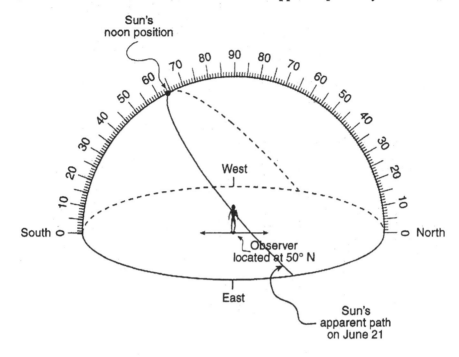

80 On the diagram provided *on your answer paper,* mark with a dot the position of Polaris as viewed by the observer. Label this dot "Polaris."   [1]

81 On the diagram provided *on your answer paper,* mark with a dot the position of the observer's zenith. Label this dot "Zenith."   [1]

82 The altitude of the Sun's position at noon on March 21 is 40° at this location. On the diagram provided *on your answer paper,* draw and label the approximate apparent path of the Sun on March 21.   [1]

---

83 Below is a list of some mineral resources and the number of years that supplies are estimated to last (supply time) if use continues at the current rate.

Mineral Resources' Future

Mineral Resource	Estimated Supply Time
Salt, magnesium metal	almost infinite
Lime, silicon	thousands of years
Potash, cobalt	200+ years
Manganese ore	200+ years
Iron ore	100 to 200 years
Chromite, feldspar	100 to 200 years
Bauxite (aluminum ore)	50 to 100 years
Phosphate rock, nickel	50 to 100 years
Copper, mercury	less than 50 years
Zinc, lead	less than 50 years

State *one* way humans could increase the estimated supply time for many of these resources.   [1]

Base your answers to questions 84 and 85 on the diagram of an ellipse below.

84 Calculate the eccentricity of the ellipse, following the directions below.

   a Write the equation used to determine eccentricity.   [1]

   b Based on measurements of the diagram, substitute values into the equation.   [1]

   c Calculate the eccentricity of the ellipse.   [1]

85 State how the eccentricity of the given ellipse
compares to the eccentricity of Earth's orbit.   [1]

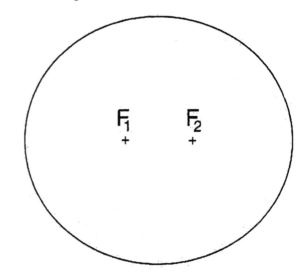

Base your answers to questions 86 through 88 on cross sections I and II shown below. Letters *A* through *J*
represent rock units. Rock units *B* and *I* are the same age. Overturning has not occurred in either cross
section.

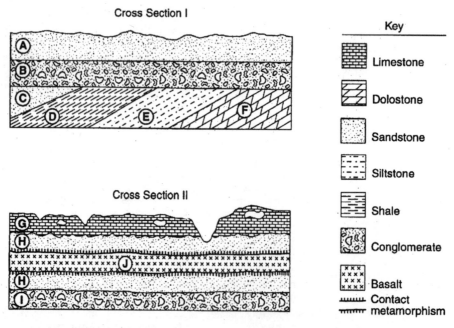

86 State the letter of the oldest rock unit shown in
the cross sections.   [1]

87 State the name of a metamorphic rock that
would be found in the zone of contact metamorphism surrounding rock unit *J*.   [1]

88 A buried erosional surface (unconformity) exists in
cross section I. Identify the position of the most
apparent unconformity by drawing a thick wavy
line ($\sim\!\!\sim\!\!\sim$) at the correct position in
cross section I *on your answer paper.*   [1]

EARTH SCIENCE
JUNE 2000

Program Modification Edition

ANSWER PAPER

Student . . . .

Teacher . . . . School . . . .

Grade (circle one)   8   9   10   11   12

Record all of your answers on this answer paper in accordance with the instructions on the front cover of the test booklet.

Part I (40 credits)

1	1 2 3 4	15	1 2 3 4	29	1 2 3 4
2	1 2 3 4	16	1 2 3 4	30	1 2 3 4
3	1 2 3 4	17	1 2 3 4	31	1 2 3 4
4	1 2 3 4	18	1 2 3 4	32	1 2 3 4
5	1 2 3 4	19	1 2 3 4	33	1 2 3 4
6	1 2 3 4	20	1 2 3 4	34	1 2 3 4
7	1 2 3 4	21	1 2 3 4	35	1 2 3 4
8	1 2 3 4	22	1 2 3 4	36	1 2 3 4
9	1 2 3 4	23	1 2 3 4	37	1 2 3 4
10	1 2 3 4	24	1 2 3 4	38	1 2 3 4
11	1 2 3 4	25	1 2 3 4	39	1 2 3 4
12	1 2 3 4	26	1 2 3 4	40	1 2 3 4
13	1 2 3 4	27	1 2 3 4		
14	1 2 3 4	28	1 2 3 4		

Answer the questions in two of the six groups in this part. Be sure to mark the answers to the groups you choose in accordance with the instructions on the front cover of the test booklet. Leave blank the spaces for the four groups of questions you do not choose to answer.

Group A Rocks and Minerals		
41	1 2 3 4	
42	1 2 3 4	
43	1 2 3 4	
44	1 2 3 4	
45	1 2 3 4	

Group B Plate Tectonics		
46	1 2 3 4	
47	1 2 3 4	
48	1 2 3 4	
49	1 2 3 4	
50	1 2 3 4	

Group C Oceanography		
51	1 2 3 4	
52	1 2 3 4	
53	1 2 3 4	
54	1 2 3 4	
55	1 2 3 4	

Group D Glacial Processes		
56	1 2 3 4	
57	1 2 3 4	
58	1 2 3 4	
59	1 2 3 4	
60	1 2 3 4	

Group E Atmospheric Energy		
61	1 2 3 4	
62	1 2 3 4	
63	1 2 3 4	
64	1 2 3 4	
65	1 2 3 4	

Group F Astronomy		
66	1 2 3 4	
67	1 2 3 4	
68	1 2 3 4	
69	1 2 3 4	
70	1 2 3 4	

Part III (25 credits)

Answer *all* questions in this part.

71

72 _____

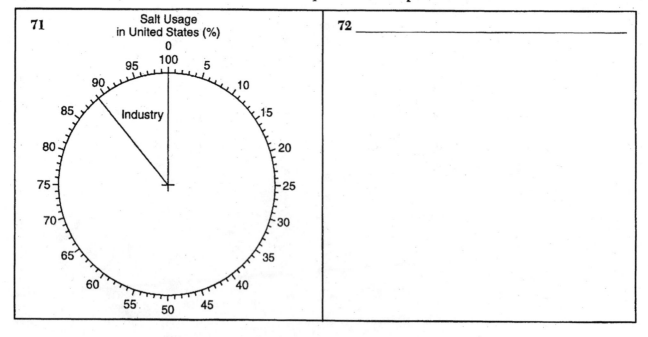

Salt Usage in United States (%)

Industry

73 a–c

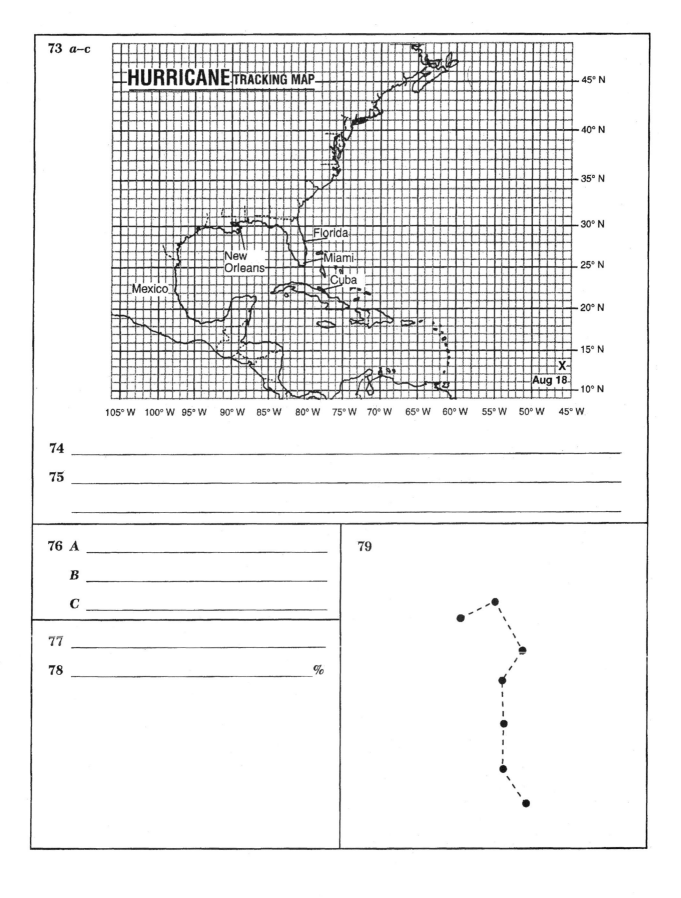

HURRICANE TRACKING MAP

Florida
New Orleans
Miami
Cuba
Mexico

X
Aug 18

45° N
40° N
35° N
30° N
25° N
20° N
15° N
10° N

105° W 100° W 95° W 90° W 85° W 80° W 75° W 70° W 65° W 60° W 55° W 50° W 45° W

74 _____

75 _____

_____

76 A _____

B _____

C _____

77 _____

78 _____ %

79

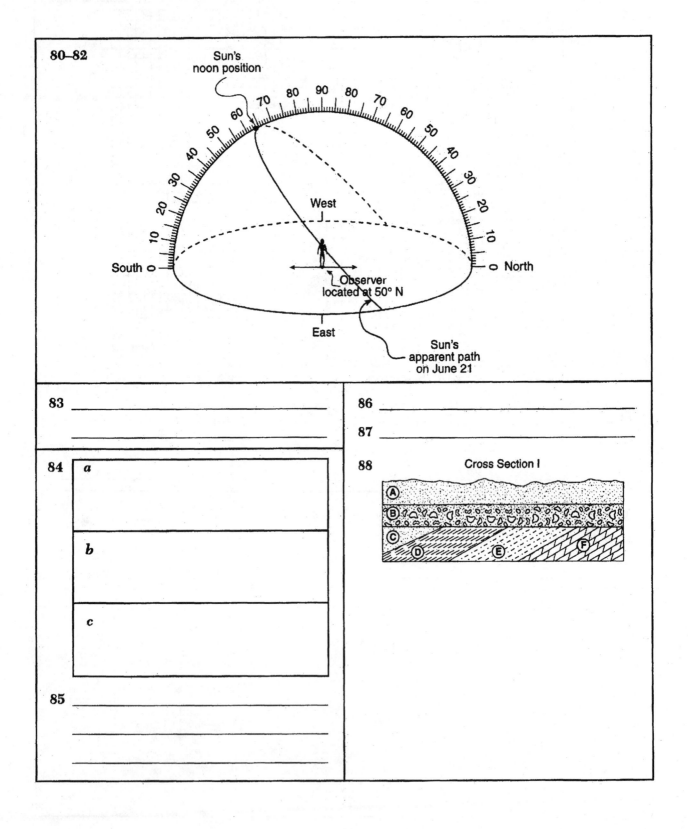

80–82

Sun's noon position

Sun's apparent path on June 21

West

South 0

North

East

Observer located at 50° N

83 _____

_____

84

| a |
| b |
| c |

85 _____

_____

_____

86 _____

87 _____

88 Cross Section I

A
B
C
D   E   F